Modern Mechanics—a vectorial approach

Modern Mechanics— A Vectorial Approach

Christopher A. L. Wragg
Head of Mathematics Department
Lord Williams's School, Thame

Edward Arnold

© Christopher A. L. Wragg 1972

First published 1972
by Edward Arnold (Publishers) Ltd.,
25, Hill Street,
London, W1X 8LL

ISBN: 0 7131 2371 0

Filmset by Keyspools Ltd, Golborne, Lancs.
Printed in Great Britain by C Tinling & Co Ltd, Prescot and London

Preface

Applied Mathematics in schools has undergone a number of changes over the past few years. Not least is the welcome diversification of topics now being studied at sixth-form level under this heading, but although a number of other branches have come to the fore, none of these can ever displace the need for a study of mechanics from the mathematical standpoint. The increasing awareness of the value of vector algebra in dealing with mechanical situations together with the adoption of SI units has given the subject a new impetus, and it is in the spirit of these developments that this text book has been written.

There are a number of other books which contain more material than is required for Advanced Level G.C.E. Courses in Applied Mathematics. In the belief that this can put off the average sixthformer of today, this textbook has been confined strictly to Advanced Level topics. However, it does aim to be suitable for all the G.C.E. Examining Boards. It should not be difficult for the student to avoid those topics not within his particular syllabus; although the subject is integrated as far as possible, each chapter is a complete study in itself and irrelevant chapters or sections can be omitted without difficulty.

Chapter exercises are relatively brief, and in general do not relate to topics outside the immediately preceding section. The student should attempt as many examples from these chapter exercises as time allows as these should enable him to gain a firm grasp of each topic before he has to integrate it with others. The support exercises are generally more difficult, and here the integration of ideas is encouraged. The purpose of these exercises is to encourage the student to look on any problem as one in its own right rather than to link it too closely with any one particular topic. It is intended that the support exercises be studied at the same time as the immediately preceding chapters, and the new topics of these chapters are introduced progressively into the exercises to make this possible.

An important part of the course is the selection of project examples. In the author's experience this type of open-ended problem has proved very valuable. Clearly many more topics could be investigated in similar ways. It is unfortunate that Applied Mathematics is often treated as the poor relation on school time-tables and is not given as much time as other subjects. This shortage of time however should not discourage the introduction of practical observation and project work. They frequently serve to deepen a student's understanding and give him increased confidence in the subject, and on the other hand can often reveal basic misconceptions and misunderstandings, which can then be rectified.

The reader will find that a number of traditional formulae may not be quoted as such. Formulae are valuable only so long as they do not short-circuit the student's understanding of the principles involved. He will quickly learn from his own experience and the advice of his teacher which formulae are most usefully remembered.

Thame   C.A.L.W.
1972

Acknowledgements

The author wishes to acknowledge the kind permission of each of the following G.C.E. Examining Boards to use certain of their Advanced Level questions from recent papers, and for permission in certain cases to adapt questions to conform to SI Units. The author accepts full responsibility for answers quoted at the end of this text, and for the adaption of questions to SI units which are clearly indicated in the text. The source of Examination questions is indicated throughout the exercises by the appropriate initial of the Examining Board concerned as follows:

Associated Examining Board	(A.E.B.)
University of Cambridge Local Examinations Syndicate	(C)
Joint Matriculation Board	(J.M.B.)
University of London	(L)
Oxford Delegacy of Local Examinations	(O)
Oxford and Cambridge Schools Examination Board	(O&C)
Northern Ireland General Certificate of Education Examinations Board	(NI)
Southern Universities' Joint Board	(S)
Welsh Joint Education Committee	(W)

The author also wishes to express his thanks to the British Standards Institute for permission to reproduce certain portions from their publications on SI Units. Their exact source is indicated with the extracts in Appendix A.

Contents

1 An Introduction

1.1 Historical background

While the geometry known to the early Greeks will always be of value to us in mechanics, it is not for such applications that we remember Euclid or Pythagoras. Perhaps the first mathematician to begin developing the subject of mechanics was Archimedes (287–212 BC).

Many readers will already be familiar with the story of how Archimedes discovered the first law of hydrostatics. Hieron, King of Syracuse, had a crown which he suspected the goldsmith of making with adulterated gold. Archimedes would have been familiar with the fact that different metals had different weights for the same volume, but how to measure the volume of a crown? The legend goes that sitting in his bath one day it suddenly dawned on him that the apparent loss of weight of a body immersed in a liquid was equal to the weight of the liquid displaced. Without further thought he jumped out of the bath and ran naked down the street shouting 'Eureka, eureka!'—'I have found it, I have found it!'.

Archimedes was primarily a pure mathematician, and although he developed an extensive theory of hydrostatics, and developed the Principles of Moments, it was with some reluctance that he adopted the guise of mechanical engineer. However, when Syracuse was under attack by the Roman general Marcellus his patriotic spirit was again successfully appealed to by King Hieron, and applying his knowledge of the principles of levers and moments, Archimedes repelled the Romans with machines far in advance of the times. Here was the great-grandfather of Applied Mathematics.

Archimedes did not limit himself even to these bounds. He was also an astronomer in his own right, and developed his own form of calculus which enabled him to find areas of most of the common figures, particularly the conics. The value of the Calculus as we know it to-day however was not realized until Newton and Leibnitz developed their theories in the 17th century. Archimedes applied his knowledge to static situations, but the problem which puzzled mathematicians for centuries was the place of time. So many practical problems involved change—the rate of change.

Newton often showed reluctance to publish his theories and discoveries, and although it was in 1665–6 that he invented his form of the Calculus, it was left for Leibnitz to publish his version first in 1684. Leibnitz's form of the Calculus was particularly well thought out, and the symbols we use to-day were his invention. But Newton was not content with the new theory for its own sake, and he began to apply it to the mechanical scene. So mechanics took its second great step forward, as Newton allied the Calculus to the Laws of Motion which he deduced from his observations and experiments. Here was the grandfather of mechanics. He opened up the whole field of dynamic theory in its vastness. The problem of time and motion was solved, at least for the present.

This new theory also enabled Newton to take astronomy a stage further. Apollonius, a contemporary of Archimedes, had analysed in great detail the properties of the conics, and Kepler had painstakingly deduced the paths of the planets as being elliptic a few years before Newton came on the scene. Kepler had deduced the basic laws of these paths from his calculations, but it was Newton who using the calculus was able to establish these laws from first principles, and to develop his theory of Gravitation.

It is chiefly the work of Archimedes and Newton that forms the basis for this text, but it should not be forgotten that Einstein's theory of Relativity has taken us yet one more step on in the development of mechanics—perhaps he is the father of 20th century progress in this field. From atomic physics to a further concept of the universe in which we live, Einstein has led the third great break-through in mechanics.

1.2 Definitions

All our theory of mechanics can be based on a few fundamental principles which have been deduced from experimental observation. It will soon become evident that we owe most of our knowledge in this field to Newton. The collective name of Newtonian Mechanics is still as valid to-day as it was 250 years ago. It was he who observed and formulated many of the basic principles which are the basis of our study. There are three such principles from which we shall begin, but first we need to define some of the terms we shall use.

From our everyday life we are familiar with the ideas of speed and acceleration, but perhaps they are not very precisely defined in our minds. To the layman, speed answers the question 'How fast?', but before we make a more formal definition we must distinguish between two kinds of quantities known as **scalars** and **vectors**. A scalar is a quantity which simply has magnitude; a vector is a quantity which has both magnitude and direction. To illustrate, the statement that an object is moving with a speed of 30 m/s is limited information—to say in which direction it is travelling adds to the information given. If we define **speed** as the rate of change of distance (or position) with respect to time then this is a scalar with no direction implied. But **velocity** is the rate of change of position with respect to time in a particular direction, and is a vector. Loosely we could say that speed plus direction = velocity.

Those who are familiar with calculus and its notation will appreciate that if distance is s, time is t, and speed is v, then

$$v = \frac{ds}{dt}.$$

When we wish to distinguish between scalars and vectors, we shall write scalars in normal type, as in the above equation, but vectors will be written in bold type,* so if velocity is **v**, and distance is measured from a particular point in a particular direction, and is **s**,** then the equivalent vector equation is

$$\mathbf{v} = \frac{d\mathbf{s}}{dt}.$$

Notice that a vector cannot equal a scalar. Further examples of scalars are temperature, lengths, volume, humidity. We go on to define two further kinds of vectors: acceleration and force.

Acceleration is the rate of change of velocity with respect to time, and is a vector. We do however use the same word in the scalar sense, meaning the rate of change of speed with respect to time. It is generally clear by the context which is meant in any particular situation. In calculus notation, acceleration **a** is defined by the equation

$$\mathbf{a} = \frac{d\mathbf{v}}{dt} = \frac{d^2\mathbf{s}}{dt^2},$$

or in scalar form,

$$a = \frac{dv}{dt} = \frac{d^2s}{dt^2}.$$

Force is that which moves or tends to move a given object. Because it will tend to move it in a particular direction it is a vector, not a scalar.

The word object is not a scientific term; it is more usual to refer to an object either as a body or as a particle. If size and shape become insignificant in a particular situation then the word **particle** is used. If however it is more complex, then we refer to it as a **body**. A collection of particles, bodies or forces, etc. is often referred to as a **system**.

When facing a particular problem for the first time we have to pick out the essential parts of the system and reduce them to the simplest possible form in keeping with the problem. When we have so reduced our problem we have what we call a **mathematical model**. As an example, if we are considering planetary motion, and in particular the motion of the moon, we will first discard the gravitational effects of more distant stars and confine ourselves to the moon, the sun and the earth. Since distances are still so great, we can represent the moon, the sun and the earth as three dots—i.e.

---

* Many notations are used for vectors. A useful one to use in handwriting (and the most common outside print) is to write **v** as v.
** We discuss the position vector more fully in Chapter 6.

treat them as particles. We have reduced our system to a mathematical model which is composed of three dots!

We can use this example to illustrate a further distinction in terms. There are two kinds of forces acting in this situation. There are a number of **external forces** due to the other stars and planets. We ruled these out in this case as being sufficiently small that they could be neglected, but forces outside the system cannot always be ignored. Suppose we were now to take out the two dots representing the sun and the earth, then if the model is to remain as meaningful we must introduce forces on the moon to represent the effects of the earth and sun. Fig. 1 illustrates this process. The forces we have 'introduced' are within the system, and are acting within the system all the time, but it is only when we begin to break the system up into components that they become evident. Such forces are called **internal forces**.

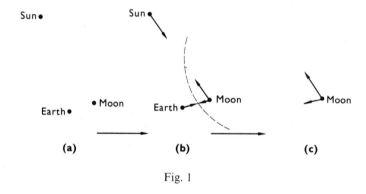

Fig. 1

As a more down-to-earth example of internal and external forces, take as a system a motor-car. The various hinges on all the doors must be exerting forces (otherwise the doors would fall off!), but are inside the system—internal forces. The force exerted by the car on the road however is outside the system—an external force.

1.3 Basic principles—Newton's Laws

We are now in a position to state our first principle—

> **Newton's 1st Law:** *A body continues in its state of rest or uniform motion unless acted upon by an external force.*

The static case (i.e. where no movement is involved) is evident. If you place a book on a table it will stay there—until an external force such as a breeze, a push, or pull exerted by a hand is applied. Since on this earth gravity always acts, it is largely hypothetical to find a moving body not acted on by some force or other. Many situations however do arise in which such forces are so small that they can be neglected. The fact that a force does cause motion is covered by the second Law.

Newton's 2nd Law: *The rate of change of momentum of a body is proportional to the impressed force and takes place in the direction of that force.*

Momentum is defined as the product: mass × velocity.
Mass is a measure of the quantity of matter within a body and is a scalar. Particular care must be taken to note the distinction between mass, weight and force:

Mass is a quantity of matter—how much.

Weight is a measure of the mass in terms of the force exerted on the mass by the gravitational pull of the Earth (or Moon, etc.)—how heavy.

Force is that which causes or tends to cause motion—how strong.

Notice that a body in space becomes virtually weightless, but will retain its mass. We measure mass in kilogrammes (kg); weight is also sometimes quoted in kilogrammes (hence the confusion), but is always understood to refer to the force exerted by gravity on a mass of so many kg. We measure force in newtons (defined below), and to evaluate this force exerted by gravity we must multiply the mass by g, the acceleration due to gravity.

Newton's 2nd Law is a statement about vectors, and from it we can form an equation which describes the motion. Thus if m = mass, $\mathbf{F}$ = force, k = a constant, and other terms are defined as in **1.2**, then

$$\frac{d}{dt}(m\mathbf{v}) = k\mathbf{F}.$$

Unless it is stated otherwise we shall assume the mass to be constant. (It is not always so, even in simple mechanics. For example, a rocket burns fuel quickly and becomes lighter with time).

$$\therefore \frac{d}{dt}(m\mathbf{v}) = m\frac{d\mathbf{v}}{dt} = m\mathbf{a}.$$

By a suitable definition of units we can make $k = 1$, and so we get Newton's 2nd Law in the important form

Force = mass × acceleration.

In SI units the basic unit of force is appropriately called the **newton** (N). The newton is that force which, when applied to a body having a mass of one kilogramme, gives it an acceleration of one metre per second squared.

While we often apply the 2nd Law in the form:
force = mass × acceleration, it is only of direct use when an external force acts. If no external force does act, then the momentum remains unchanged.

We refer to the Law in this form as the **Principle of Conservation of Linear Momentum**. The word 'linear' is important to distinguish it from the Principle of Conservation of Angular Momentum which is discussed in Chapter 12. We do however drop the word 'linear' in problems where confusion cannot arise.

The third Law is very simple but very fundamental:

> **Newton's 3rd Law:** *To every action there is an equal and opposite reaction.*

Action and reaction are names given to those forces which act in pairs, always balancing each other as the Law states. It means that a weight on a table-top exerts the same force on the table as the table has to exert on the weight to hold it up. It means that if two cars collide then the effective force on one is the same as the effective force on the other. Action and reaction are the two forces two bodies exert on each other.

EXAMPLE 1   *A force of 5 kilonewtons (kN) acts on a mass of 15 tonnes. Calculate the acceleration in m/s².*

Where units are mixed in a question, as they are here, it is a safe rule to convert all units to basic units (newtons, metres, kilogrammes) immediately. Thus 5 kN is 5000 N, and 15 tonnes is 15 000 kg.

Let the acceleration be of magnitude a m/s², then using the principle:
Force = mass × acceleration,

$$5000 = 15\,000a.$$
$$\therefore \quad a = \tfrac{1}{3},$$

and the <u>acceleration of the mass is $\tfrac{1}{3}$ m/s²</u>.

EXAMPLE 2   *Two masses, one of 10 kg and the other of 250 g, are acted on by forces of magnitude 10 N and 5 N respectively in opposite directions, and at a certain instant they collide and coalesce. The forces remain the same both before and after the collision.*

Calculate (a) their relative acceleration before impact, and (b) their acceleration after the collision.

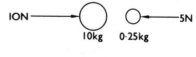

ION ————➤ 〇 〇◄————5N
10kg   0·25kg

Fig. 2

Let the acceleration of the two separate masses have magnitudes a_1 and a_2 m/s² respectively. 250 g is 0·25 kg.

From the Principle: Force = mass × acceleration,

for the first mass: $\qquad$ $10 = 10a_1,$
and for the second: $\qquad$ $5 = 0.25a_2.$

Hence $\qquad$ $a_1 = 1$ and $a_2 = 20$, and

the relative acceleration before the impact was 21 m/s².

After impact, if the acceleration is a_3 m/s², then by the same principle,

$$10 - 5 = (10 + \tfrac{1}{4})a_3.$$

Hence $\qquad$ $\dfrac{41}{4}a_3 = 5,$

$$a_3 = \frac{20}{41}.$$

The acceleration of the combined masses is $\frac{20}{41}$ m/s².

Exercise 1

1 Find the acceleration of a mass of 250 kg when acted on by a force of 10 N.
2 Find the mass that is given an acceleration of 40 m/s² by a force of 720 N.
3 Find the force in millinewtons (mN) required to give 10 g an acceleration of 25 mm/min².
4 A car of 800 kg can accelerate at 12 m/s² when driven by a man who weighs 89 kg. He stops to pick up 3 passengers of average weight 81 kg. What will his maximum acceleration now be?
5 Assuming that an engine can exert a constant maximum force of 2/9 hN irrespective of speed, find the maximum speed of the car if it has a mass of 1·2 Mg and if internal resistances exert a retarding force of $\frac{1}{2}V$ N and the wind resistance is $V^2/200$ N, where V is its speed in m/s. Find also the acceleration at 20 m/s.
6 Project Example:
Investigate the effect of variable mass due to burning of fuel.

2 One Dimensional Motion under a Constant Force

2.1 Equations of motion under constant acceleration

Any equation or set of equations which describe a particular motion are called Equations of Motion. One particular set occur very frequently and are generally memorized, and are even referred to by some as *the* equations of motion as if no others existed. This latter practice is misleading and should be avoided. The equations of motion to which we refer in this chapter concern motion under a constant acceleration only.

From Newton's 2nd Law we saw that force = mass × acceleration, and we wrote this in the form

$$\mathbf{F} = m\mathbf{a}.$$

In this chapter we confine ourselves to motion in one dimension, i.e. in one direction, and so it is sufficient to use scalar quantities which correspond to the magnitudes of the vectors in calculation. Therefore, for this chapter only, we shall drop the vector notation. We shall however understand a speed $-v$ to be in the opposite direction to a speed of $+v$, and similarly for distances and accelerations. We write the above equation as

$$F = ma.$$

In the situation we are considering, the acceleration a is constant. Let s be distance, then

$$\frac{d^2 s}{dt^2} = a.$$

Integrating with respect to time t,

$$\frac{ds}{dt} = at + k.$$

Now $\frac{ds}{dt}$ is the speed v after time t. If the speed is u when $t = 0$, then the constant $k = u$, giving

$$v = u + at. \qquad 2.1$$

Integrating again with respect to time,

$$s = ut + \tfrac{1}{2}at^2 + K.$$

If we agree to measure the distance from the point where the particle was when $t = 0$, then $K = 0$, giving

$$s = ut + \tfrac{1}{2}at^2. \qquad\qquad 2.2$$

We can deduce from these two equations a relationship independent of t by substituting from 2.1 into 2.2. This relationship can be written as

$$v^2 = u^2 + 2as. \qquad\qquad 2.3$$

These equations of motion describe the motion of a body under the action of a constant force, and should be memorized. The reader will appreciate that the third equation, 2.3, was obtained from 2.1 and 2.2, and when we are using these equations we will generally use only two of them, whichever are the most convenient for the problem.

EXAMPLE 1   *A bullet of mass 0.4 g moving with speed 320 m/s strikes a block of wood which offers a constant resistance of 80 N. Find how deep the bullet will go into the block.*

From the principle: force = mass × acceleration,

$$80 = 0.4 \times 10^{-3} \times a$$

where a m/s^2 is the acceleration. Hence

$$a = 2 \times 10^5.$$

From the equation of motion, $v^2 = u^2 + 2as$,

$$0 = 320^2 - 2 \times 2 \times 10^5 \times s,$$

where s is the distance in metres it penetrates into the block.

Thus,
$$s = 16^2/10^3$$
$$= 0.256.$$

∴ Bullet goes 25·6 cm into the block.

EXAMPLE 2   *Suppose that in Example 1 the block was only 15 cm thick. Find the speed at which the bullet leaves the block.*

Using the same equation of motion, $v^2 = u^2 + 2as$, the bullet leaves the block with speed v m/s, where

$$v^2 = 320^2 - 2 \times 2 \times 10^5 \times 0.15$$
$$= 20^2(256 - 150)$$
$$= 20^2 \times 106.$$
$$\therefore \ v = 20 \times 10.3 = 206.$$

The bullet leaves the block with a speed of 206 m/s.

EXAMPLE 3   *A particle is moving with a constant speed of 230 cm/s across a smooth part of a table when it suddenly begins to pass over a rough section which slows it down to rest by a constant frictional force of 115 N. If the mass of the particle is 5 kg, find the distance travelled over the rough part, and the time it takes to slow down to a standstill.*

From the principle: force = mass × acceleration,

$$115 = -5a,$$

where the acceleration is a m/s^2. Hence

$$a = -23.$$

From the equation of motion, $v = u + at$,

$$0 = 2 \cdot 3 - 23t.$$
$$\therefore \ t = 1/10.$$

To find the distance travelled, s, we can use either of the equations *2.2* or *2.3*, but the latter makes the working easier. Using the equation of motion, $v^2 = u^2 + 2as$,

$$0 = 2 \cdot 3^2 - 2 \times 23s,$$
$$s = \frac{2 \cdot 3}{20}$$
$$= 0 \cdot 115.$$

∴ Particle moves 11·5 cm over the rough portion, and takes 0·1 s to come to rest.

EXAMPLE 4   *A train travels from one station A to another B 5 km distant. It starts from rest at A accelerating uniformly for $\frac{3}{4}$ min, by which time it has attained a speed of 60 km/h. It maintains this speed until it is 800 m from B. The brakes are then applied to bring the train to rest at B with uniform retardation. Calculate*
   (a) *the distance travelled while accelerating, and*
   (b) *the time taken for the whole journey.*

The conversion factor from km/h to m/s is $10^3/60^2$, which is 5/18. It is a factor worth remembering, but probably in the form 10/36 rather than 5/18 as the 10 is so easily absorbed into other factors.
   In this example, 60 km/h ≡ $60 \times \frac{10}{36}$ = 100/6 m/s.
   From the equation of motion, $v = u + at$, if the acceleration is a m/s^2, then

$$100/6 = 0 + 45a.$$
$$\therefore \ a = \frac{100}{270}$$
$$= 10/27.$$

If d m is the distance travelled while accelerating, then from the equation of motion, $v^2 = u^2 + 2as$,

$$(100/6)^2 = 0 + 20d/27.$$

$$\therefore d = \frac{2500}{9} \times \frac{27}{20}$$

$$= \frac{750}{2}$$

$$= 375.$$

The train accelerates for 375 m.

Let the brakes retard the train at a rate of r m/s², then applying the equation of motion $v^2 = u^2 + 2as$ to the last part of the motion,

$$0 = (100/6)^2 - 2 \times 800r,$$

giving

$$r = \frac{2500}{9} \times \frac{1}{1600}$$

$$= 25/144.$$

If the time to stop the train is T s, then using the equation of motion, $v = u + at$,

$$0 = 100/6 - \frac{25}{144}T.$$

$$\therefore T = \frac{100 \times 144}{6 \times 25}$$

$$= 4 \times 24$$

$$= 96.$$

But the train covers a distance of $(5000 - 375 - 800)$ m at a constant speed of $100/6$ m/s, i.e. 3825 m at this speed.

$\therefore$ Time for the whole journey was

$$\left(45 + \frac{3825}{100/6} + 96\right) \text{ s}$$

$$= (141 + 38 \cdot 25 \times 6) \text{ s}$$

$$= (141 + 229 \cdot 5) \text{ s}$$

$$= 370 \cdot 5 \text{ s}.$$

Time for the whole journey was $370 \cdot 5$ s $= 6$ min 10 s (to nearest second).

Exercise 2

1 Calculate how long it takes a car accelerating at $2 \cdot 5$ m/s² to reach a speed of 50 km/h from rest.

2 A body accelerates uniformly from a speed of 15 m/s to one of 30 m/s over a distance of 360 m. Find how long it takes to do this.

Find also how much further it would travel increasing speed from 30 m/s to 45 m/s at the same rate, and how long this would take.

3 A car accelerates uniformly from 30 km/h to 50 km/h in a distance of 50 m. Find the time taken to cover this distance, and the acceleration in m/s².

4 A car starting from rest accelerates uniformly, travelling 100 m in 7·5 s. Determine the speed after this 7·5 s in km/h, and the acceleration in m/s².

5 A particle passes through a point 0 at time t = 0 at 28 m/s, being retarded at a constant rate of 4 m/s². Calculate at what times it is moving with speed 10 m/s, assuming the motion continues unhindered.

6 Assume that a car is able to stop with a uniform retardation of 7·4 m/s², and that a driver can react to an emergency in 0·6 s. Calculate the overall stopping distance of the car from speeds of (i) 30 km/h, (ii) 60 km/h, (iii) 90 km/h. (Give your answers to the nearest metre.)

7 A train accelerating uniformly passes three successive kilometre posts at times t = 0, t = 75 and t = 125 (all in seconds). Calculate the acceleration of the train, and also the speed at the last of these posts.

8 Cyclist A sets out from a town with a constant acceleration of 0·5 m/s² until he reaches a speed of 20 km/h which he then maintains. Half a minute later cyclist B sets out in pursuit, accelerating at 1·5 m/s² to a speed of 24 km/h, and then travelling at constant speed. Find when and where B overtakes A.

It is often possible to eliminate some of the tedium of repeated substitution and calculation in the Equations *2.1–2.3* by considering instead the properties of graphs describing the motion.

2.2 Distance-time graph

The distance-time graph is that of the function $s = f(t)$, where s is distance and t is time. In motion under a constant force this is a quadratic function (Equation *2.2*), but *provided the motion is confined to one dimension* what follows will apply whatever the nature of the function.

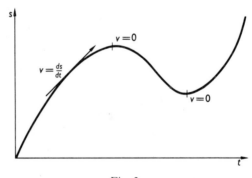

Fig. 3

The reader will be familiar with the use of this graph to find without calculation when and where two things meet. It is the shape of the curve however which is important too, indicating as it does the magnitude of the velocity at any time by the gradient of the curve:

$$v = \frac{ds}{dt}.$$

Hence at a maximum or minimum point on the curve the gradient is zero indicating that the velocity is zero. The sign of the gradient indicates the direction of motion.

2.3 Velocity-time graph

The velocity-time graph is that of the function $v = F(t)$. If the motion takes place *in a straight line*, i.e. in one dimension, then the gradient of the curve $\frac{v}{dt}$ corresponds to the magnitude of the acceleration. If the gradient is zero—at the stationary points on the curve—the acceleration will be zero and the body will be moving with constant velocity.

From our knowledge of calculus we also know that the area bounded by the curve, the t-axis and the ordinates $t = t_1$, $t = t_2$ is

$$\int_{t_1}^{t_2} v\, dt.$$

But this is

$$[s]_{t_1}^{t_2}.$$

i.e. for motion in a straight line, the area bounded by the curve and the axis is equal to the distance travelled.

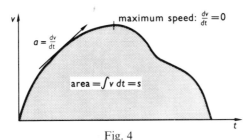

Fig. 4

EXAMPLE 5   *We consider again Example 4 on page 10.*

First we draw the velocity-time graph for the motion, as in Fig. 5.

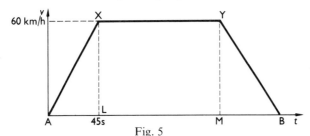

Fig. 5

The shape of the function v is a trapezium which we label AXYBML as shown. L and M are the feet of perpendiculars from X and Y.

Triangle AXL is equal to the distance covered in the first 45 seconds, i.e., the distance covered was

$$\frac{1}{2} \times 45 \times 60 \times \frac{10}{36} \, \text{m} = \frac{4500}{12} \, \text{m}$$
$$= 375 \, \text{m}.$$

If LM is equivalent to t seconds, then

$$\text{XYML} = \frac{100}{6} \times t = 4200 - 375.$$

$$\therefore \ t = \frac{6}{100} \times 3825$$
$$= 229 \cdot 5.$$

If MB is equivalent to T seconds, then

$$\text{MBY} = \frac{1}{2} T \times \frac{100}{6} = 800.$$
$$\therefore \ T = 8 \times 12 = 96.$$

Thus the time for the whole journey was 370·5 s.

We have come to this conclusion purely from consideration of the velocity-time graph; no reference at all has been made to the equations of motion. In this instance this working is not very much shorter, but in many examples the method reduces the length considerably. Each problem has to be approached on its own merits.

2.4 Motion under gravity

Newton's Law of Gravitation enounced the principle that the force of attraction between two bodies is directly proportional to their masses, and inversely proportional to the square of the distance between them. If this force is F, the distance between them d, and the masses are M and m, then this can be written as

$$F = G\frac{Mm}{d^2} \qquad\qquad 2.4$$

where G is a constant. The distance d is measured between the centres of the two masses.

If M is taken as the mass of the earth, and m is the mass of some body close to the surface of the earth, then F is the force attracting that body towards the ground—the force of gravity. The distance d will be so nearly equal to the radius of the earth for a body sufficiently close to the ground that we can take d to be constant. Thus $\frac{GM}{d^2}$ is constant, equal to g, say. Then equation 2.4 becomes

$$F = mg. \qquad\qquad 2.5$$

From Newton's 2nd Law we know that Force = mass × acceleration, and so g must be the acceleration of the body. Since this is independent of the mass, a body free to move under gravity will fall with a constant acceleration of g (so long as we neglect air resistance, etc.). This constant acceleration is universally designated by the symbol 'g', and we can deduce experimentally that its value is 9·81 m/s^2 approximately.* If we wish to be precise we must remember that this value will vary slightly from place to place, due to the earth being an imperfect sphere, variations in altitude, and other causes.

EXAMPLE 6   *A boy standing at the foot of a tower 24 m high throws a stone vertically upwards with a velocity of V m/s. At the same instant a stone is released from the top of the tower. If they collide 15 m above the ground, find the value of V. Find also the minimum value of V if they are to be able to collide while in the air. (Take g as 9·81 m/s².)*

Let the stones collide after time t, then using the equation of motion,

$$s = ut + \tfrac{1}{2}at^2,$$

for the first stone: $15 = Vt - \tfrac{1}{2}gt^2,$ (1)

for the second stone: $9 = \tfrac{1}{2}gt^2.$ (2)

Adding (1) and (2),

$$24 = Vt,$$

and from (2),

$$t = \sqrt{\frac{18}{g}}.$$

Hence

$$V = 24\sqrt{\frac{9\cdot81}{18}}$$
$$\doteqdot 17\cdot7.$$

The boy throws the stone at 17·7 m/s (to 3 significant figures).

To find the minimum value of V such that the stones collide in the air,

---

* The Universal Constant G, called the Gravitational Constant, is approximately $6\cdot67 \times 10^{-11}$ in SI units. The rather sophisticated experiments designed to evaluate G will be found described in appropriate physics texts.

let the collision occur at a height h m above the ground. The equation of motion $s = ut + \frac{1}{2}at^2$ now gives for the two stones

$$h = Vt - \tfrac{1}{2}gt^2 \tag{3}$$

and
$$24 - h = \tfrac{1}{2}gt^2, \tag{4}$$

where they collide after time t. Adding (3) and (4)

$$24 = Vt,$$

and from (4)

$$t = \sqrt{2(24 - h)/g}.$$

But in the limiting case, $h = 0$, giving

$$t = \sqrt{\frac{48}{g}}$$
$$= 4\sqrt{\frac{3}{g}}.$$

Hence
$$V = \frac{24}{4}\sqrt{\frac{g}{3}}$$

$$= 6\sqrt{\frac{g}{3}}.$$

The minimum value of V if the stones collide in the air is $6\sqrt{g/3}$ m/s.

Exercise 3

1 It takes 2·3 s for a stone to fall from the top to the bottom of a vertical cliff. How high is the cliff? (Take g as 9·8 m/s².)

2 Prove that the difference in speeds of two particles both moving vertically under gravity is constant.

3 A train accelerates uniformly from rest to 50 km/h in 15 s, and immediately retards uniformly to rest in a further 12 s. Use the velocity-time graph to find the distance travelled.

4 Find the speed at which a stone must be thrown vertically downwards a distance of 20 m (a) to strike an object with speed 20 m/s, (b) to strike the object 1·2 s after it is thrown. (Take g as 9·8 m/s².)

5 A coach accelerates from rest uniformly to 72 km/h, travels at this speed for 1 min, and retards uniformly to rest. It covers a total distance of 1700 m. Find the total time taken for the journey.

6 A railcar accelerates at a rate of a m/s² until it reaches a speed of 72 km/h. It then travels at this constant speed until, approaching a stopping point, it retards uniformly at $\frac{1}{2}a$ m/s². If the distance travelled is 3000 m and the time taken for the whole journey is 4 min, find the value of a.

7 A vehicle moves 3 km from rest to rest in $3\frac{1}{2}$ min. If it accelerates uniformly, then travels at a constant speed of 90 km/h, and finally retards uniformly, find how far it travelled at full speed, and for how long.

8 A boy fires a home-made rocket vertically into the air. He estimates that the fuel will burn for three seconds and exert a force of 0·935 N. If the mass of the rocket is 50 g, and the mass of the fuel can be neglected, find the maximum speed (going upwards), and the maximum height attained. (Take g as 9·8 m/s².)

9 Train A leaves X with constant acceleration which it maintains until it reaches a speed of 80 km/h. It maintains this speed for 7 min and then decelerates uniformly to arrive at Y exactly $8\frac{1}{2}$ min after leaving X. Find the distance from X to Y.

Train B passes through X at a steady speed of 60 km/h which it maintains until, by a uniform retardation of $\frac{5}{6}$ m/s², it comes to rest at Y. B must leave Y 2 min before A arrives there, and must also allow $1\frac{1}{2}$ min for passengers to disembark, etc. Find how far from Y that B must apply the brakes, and how long after B passes through X that A leaves X.

10 A particle is thrown vertically downwards from a point height h above the ground with speed V. A second particle is thrown at the same instant from the ground with speed $5V$ in the same vertical line. Show that they collide at a point $\dfrac{5h}{6} - \dfrac{gh^2}{72V^2}$ above the ground, on the assumption that they collide in the air, and deduce the condition on h that this should be so.

11 A particle of mass 0·7 μg is accelerated by a constant force F for 1 ms to a speed of 700 m/s. It maintains this speed for 0·05 s, after which a second force $\frac{2}{3}F$ retards the particle and continues to act until it returns through the starting point. Find the value of F, the time that elapses during the complete motion (starting point to starting point), and the speed at which the particle passes through the starting point.

12 Two cars starting from rest at the same point and time accelerate uniformly, the first reaching 56 km/h in 8 s, and the second accelerating at a rate of 6 km/h/s. When the first car reaches 80 km/h it continues at constant speed. The second car reaches 100 km/h and then also continues at constant speed. Draw in one diagram the velocity-time graphs for the two cars.

Find the time that elapses from the start until the second car overtakes the first, and calculate the distance travelled in this time.

13 The times after the start of a car from rest at a point A are recorded at given distances from A according to the following table.

Distance from A (in metres)	0	10	20	28	36	50	60	70	80	95
Time after start (in seconds)	0	4·1	7·0	10.2	13·4	15·9	17·2	18·4	19·5	21·1

Plot the distance-time graph, and assess as accurately as possible the speed in metres per second after successive periods of 2 s. Hence plot the velocity-time graph and estimate the maximum acceleration of the car (ignoring the acceleration in the first second).

2.5 Simple pulley systems

In the examples we shall consider in this section, all the pulleys will be smooth, and all the strings will be vertical where they are not in contact with the pulleys. It could be argued that when we turn to the motion of pulley systems we are no longer in one dimension, but mathematically they are equivalent to one-dimensional motion as we demonstrate in the first example. The provision that the pulleys must be smooth is partly necessary so that we can assume the tensions in the strings are the same throughout their lengths, and partly so that we can ignore their effect on the acceleration of the system. Tension is the name we give to the internal force within the string (or rod, bar, etc.) and is the reaction to the forces acting at the two ends.

To explain the mathematics involved in simple pulley systems we shall consider five examples. The main principle that we use in every case is Newton's 2nd Law in the form

$$\text{Force} = \text{mass} \times \text{acceleration}.$$

Throughout this section we shall refer to this principle as $F = ma$.

EXAMPLE 7   *Two particles of masses m and 3m are connected by a light inextensible string over a smooth pulley. If they are released from rest, find the acceleration of the system.*

The fact that the string is light and inextensible is a detail, but is nonetheless significant. The string is light by comparison with the weights of the particles and can therefore be ignored, and the fact that it is inextensible tells us that the tension in the string will not vary during the motion.

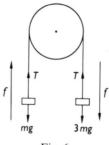

Fig. 6

Suppose that the acceleration of the system is f, and that the tension in the string is T, then applying $F = ma$ to the smaller particle:

$$T - mg = mf. \tag{1}$$

Similarly for the larger particle:

$$3mg - T = 3mf. \tag{2}$$

Adding (1) and (2)

$$2mg = 4mf,$$
$$\therefore f = \tfrac{1}{2}g.$$

There are two things to note at this point. The first is to remind ourselves that the mass m is not the gravitational force, even though we may talk of the weight m. The force (the principle $F = ma$ should be a reminder) is the product mg. Secondly it is easy to demonstrate that this relatively simple example is equivalent to a one-dimensional motion, and in fact we can make the working shorter if we consider the system as being the situation illustrated in Fig. 7. The tension in the string now becomes an internal force, and we consider the mass of the whole system rather than its separate parts. Applying $F = ma$ in this situation we go straight to the equation

$$3mg - mg = (3m + m)f$$

i.e. $$2mg = 4mf,$$

and as before, the acceleration $= \frac{1}{2}g.$

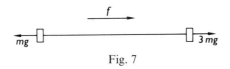

Fig. 7

EXAMPLE 8   *Two masses, one 2m, the other 5m, are connected by a light inextensible string over a smooth pulley, and they are held with the string just taut both 50 cm above a horizontal table. The pulley is 125 cm above the table. The masses are released. As the 5m weight hits the table it becomes unhitched from the string. Show that in the motion that follows the 2m mass does not quite reach the pulley, and find with what speed it hits the table. (Take g as 9·8 m/s².)*

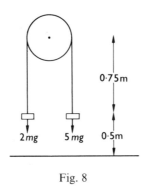

Fig. 8

Fig. 8 illustrates the situation. Applying $F = ma$ to the system as a whole, the acceleration f of the first stage of the motion is given by

$$5mg - 2mg = (5m + 2m)f.$$

$$\therefore f = \frac{3}{7}g.$$

If they are moving with velocity v m/s when the 5m weight hits the table, then from the equation of motion $v^2 = u^2 + 2as$,

$$v^2 = 0 + 2 \times \frac{3}{7}g \times \frac{1}{2}$$

$$= \frac{3 \times 9 \cdot 8}{7}$$

$$= 4 \cdot 2.$$

Thus the 2m weight continues upwards with speed $\sqrt{4 \cdot 2}$ m/s. If it reaches a maximum height of $(1 + x)$ m above the table, then by the same equation of motion,

$$0 = 4 \cdot 2 - 2gx.$$

$$\therefore x = \frac{2 \cdot 1}{9 \cdot 8}$$

$$= 3/14.$$

Since $\frac{3}{14} < \frac{1}{4}$, the 2$m$ weight does not reach a height of 125 cm.
    i.e. the 2m weight does not reach the pulley.

Let the speed of the 2m weight be V m/s when it strikes the table, then from the same equation of motion,

$$V^2 = 4 \cdot 2 - 2g(-1),$$

(distance s is measured in the negative direction—downwards).

$$V^2 = 4 \cdot 2 + 19 \cdot 6$$

$$= 23 \cdot 8.$$

$$\therefore V \doteqdot 4 \cdot 88.$$

The 2m weight strikes the table at a speed of 4·88 m/s.

EXAMPLE 9   *Two weights of masses 3m and 4m are connected by a light inextensible string over a smooth pulley. The 4m weight is held with the string just taut and the 3m weight just resting on a horizontal table below the pulley. The system is released. 70 cm above the table, the 3m weight picks up another weight of mass 7m. Determine the maximum height above the table reached by the 3m weight, and the time that elapses from the start of the motion to the instant the combined masses strike the table. (Take g as 9·8 m/s².)*

This situation differs from the preceding one in that a third weight is added to the system half-way through the motion. To tackle this new aspect we shall need to apply the Principle of Conservation of Momentum which we deduced from Newton's 2nd Law (p. 6). First, however, we analyse the motion before the 7m weight is picked up.

As before, we apply the principle $F = ma$ to find the acceleration f of the first stage of the motion. Thus

$$4mg - 3mg = (3m + 4m)f,$$

$$f = g/7.$$

If the weights are moving with speed v m/s when the $3m$ weight has reached a height of 70 cm above the table, then using the equation of motion $v^2 = u^2 + 2as$,

$$v^2 = 0 + 2g \times 0.7/7$$

$$= 19.6 \times 0.1.$$

$$\therefore v = 1.4.$$

Now the system does not continue with this velocity when the third weight is picked up. By Newton's 2nd Law, the momentum of the whole system will not change unless an external force is applied. The $7m$ weight is an integral part of the system, and any force which acts between the two connecting weights is internal. So the momentum of the system before the pick-up equals the momentum afterwards. We defined momentum as mv, mass × velocity. Since the mass has increased by $7m$, the velocity must decrease proportionately. If the new velocity immediately after pick-up is w m/s, then by the Conservation of Momentum,

$$3m \times 1.4 + 4m \times 1.4 = 3mw + 4mw + 7mw,$$

$$14mw = 9.8m,$$

$$w = 0.7.$$

Because of the added weight, the acceleration of the system has also altered. Applying $F = ma$, if the new acceleration is f' m/s^2 in the opposite direction to the previous acceleration,

$$10mg - 4mg = 14mf',$$

$$f' = \frac{6g}{14}$$

$$= 4.2.$$

Suppose the connected weights now rise a further h m before coming momentarily to rest, then applying the equation of motion $v^2 = u^2 + 2as$,

$$0 = w^2 - 2f'h.$$

$$\therefore 2 \times 4.2h = 0.7^2,$$

$$h = \frac{0.7}{12}$$

$$\doteqdot 0.058.$$

Maximum height above the table is 76 cm (to nearest cm).

To find the time that elapses during the complete motion we must consider each part of the motion separately, and this time we can use either of the Equations *2.1* or *2.2*. In the first part the former equation is simpler (being linear rather than quadratic), and so using the equation of motion $v = u + at$ for the first stage of the motion, if it takes T_1 s, then

$$1\cdot4 = 0 + gT_1/7.$$
$$T_1 = (7 \times 1\cdot4)/g$$
$$= 1.$$

For the second part of the motion, since we do not know the velocity with which the weights strike the table, we use the Equation *2.2*. Using the equation of motion $s = ut + \frac{1}{2}at^2$, if the time for this part of the motion is T_2, then

$$-0\cdot7 = 0\cdot7T_2 - \tfrac{1}{2} \times 4\cdot2T_2^2.$$

(The distance s is negative since it is below the point at which we consider the motion to begin.)

$$\therefore\ 21T_2^2 - 7T_2 - 7 = 0,$$
$$3T_2^2 - T_2 - 1 = 0.$$
$$T_2 = \frac{1 \pm \sqrt{1+12}}{6}$$
$$= (1 \pm \sqrt{13})/6.$$

Discounting the negative value, the total time for the whole motion is $T_1 + T_2$ which is

$$1 + (1 + \sqrt{13})/6 = \underline{(7 + \sqrt{13})/6 \text{ seconds.}}$$

EXAMPLE 10   *Fig. 9 shows a pulley system in which both pulleys A and B are smooth, but A is fixed, whereas B is on one end of a light inextensible string passing over A, on the other end of which is a weight of mass 2·1 kg. Over pulley B is another light inextensible string with masses of 0·9 kg and 0·5 kg on the ends. If the system is free to move, find the acceleration of B.*

It is very easy to be confused by this more complex situation, and we must take care to be systematic in our approach. There are three different accelerations which we might be asked to find. The acceleration of B is the same as that of the 2·1 kg weight—let this acceleration be a_1 m/s². The 0·5 kg weight will be moving towards B with an acceleration of a_2 m/s², say. It is important to understand that we mean this acceleration is relative to the *fixed* background, and not relative to any other part of the system. We cannot tell at this point whether the 0·9 kg weight will move up or down, but we can form our equations more easily if we take it to be moving upwards also, and we will take its acceleration to be a_3 m/s^2. If we are wrong in choosing this direction then a_3 will work out to be negative.

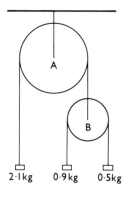

2·1kg   0·9kg   0·5kg

Fig. 9

We now apply the principle $F = ma$ to each of the separate masses. Suppose the tension in the string over A is T N. Since B is itself weightless the resultant force on B is zero, and so the tension in the string over B is $T/2$ N. Now applying $F = ma$ to each mass in turn.

For the 2·1 kg weight:

$$2·1g - T = 2·1a_1,$$
$$21g - 10T = 21a_1. \tag{1}$$

For the 0·5 kg weight:

$$T/2 - 0·5g = 0·5a_2,$$
$$T - g = a_2. \tag{2}$$

For the 0·9 kg weight:

$$T/2 - 0·9g = 0·9a_3,$$
$$5T - 9g = 9a_3. \tag{3}$$

We now have three equations in four unknowns: a_1, a_2, a_3 and T. The necessary fourth equation is the relationship between the three accelerations. By considering Fig. 10 we see that the velocity of the string over B relative to B is $a_2 - a_1$ on one side, but is $a_1 - a_3$ on the other.

Thus

$$a_2 - a_1 = a_1 - a_3,$$
$$2a_1 = a_2 + a_3. \tag{4}$$

Adding (1) to $10 \times (2)$

$$11g = 21a_1 + 10a_2,$$

and adding (1) to $2 \times (3)$

$$3g = 21a_1 + 18a_3.$$

Hence
$$a_2 + a_3 = \frac{11g - 21a_1}{10} + \frac{g - 7a_1}{6},$$

$$= 2a_1 \quad \text{by (4)}.$$

$$\therefore \quad 60a_1 = 33g - 63a_1 + 5g - 35a_1,$$

$$158a_1 = 38g,$$

$$a_1 = \frac{19g}{79}.$$

Pulley B moves upwards with an acceleration of $\dfrac{19g}{79}$ m/s^2.

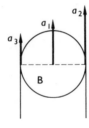

Fig. 10

EXAMPLE 11   *Let the pulley B in Example 10 have a mass of 1·2 kg. Find the acceleration of B.*

Let the accelerations be a_1, a_2 and a_3 m/s^2 as defined in Example 10. Let the tensions in the strings over A and B now be T N and S N respectively. Applying the principle $F = ma$.
For the 2·1 kg weight:

$$2 \cdot 1g - T = 2 \cdot 1a_1,$$

$$21g - 10T = 21a_1. \tag{1}$$

For the 0·5 kg weight:

$$S - 0 \cdot 5g = 0 \cdot 5a_2,$$

$$2S - g = a_2. \tag{2}$$

For the 0·9 kg weight:

$$S - 0·9g = 0·9a_3,$$

$$10S - 9g = 9a_3. \tag{3}$$

For pulley B:

$$T - 2S - 1·2g = 1·2a_1,$$

$$5T - 10S - 6g = 6a_1. \tag{4}$$

Comparing accelerations,

$$2a_1 = a_2 + a_3. \tag{5}$$

The working of these equations is left to the reader. He will find that the

acceleration of B is now $-\dfrac{9g}{107}$ m/s^2, i.e. B moves downwards.

Exercise 4

1 Find the acceleration of a system composed of two weights, masses 0·35 kg and 0·63 kg, attached by a light inextensible string passing over a smooth fixed pulley. Find also the tension in the string. (Take g as 9·8 m/s^2.)

2 Two masses of magnitudes m and xm are attached by a light inextensible string passing over a smooth fixed pulley. Find the two possible values of x if the acceleration of the system is $g/4$.

3 Two weights of masses m and $2m$ are attached by a light inextensible string which passes over a smooth light pulley. The string is just taut, the free portions being vertical, and the masses held at the same horizontal level at a height d above a horizontal table. Show that if the system is released the heavier mass strikes the table with speed $\sqrt{(2gd/3)}$. (Assume that the string is long enough for the pulley not to interfere with the motion.)

4 A system is composed of two weights, masses M kg and m kg, $M > m$, connected by a light inextensible string over a smooth pulley. They are held with the string taut and vertical at a height d m above a table and are released at the same instant. Find the ratio $M:m$ if it is 0·7 s before the heavier mass strikes the table.

5 Two weights connected by a light inextensible string over a smooth pulley are held at rest side by side distant d above a horizontal table, with the string taut. Their masses are m_1 and m_2, $m_1 > m_2$. Find the maximum distance through which the smaller mass rises, assuming that it does not reach the pulley.

6 Two weights of masses m and M ($M > m$) are held side by side vertically below a fixed smooth pulley. A light inextensible string connecting the two weights and passing over the pulley is just taut. If the weights are at a height h above an inelastic horizontal table, show that the height to which the heavier mass will rise after it is first jerked off the table is

$$\frac{m^2 h}{(M+m)^2}.$$

7 A weight of mass 15 g resting on a horizontal table is connected by a light inextensible string over a smooth pulley to a weight of mass 55 g, which is held with the string just taut 0·8 m above the table. The system is released. At a height h above the table a mass of 105 g becomes attached to the 15 g mass, and the ensuing motion is such that the 55 g mass only just reaches the table. Find h. (Take g as 9·8 m/s^2.)

8 Two particles of masses $2m$ and $5m$ are attached to the ends of a light inextensible string passing over a smooth fixed pulley. They are held at a height of 400 mm above a horizontal table with the string just taut. If they are released and after $0 \cdot 2$ s the string snaps, find the speeds at which the particles strike the table.

9 A light inextensible string is attached by one end to a fixed point from which it passes under a smooth pulley A of mass $3m$, and up over a second smooth pulley B which is fixed. A weight of mass m is attached to the free end of the string. Find the tension in the string and the acceleration of A.

10 Three pulleys A, B and C are light and smooth. A string of fixed length is attached at X and Y to points on a horizontal ceiling, and it passes under A, over B and under C. B is fixed to the ceiling between X and Y, and all parts of the string not touching the pulleys are vertical. If weights of masses $2m$ and $3m$ are attached to A and C respectively find the acceleration of A, and the tension in the string.

11 Two weights of masses m_1 and m_2 are connected by a light inextensible string passing over a smooth pulley, which is in turn connected by a light inextensible string over a smooth fixed pulley to a weight of mass m_3. Find m_1 in terms of m_2 and m_3 if, when the system is free to move, the weight of mass m_1 remains stationary.

12 Three masses, m, $2m$ and $3m$, are suspended on light inextensible strings over two smooth pulleys A and B as illustrated in Fig. 11, A being fixed. If the system is free to move, determine the acceleration of the $3m$ mass.

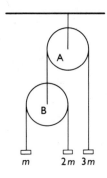

Fig. 11

3 Vectors (1)

3.1 Representation by directed line segments

In Chapter 2 we saw that so long as we were considering motion in one dimension we could ignore the distinction between scalars and vectors. We must now return however and consider the laws that vectors obey in two or more dimensions.

A vector is defined as that which has both magnitude and direction, and we can illustrate this very easily by a straight line, as in Fig. 12. The length of the line AB is in proportion to the magnitude of the vector, and the direction of the line also corresponds to that of the vector. When using points at the ends of lines representing vectors we sometimes use an extra notation for the vector. If the vector here is **r**, then we will sometimes write

r as $\overrightarrow{AB}$.

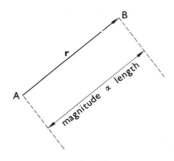

Fig. 12

To increase the size of a vector does not alter its direction, and when we multiply a vector by a scalar then its magnitude is altered by that factor. For example, Fig. 13 shows the vector **r** represented by the line AB. The vector 3**r** is then represented by the line AC, where AC = 3 AB. Similarly the vector $\frac{1}{2}$**r** is represented by the line AD, where D is the mid-point of AB.

If two vectors, 2**r** and 3**r**, act in the same straight line AB, then we say that their combined effect—i.e. their sum, follows the scalar rule of addition and is 5**r**. In more general terms,

$$m\mathbf{r} + n\mathbf{r} = (m+n)\mathbf{r}. \qquad 3.1$$

Now suppose that a vector **r** can be represented by the line joining A to B, then we say the vector −**r** is represented in magnitude and direction by the line joining B to A, and that

$$\mathbf{r}+(-\mathbf{r}) = \mathbf{0},$$

i.e. their combined effect is zero. It follows that *3.1* is true for all scalar *m*, *n*, whether positive or negative.

The reader may realize that we have already assumed *3.1* in Chapter 1, Example 2, and in most of the pulley problems of Chapter 2. It is unlikely that it caused you concern at that stage, but in this chapter we need to be a little more rigorous.

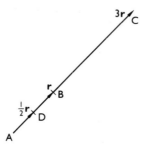

Fig. 13

3.2 The parallelogram of vectors

So far what we have said still only applies to one dimension. Suppose that we now have two vectors **r** and **s** both of which act at a point A but do not act in the same direction. Suppose **r** can be represented by the line AB, and that **s** can be represented by the line AD (see Fig. 14), then we state a further principle:

> **The parallelogram of vectors:** *If two vectors* **r** *and* **s** *acting at a point can be represented in magnitude and direction by the two sides* AB *and* AD *of a parallelogram* ABCD, *then their sum,* **r**+**s**, *is represented in magnitude and direction by the diagonal* AC.

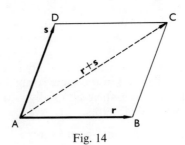

Fig. 14

We frequently refer to the sum of two vectors as their resultant. It is a very short step from here to show that we can add any number of vectors together in this way by just taking them two at a time.

Since opposite sides of a parallelogram are equal it follows that we could represent **s** by the side BC. The resultant is then the closing side of the triangle AC. It may be wondered why we do not give the Principle in this form to start with, but the parallelogram law retains the point of action of each vector—**r**, **s**, and their sum **r**+**s** all act at A, and are represented as such. To move **s** from A to B is to diverge from the true situation.

Suppose now that we have a vector **r** represented by a line OP of length r, and that N is any point on the circle with OP as diameter, then angle ONP, since it is subtended by the diameter, is 90°. Let the line perpendicular to ON through O cut the circle again at L, then angle OLP is also 90°, and OLPN is a rectangle. But ON represents a vector—call it **s**, and OL represents a vector—call it **t**. Then, by the parallelogram of vectors,

$$\mathbf{s}+\mathbf{t} = \mathbf{r}. \qquad\qquad 3.2$$

But N can be any point on the circle, and angle PON can lie anywhere in the range 0°–90°. Thus we can always find two perpendicular vectors **s** and **t** in any particular direction we choose so that *3.2* holds.

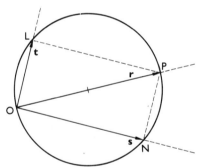

Fig. 15

For a particular direction these two vectors are unique, and since they are at right-angles they each independently represent the total effect of **r** in their particular directions. **s** and **t** are called components of **r**. The process of finding such components is called resolving; if we resolve **r** in the direction ON then the result is **s**. If the angle PON is θ then the magnitude of **s** is $r \cos \theta$, and of **t** is $r \sin \theta$.

The examples that follow are generally based on the resolution of forces, but we should not forget that all types of vectors can be treated in this way.

EXAMPLE 1   *Three forces of magnitudes 3 N, 2 N and 5 N act on a particle O in directions* OA, OB *and* OC *respectively, where angles* AOB,

BOC *and* AOC *are 90°, 60° and 150° respectively. Find the resultant (i.e. the sum) of these forces.*

Since OA and OB are already perpendicular, we shall resolve the forces in those two perpendicular directions. Resolving forces in the direction OA the resultant has component:

$$(3 - 5\cos 30°) = (3 - \frac{5\sqrt{3}}{2}) \text{ N.}$$

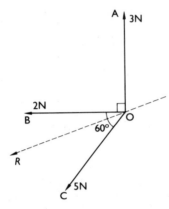

Fig. 16

Resolving in the direction OB, the resultant has component

$$2 + 5\cos 60° = 2 + 2\tfrac{1}{2}$$
$$= 4\tfrac{1}{2} \text{ N.}$$

The magnitude of the resultant then comes using Pythagoras's Theorem (as you would find OP in Fig. 15 from ON and OL), and is R N where

$$R^2 = 4\tfrac{1}{2}^2 + (3 - \frac{5\sqrt{3}}{2})^2$$

$$= 20 \cdot 25 + 9 - 15\sqrt{3} + \frac{75}{4}$$

$$= 48 - 25 \cdot 98$$

$$= 22 \cdot 02.$$

$$\therefore \ R \fallingdotseq 4 \cdot 69.$$

The direction of R is $\tan^{-1}(4\tfrac{1}{2}/(3 - 5\sqrt{3}/2))$ to OA $= \tan^{-1} 9/(6 - 5\sqrt{3})$.

$\therefore$ Resultant is 4·69 N at $\tan^{-1} 9/(6 - 5\sqrt{3})$ to OA.

EXAMPLE 2   *A parallelogram* ABCD *has angle* B = 60°, *and* AB = 2 BC = 2 *units.* AC *cuts* BD *at* O, *and forces represented in magnitude and direction by* OA, AD, OD *and* CD *all act at* O. *Find their resultant.*

From the trigonometry of the figure (Fig. 17), angle ACB = 90°, so we resolve in directions AD and CA. AC is of length $\sqrt{3}$, and so OA is of length $\frac{\sqrt{3}}{2}$. By Pythagoras OD^2 is then $\frac{3}{4}+1$, and hence OD = $\frac{\sqrt{7}}{2}$.

Resolving parallel to AD, the resultant has component

$$1 + \frac{\sqrt{7}}{2} \cos BDA + 2 \cos 60° = 1 + \frac{\sqrt{7}}{2} \cdot \frac{2}{\sqrt{7}} + 1$$

$$= 3.$$

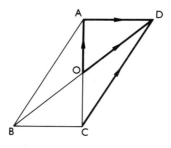

Fig. 17

Resolving parallel to CA, the resultant has component

$$\frac{\sqrt{3}}{2} + \frac{\sqrt{7}}{2} \sin BDA + 2 \sin 60° = \frac{\sqrt{3}}{2} + \frac{\sqrt{7}}{2} \cdot \frac{\sqrt{3}}{\sqrt{7}} + \sqrt{3}$$

$$= 2\sqrt{3}.$$

Hence the magnitude of the resultant is $((2\sqrt{3})^2 + 3^2)^{\frac{1}{2}} = \sqrt{21}$.

The direction of the resultant is at an angle $\tan^{-1} \frac{2\sqrt{3}}{3}$ to AD.

∴ The resultant is $\sqrt{21}$ units at $\tan^{-1} 2/\sqrt{3}$ to AD.

Exercise 5

1 Find the resultant of two forces of magnitudes 12 N and 18 N acting at a point O along OX and OY respectively if angle XOY is 90°.

2 Forces of 1, 2, 3 and 4 newtons act at a point O in directions OA, OB, OC and OD where angles AOB, BOC, COD and DOA are all 90°. Find the magnitude and direction of their resultant.

3 Find the resultant of two forces P N and Q N acting at a point O in directions at $\alpha°$ and $\beta°$ to a line OA (in an anticlockwise sense) if

(a) P = 2, Q = 3, α = 60, β = 270;
(b) P = 4, Q = 24, α = 45, β = 240;
(c) P = 10, Q = 15, α = 22·5, β = 138.

4 Find the magnitude and direction of the resultant of three vectors acting at a point O, each being of magnitude 6 units, along lines OA, OB and OC if angles AOB, BOC and AOC are 90°, 120° and 210° respectively.

5 Given a rectangle ABCD and any point P inside the rectangle, prove that

$$\overrightarrow{PA}+\overrightarrow{PB}+\overrightarrow{PC}+\overrightarrow{PD} = n\overrightarrow{PO}$$

where O is the intersection of the diagonals and n is a constant. (The notation $\overrightarrow{XY}$ stands for the vector represented in magnitude, direction and position by the line XY.)

6 Prove that if 5 forces acting at a point can be represented in magnitude and direction by the sides AB, BC, CD, DE and EF of a hexagon, then their resultant is represented in magnitude and direction by AF.

Hence find graphically the resultant of forces of magnitude P, 3P, 2P, 2P and 4P acting at O which act so that the angles between them taken in an anti-clockwise direction are 30°, 70°, 110° and 20° respectively.

7 A particle of mass 145 g is acted on by three separate forces of magnitudes 3 N, 5 N and 6 N in directions making angles of 30°, 60° and 150° with a line OA, measured anticlockwise round O. Find the acceleration of the particle.

8 Forces act radially from the centre of a regular hexagon ABCDEF with magnitudes 1 along OA, 2 along OB, 3 along OC, 2 along OD, and 1 along OE. Find the resultant.

An alternative system of forces having the same resultant as the first system is composed of forces P along FA, Q along FB, and R along FE. If $P = 2$ units find Q and R.

9 A telegraph pole supports 3 wires from a northerly direction, 5 wires from the south-east and 2 wires from the west. Each wire exerts a force of 10 N on the pole. Find the magnitude of the resultant force to the nearest 0·1 N, and its direction to the nearest 10′.

3.3 The triangle of vectors

When the resultant of a set of vectors acting at a point is zero they are said to be in equilibrium. If the resultant is not zero, then whenever we resolve in two perpendicular directions we must always get at least one non-zero component. We would in fact always get two non-zero components unless we happened to choose one of the directions to coincide with the resultant itself. Consequently we conclude that it is sufficient proof that such a system is in equilibrium if the components in any two perpendicular directions are both zero. Even this is more stringent than is really necessary; to resolve in any two non-parallel directions would be sufficient.

Many problems begin from the other end—namely that a system is assumed to be in equilibrium to start with. If we take a simple case where three forces acting at a point are in equilibrium certain important results follow.

On page 28 we stated the principle of the Parallelogram of Vectors. We represented vectors **r** and **s** by the sides AB and AD of the parallelogram ABCD, and said that **r**+**s** was represented by AC. Thus if we added a third vector **t** to **r** and **s** where **t** is represented by CA, the resultant is zero—

i.e. **r**, **s** and **t** are in equilibrium. We thus arrive at a result referred to as the **Triangle of Vectors** which states that:

> *If three vectors acting at a point can be represented in magnitude and direction by the three sides of a triangle taken in order, then they are in equilibrium.*

The phrase 'taken in order' is important, and means that if the directions of the vectors are marked on the sides of the triangle (as in Fig. 19) they will be either all clockwise or all anti-clockwise round the triangle. Remember that the Parallelogram of Vectors and the Triangle of Vectors are two distinct statements. The former concerns the resultant of two vectors; the latter concerns the equilibrium of three vectors.

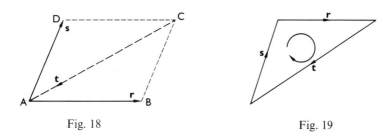

Fig. 18   Fig. 19

3.4 Lami's Theorem

A corollary to the Triangle of Vectors is **Lami's Theorem** which although traditionally associated with forces applies to all vectors. We state it here in the vector form:

> *If the resultant of three vectors acting at a point is zero, then each vector is proportional to the sine of the angle between the other two.*

Let the vectors have magnitudes V_1, V_2 and V_3, and the angles between them be α, β, γ as shown in Fig. 20(a). Since the vector sum is zero we can represent the three vectors by the sides of a triangle ABC, where BC $= V_1$, CA $= V_2$ and AB $= V_3$. Then since the sides represent the directions as well as magnitudes, the exterior angles at A, B and C are α, β and γ respectively (Fig. 20(b)). But the sine of an angle is the sine of its supplement, and by the Sine Rule

$$\frac{V_1}{\sin A} = \frac{V_2}{\sin B} = \frac{V_3}{\sin C}.$$

Hence

$$\frac{V_1}{\sin \alpha} = \frac{V_2}{\sin \beta} = \frac{V_3}{\sin \gamma}$$

which is Lami's Theorem.

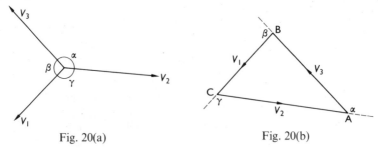

Fig. 20(a)   Fig. 20(b)

It is an important fact that if a system is in equilibrium under the action of three non-parallel forces, then these three forces must all act through (i.e. be directed through) the same point. The case often arises where the vector sum of three forces is zero but the system is not in equilibrium because they do not pass through the same point. A simple example of this is to imagine three equal forces acting along the sides of an equilateral triangle, all in the same sense round the figure. Their sum is zero, but it will be readily appreciated that these forces will tend to turn the triangle about its centre, and it is not in equilibrium. We discuss this type of situation in Chapter 4; at this point we wish to apply the Triangle of Vectors and Lami's Theorem to systems which are in equilibrium under three forces.

In a number of examples that follow, the systems will involve points of contact between components of the system, and we need to know how the internal forces act between these different components. So long as these components are smooth, intuition leads us to observe that

(i) the reaction between a rod and a plane acts perpendicularly to the plane, and

(ii) the reaction between a rod and a peg is perpendicular to the rod.

These situations are illustrated in Figs. 21 and 22. If (i) and (ii) were not true, then an arbitrary factor would be introduced which would be quite contrary to our experience of the consistency of the world in which we live. To illustrate this, consider the situation pictured in Fig. 23 where we have a rod AB in contact with a peg P. We say that the reaction between them

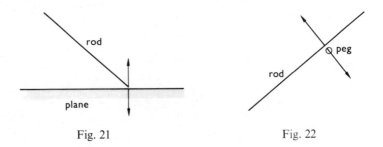

Fig. 21   Fig. 22

lies in the line PN where PN is perpendicular to AB. But suppose it is argued that the reaction lies along PX at an angle to PN, then we could equally argue that it lies along PY, where Y is on the opposite side of PN to X and angle NPX = angle NPY. Since both cannot be true, neither can be true. Therefore the reaction lies along PN.

We can follow a similar argument for the rod in contact with a plane.

The direction of the reaction at a hinge is determined solely by the other forces of the system.

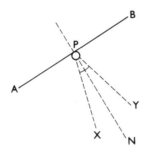

Fig. 23

EXAMPLE 3   *A uniform rod AB of weight $\frac{1}{2}$ kg rests in equilibrium with the end A in contact with a smooth vertical wall, and is supported by a peg P a third of the way along its length from A. Find the angle of the rod to the vertical, and the reactions at the wall and at the peg.*

The fact that the rod is uniform implies that the weight of the rod acts at the mid-point of AB—call this point G. (This point is often referred to as the centre of gravity, or as the centre of mass.) There are three forces acting: the reaction at the wall, the reaction at the peg, and the weight of the rod. These must act through a point—call it O. Then the forces act along AO, OP and GO as shown in Fig. 24. Note that angles XAO and APO must both be 90°.

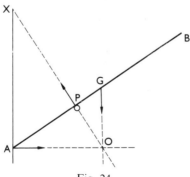

Fig. 24

By the geometry of the figure triangles APO and AOG are similar. Thus

$$\frac{AP}{AO} = \frac{AO}{AG},$$

$$\frac{AB}{3AO} = \frac{2AO}{AB}$$

$$AO^2 = AB^2/6.$$

If AB makes an angle θ to the vertical, then

$$\sin \theta = \frac{AO}{AG}$$

$$= \frac{AB}{\sqrt{6}} \cdot \frac{2}{AB}$$

$$= \sqrt{\frac{2}{3}}.$$

Angle of the rod to the vertical is $\sin^{-1} \sqrt{\frac{2}{3}}$.

If we now produce OP to meet the wall vertically above A at X, then triangle AXO is the triangle of vectors—AX has the direction of the weight, AO of the reaction to the wall, and OX of the reaction at the peg. But

$$OX = AX/\sin AOX$$

$$= \sqrt{\frac{3}{2}} \cdot AX.$$

$\therefore$ Reaction at the peg is $\sqrt{\frac{3}{2}}$.weight $= \sqrt{\frac{3}{2}} \cdot \frac{1}{2}$ kg.

Reaction at the peg is $\frac{g}{2}\sqrt{\frac{3}{2}}$ N.

Similarly, using Pythagoras's Theorem,

$$AO^2 = OX^2 - AX^2$$

$$= \left(\frac{3}{2} - 1\right) AX^2,$$

and $$AO = AX/\sqrt{2}.$$

$\therefore$ The reaction at the wall is $g/2\sqrt{2}$ N.

Problems such as this last example often lend themselves to several methods of solution. Spotting the triangle of vectors within the diagram frequently proves to be the best and easiest. We could however have used Lami's Theorem applied at O, or alternatively given the reactions labels and resolved horizontally and vertically getting a pair of simultaneous

equations. An example obviously appropriate to Lami's Theorem follows.

EXAMPLE 4   *A mass* C *of weight* W N *is suspended by two light strings*
AC *and* BC *from points* A *and* B *on the same horizontal level above* C.
AB = AC = 12 cm, CB = 8 cm. *Find the tensions in* AC *and* BC.

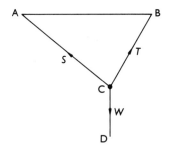

Fig. 25

Let the tension in AC be S and in BC be T. If D is a point vertically
below C, then Lami's Theorem gives

$$\frac{W}{\sin ACB} = \frac{S}{\sin BCD} = \frac{T}{\sin ACD} \qquad (1)$$

But $\sin BCD = \cos ABC,$

and $\sin ACD = \cos BAC.$

Since triangle ABC is isosceles,

$$\cos ABC = 4/12 = \tfrac{1}{3}.$$

Further, $\sin ACB = \frac{2\sqrt{2}}{3}.$

∴ From (1) $\dfrac{3W}{2\sqrt{2}} = 3S,$

$$S = \frac{W}{2\sqrt{2}}.$$

Let angle BAC = 2θ, then if the reader is familiar with trigonometrical
formulae he will know that

$$\cos 2\theta = 1 - 2 \sin^2 \theta$$

giving $\cos 2\theta = 1 - 2/9$

$$= 7/9.$$

Alternatively we can arrive at the same result using the Cosine Rule which gives

$$\cos \text{BAC} = \frac{12^2 + 12^2 - 8^2}{2 \times 12 \times 12}$$

$$= \frac{288 - 64}{2 \times 12 \times 12}$$

$$= \frac{224}{32 \times 9}$$

$$= 7/9.$$

From (1)
$$\frac{3W}{2\sqrt{2}} = 9T/7,$$

$$T = \frac{7W}{6\sqrt{2}}.$$

$\therefore$ The tensions in AC and BC are $\dfrac{W}{2\sqrt{2}}$ and $\dfrac{7W}{6\sqrt{2}}$ respectively.

EXAMPLE 5   *A uniform trap-door of weight $20\sqrt{3}$ N leans against a smooth wall at an angle of $30°$ to the vertical when open. Find the reaction at the hinge.*

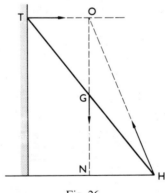

Fig. 26

Let the centre of mass of the door be G, the hinge be H, and the top edge of the door against the wall be T. The weight acts vertically through G, and the reaction at T acts horizontally through T, the lines of action of the two forces meeting at O. Since the system is in equilibrium under three forces, the reaction at H must act along HO (Fig. 26).

If OG produced meets the horizontal through H at N, triangle ONH is the triangle of forces. But

$$\text{angle OHN} = \tan^{-1} 2\sqrt{3},$$

since $\tan \text{THN} = \tan 60° = \sqrt{3}$, and G is the mid-point of TH.

$$\therefore \quad \sin \text{OHN} = \frac{2\sqrt{3}}{\sqrt{13}},$$

and $$\text{OH} = \text{ON}/\sin \text{OHN}.$$

Thus the reaction at H is

$$20\sqrt{3}.\frac{\sqrt{13}}{2\sqrt{3}} \text{ N} = 10\sqrt{13} \text{ N}.$$

Reaction at H is $10\sqrt{13}$ N at an angle $\tan^{-1} 2\sqrt{3}$ to the horizontal.

Exercise 6

1 A uniform rod XY is smoothly hinged at X to a vertical wall, at an angle of 60° to the wall, and it is held in this position by a light horizontal wire to the wall attached at the mid-point of the rod. Find the tension in the wire and the reaction at X if the mass of the rod is 5 kg. (Take g as 9·8 m/s².)

2 A uniform rod AB of mass 10 g is hinged to a vertical wall at A and a string BC supports the rod so that triangle ABC is equilateral, with C vertically above A. Find the reaction at A.

3 A smooth sphere of radius a and weight mg has a light inextensible string attached by one end to a point on its surface, the other end being attached to a point on a vertical wall. If the tension in the string is $4mg$, find the length of the string and the reaction between the sphere and the wall.

4 A particle of weight 12 N is supported by two strings, one of which is under a tension of 5 N and is at 45° to the vertical. Find the position and the tension of the other string to the nearest 10′ and 0·1 N respectively.

5 A light inextensible string ABCD is hung from its ends A and D so that AD is horizontal. Weights of masses M_1 and M_2 are hung from points B and C respectively, and it is observed that angle DAB = 60°, angle ABC = 150°, and angle ADC = 45°. Show that

$$M_1 : M_2 = 1 : \sqrt{2} \sin 75°.$$

6 A cube with edges a units long and mass m has a string of length l attached to the mid-point of one face and is hung by the string from a point on a smooth vertical wall. Show that, provided $l < a/2$, the angle the string makes with the wall is independent of a and l, and deduce the tension in the string for $l < a/2$.

7 A sphere of mass 0·85 kg and radius 45 mm rests on a smooth plane inclined at an angle of 30° to the horizontal. The sphere is held in this position by a string of length 90 mm attached by one end to a point on its surface and by the other to a point on the plane. Find the tension in the string.

8 A uniform plank AB of length $4a$ rests, with its lower end A at the foot of a vertical wall, against a smooth fixed cylinder, the axis of which is horizontal and perpendicular to the plank. The distance from A to the point of contact with the cylinder is $3a$, and AB is at 60° to the horizontal. If the weight of the plank is W, find the reaction between the plank and the cylinder.

3.5 Parallel vectors—moments

It is not difficult to see that we now have the mathematics to be able to analyse any static problem where all the forces act at one point, and we have noted that if there are only three forces involved in a given system in equilibrium then they must act through just one point or else be parallel. In this section we consider this latter case.

Suppose we have two parallel forces of magnitudes P and Q acting at points A and B respectively. If we add a force of magnitude T in the direction BA at A and in the direction AB at B then since these are equal, opposite and in the same line, the situation remains unaltered. Let AF represent the force T at A and AH the force P, and let G be such that AFGH is a parallelogram (Fig. 27). Similarly at B, BC represents the

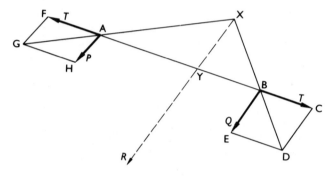

Fig. 27

force T, BE the force Q, and BCDE is a parallelogram. By the Parallelogram of Vectors, AG represents the resultant of T with P, and BD represents the resultant of T with Q. Let GA and DB produced meet at X. The resultant of the system R must be parallel to P and Q and must pass through X. Let it cut AB at a point Y. Then by similar triangles

$$\frac{XY}{YB} = \frac{Q}{T},$$

and similarly

$$\frac{XY}{YA} = \frac{P}{T},$$

Hence

$$AY/BY = Q/P.$$

Also, if we replace P and Q by forces of magnitudes and directions the same as AG and BD but acting at X, we see the resultant must have magnitude $P+Q$.

Thus, the resultant of two parallel forces P and Q is equal to their sum, $P+Q$, and divides the line between them in the ratio Q to P.

Suppose now that AB represents a light but rigid rod, then from what we have just deduced a peg placed at Y would keep the rod in equilibrium under the two forces P and Q. You may then observe that

$$P \times AY = Q \times YB.$$

This is just a simple case of a very important principle. Before we quote it we define what we mean by the **Moment of a Vector**. The moment of a vector **V** about a point P is defined as the product $V \times d$, where d is the perpendicular distance of the line of action of **V** from P. Similarly the moment of a vector **V** about a line L is the product $V_1 \times d$, where d is the perpendicular distance of the line of action **V** from L, and V_1 is the component of **V** perpendicular to L.

The moment of a force is a measure of the turning effect it produces. By increasing the value of d we can increase the moment—the turning effect—of our force, which is the principle behind our use of levers, and gave rise to the claim of Archimedes: 'Give me a place to stand and to rest my lever on and I will move the earth.'

The turning effect of a force can be in either an anticlockwise or a clockwise direction. It is normal convention to take an anticlockwise moment as positive, and a clockwise one as negative. We are now in a position to state the principle.

> **Principle of moments:** *For a system in equilibrium, the sum of the moments of all the forces about any point in the system will be zero.*

This principle is valid whether the forces are parallel or not, and gives us another very useful way of obtaining an equation to solve an equilibrium problem. We illustrate this in the examples that follow.

EXAMPLE 6   *A uniform beam AB of length 1·5 m and weight 4 kg rests horizontally on supports at A and B. Masses of 3 kg, 2 kg and 1 kg are placed on the beam 30 cm, 60 cm and 110 cm from A respectively. Find (i) the resultant force exerted by the three masses on the beam, (ii) the reactions at the two supports.*

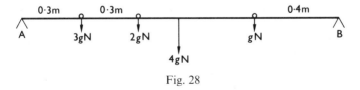

Fig. 28

Fig. 28 illustrates the situation. To answer the first part of the question we could combine the three forces two at a time as outlined in the beginning of this section. The resultant must have magnitude

$$(3+2+1)g \text{ N} = 6g \text{ N}.$$

The 3 kg and 1 kg masses are separated by a distance of $(150-70) = 80$ cm, and their resultant divides this in the ratio $1:3$ (see Fig. 29).

We now must find the resultant of 4 kg 50 cm from A and 2 kg 60 cm from A (see Fig. 30). The resultant must divide the distance between them in the ratio $1:2$, i.e. the resultant has magnitude $6g$ N and acts $53\frac{1}{3}$ cm from A.

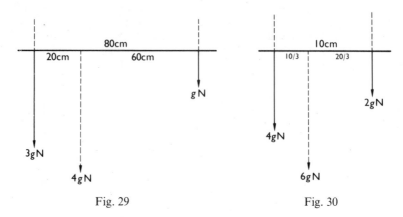

Fig. 29   Fig. 30

This method, while it stresses the points made in the text, is not the most convenient. It is quicker to take moments about a suitably chosen point—e.g. A or B. We reason that the moment of the three forces about A, say, must equal the moment of the resultant about A. We know that the resultant must be $6g$ N, and we let the resultant act at a point distant d cm from A. Then taking moments about A:

$$3g \times 30 + 2g \times 60 + g \times 110 = 6g \times d.$$

Hence
$$d = (90 + 120 + 110)/6$$
$$= 320/6$$
$$= 53\tfrac{1}{3}, \text{ as before.}$$

Thus the resultant force exerted by the three masses is $6g$ N, $53\frac{1}{3}$ cm from A.

Let the reactions at the supports A and B be R_a and R_b respectively. Taking moments about A, this time for the whole system, we get

$$150R_b - 3g \times 30 - 2g \times 60 - 4g \times 75 - g \times 110 = 0,$$

or more simply since we have found the resultant of the three weights already:

$$150R_b - 6g \times 53\tfrac{1}{3} - 4g \times 75 = 0. \tag{1}$$

An alternative way of forming the equation would be to equate the anti-clockwise moments to the clockwise moments.

It follows from (1) that

$$150R_b = 300g + 320g$$
$$= 620g.$$
$$\therefore \ R_b = 62g/15.$$

We can find R_a in a similar way by taking moments about B or some other convenient point. But this would be more tedious than necessary since $R_a + R_b$ must equal the sum of all the other forces—i.e.

$$R_a + R_b = (3+2+4+1)g.$$
$$R_a = 10g - 62g/15$$
$$= 88g/15.$$

$\therefore$ The reactions at A and B are $88g/15$ and $62g/15$ N respectively.

EXAMPLE 7   *A uniform plank 2 m long is supported at one end A and at a point B 1·4 m from A. Its mass is 3·5 kg. Find the maximum weight that can be placed at C, the opposite end of the plank to A, if the plank is not to topple.*

The essential fact in this type of problem is that if the plank is going to topple, i.e. turn about B, then the reaction at A must disappear. To find the limiting condition therefore we put this reaction at A equal to zero. If the maximum weight is then W N, taking moments about B:

$$60 \times W = 40 \times 3\cdot5g,$$
$$W = 7g/3.$$

The maximum weight that can be placed at C is $7g/3$ N.

EXAMPLE 8   *A uniform rod of mass 10 kg is hinged at one end A, and rests against a peg at an angle of 30° to the horizontal. If the rod is 6 units long and the peg is 5 units from A, find the reaction at the peg.*

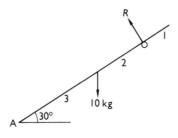

Fig. 31

This problem is essentially the same as number 6 of Exercise 6, but we include it here to show how we can solve this kind of problem using moments as an alternative to the Triangle of Vectors etc.

Remembering that it is the perpendicular distance which gives us the moment of a force, we take moments about the hinge A, taking the reaction at the peg to be R:

$$10g \times 3 \cos 30° = R \times 5,$$

$$R = 6g \cos 30°$$

$$= 3\sqrt{3}g.$$

The reaction at the peg is $3\sqrt{3g}$ N.

Exercise 7

1 A, B and C are three points lying in the same straight line ABC so that AB = 2BC. Parallel forces of magnitudes P, $3P$ and $4P$ act through A, B and C respectively. If their resultant cuts AC at D, find the ratio AD:DC.

2 A man and a boy carry a uniform plank of length 1·6 m and mass 8 kg on top of which they have placed tools weighing 3 kg 0·6 m from the boy, and pots of paint weighing 4 kg 0·4 m from the man. Find the weight in kg that the boy supports.

3 A uniform plank AB 2·5 m long is supported by two ladders at points C and D where AC = DB = 0·5 m. The plank weighs 12 kg. How close to the ends can a painter stand if he weighs 76 kg? (Give your answer to the nearest cm.)

4 A, B, C, D and E are points on a uniform rod AE such that AB = BC = 20 cm; CD = 40 cm; DE = 50 cm. The rod is supported at points B and E, and masses of 6 kg, 10 kg, and 14 kg are placed at points A, C and D respectively. The rod weighs 12 kg. Find the reactions at the two supports.

5 A large stone weighing 40 kg is to be levered upwards against a pivot lying 25 cm from the stone. Calculate the minimum length of the lever if the maximum force that can be exerted at the free end of the lever is 50 N. (Take g as 9·8 m/s².)

6 A uniform bar 1·2 m long is supported symmetrically by two vertical strings 1 m apart. If the bar weighs 5 kg and a weight of 4 kg is hung 0·75 m from one end, find the tension in newtons in each string.

If neither string can stand a tension of more than 60 N, find the furthest position from the centre at which the weight can safely be hung. (Take g as 9·8 m/s².)

7 The figure represents a beam balance. The pan is positioned 10 cm from the pivot and is exactly balanced when two weights A and B rest on the zero marks of sliding

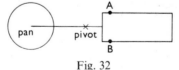

Fig. 32

scales on the opposite arm. A is of mass 50 g, and B is of mass 5 g. Each sliding scale is 20 cm long. Calculate the maximum mass that can be weighed on the pan. How should the sliding scales be calibrated? Where will the masses A and B be placed to balance a mass of 25·5 g on the pan?

8 A uniform rod AB of mass 2 kg is hinged at A and is held by a string at B so that AB is at an angle of 30° to the horizontal, and the string at B is at an angle of 45° to BA. Find the tension in the string, and the reaction at the hinge.

4 Applications

4.1 Reduction to a single force or couple

It should be recalled that referring only to the components of the resultant of a set of forces as a proof of equilibrium is only satisfactory if all the forces act through a point (see p. 34). We made the point by referring to an equilateral triangle with three forces of equal magnitude acting along its sides taken in order (Fig. 33). We observed that in this situation the triangle would tend to rotate. Now that we have defined the moment of a vector we are in a position to measure this turning effect.

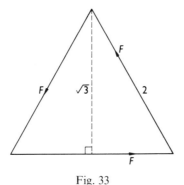

Fig. 33

Suppose that the triangle in question has sides of length 2 units, and that the forces each have magnitude F. Irrespective of which vertex I choose, the moment about that vertex of the system will be $\sqrt{3}F$. When a system has no resultant force but does have a moment about any point in the system we say that it reduces to a **couple**.

To understand more clearly what constitutes a couple, we consider two equal but opposite parallel forces not acting in the same line. Since they have no resultant they must represent a couple. Let the magnitude of each of these forces be P, and the perpendicular distance between them be d (Fig. 34). The moment of one of these forces about any point on the line of the other is Pd.

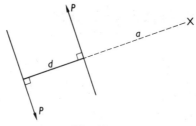

Fig. 34

Suppose now that we take moments about a point X which is a distance a from the nearer of the two forces, then the moment is

$$P(d+a) - Pa = Pd, \text{ as before.}$$

If we had considered two forces twice as large—each $2P$, but only half as far apart—$\frac{1}{2}d$, then the moment would still be the same—Pd. So we conclude that a couple can always be represented as two equal but opposite forces, but that it should be defined in terms of the moment of the couple since this is a constant independent of the point we take moments about. We refer to this moment as the magnitude of the couple. As before convention has it that an anticlockwise couple is positive, and a clockwise couple is negative.

We can now state some important general results applicable to any system of forces acting in a plane. The first is that:

> *Any system of forces acting in a plane is equivalent to a single force applied at an arbitrary point together with a couple.*

The single force will of course be equal to the vector sum of all the forces acting in the system.

The second important fact is that:

> *Any system of forces acting in a plane can be reduced either to a single force or to a couple.*

The single force will again be the vector sum of all the forces, but positioned in such a way as to eliminate the couple. The system can only be reduced to a couple if this vector sum is zero. It is not immediately obvious that the couple and single force that we generally get as equivalent to a given system can in fact be reduced to just a single force, but we can demonstrate this as follows.

Suppose that a system of forces acting in a plane has been reduced to a single force R acting through a point A in a direction perpendicular to a line AB, together with a couple of moment M. Let us represent the couple by two equal but opposite forces each of magnitude R, then these forces will be a distance d apart where $Rd = M$. Further, let these forces representing the couple be parallel to the single force R. We position the couple force which acts in the opposite direction to the single force at A. Then taking the vector sum of the three forces the resultant is a single force of magnitude R acting through a point distance d from A on AB.

It should now be clear that to prove a system is in equilibrium when forces do not all act through one point we both resolve the forces and take moments. This will normally allow us to form three equations. Resolving and taking moments is the basis of all analytical work on systems in equilibrium and systems not in equilibrium; any static problem should be analysed in this way.

EXAMPLE 1   *A square ABCD has forces acting along its sides; P along AB, Q along BC, R along CD, 2R along DA and 3R along AC in the senses indicated by the order of the letters. Find P and Q in terms of R if the system reduces to a couple, and find the magnitude of this couple if AB is 1 unit long.*

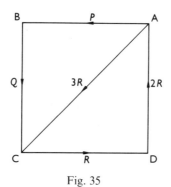

Fig. 35

Since the system reduces to a couple, the resultant force is zero, i.e. the sum of the components in any particular direction is zero. Considering components parallel to **AB**:

$$P + 3R \cos 45° - R = 0.$$

$$\therefore P = \underline{R(1 - 3/\sqrt{2}).}$$

Similarly, considering components parallel to **AD**:

$$Q + 3R \cos 45° - 2R = 0.$$

$$\therefore Q = \underline{R(2 - 3/\sqrt{2}).}$$

Taking moments about B (since this enables us to avoid the complex expressions we have formed for P and Q), the moment of the couple is

$$2R + R - 3R/\sqrt{2}.$$

Moment of the couple is $3R(1 - 1/\sqrt{2})$.

EXAMPLE 2   *A rectangle* ABCD *has sides* AB = *4a units and* BC = *3a units. Forces of magnitudes 2P, P, 3P, 3P and P act along the lines* AB, BC, CD, DA *and* CA *in the senses indicated by the order of the letters. Find the magnitude, position and direction of the resultant. The system is to be reduced to a couple of magnitude 4aP by the addition of a force through* D *and two equal but opposite forces acting along* AB *and* CD. *Find these forces.*

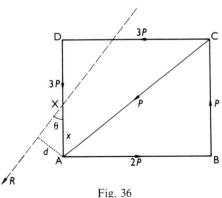

Fig. 36

Fig. 36 illustrates the initial situation. Note that triangle ABC is Pythagorean and that AC = 5a.

Let the resultant be R acting through a point X distant x from A on AD. The component of R parallel to BA is

$$3P + \tfrac{4}{5}P - 2P = 9P/5.$$

The component of R parallel to DA is

$$3P + \tfrac{3}{5}P - P = 13P/5.$$

Hence the resultant acts at an angle $\tan^{-1} \dfrac{9P/5}{13P/5} = \tan^{-1} \dfrac{9}{13}$ to AD, and by Pythagoras

$$R^2 = \left(\frac{9P}{5}\right)^2 + \left(\frac{13P}{5}\right)^2$$

$$= \frac{250P^2}{25}.$$

$$\therefore\ R = \sqrt{10}P.$$

To find x we equate the moments of the given forces about a point on the plane to the moment of the resultant about the same point. In this case we take moments about A. To find the moment of the resultant about A we suppose that it acts at X, and take the moment of the components.

Then the moment is

$$\tfrac{9}{5}P.x + \tfrac{13}{5}P.0 = 9Px/5.$$

We can justify this as follows. Let $\tan^{-1}\tfrac{9}{13}$ be θ, and let the perpendicular distance from A to R be d, then the moment of R about A is

$$Rd = R.x \sin\theta$$

$$= x.R \sin\theta$$

$$= x.(\text{component parallel to BA}).$$

Taking moments about A,

$$3a.3P + 4a.P = \frac{9P}{5}.x,$$

$$9x = 65a,$$

$$x = \frac{65a}{9}.$$

The resultant has magnitude $\sqrt{10}P$ and acts through a point $65a/9$ units from A on AD produced at $\tan^{-1}\tfrac{9}{13}$ to DA.

To answer the second part of the question we first reduce the system to a couple. We do this by introducing a force equal and opposite to the resultant acting through D. The moment of the couple is then the moment of the resultant about D, which is

$$\frac{9P}{5}.\left(\frac{65a}{9} - 3a\right) = \frac{9P}{5}.\frac{38a}{9}$$

$$= 38aP/5.$$

But the couple is to have magnitude $4aP$. We must therefore add to the system a couple of magnitude $-\tfrac{18}{5}aP$ by inserting the forces along AB and CD. If we add in forces of magnitude F in the directions BA and DC, then the magnitude of this couple will be $-3aF$. Therefore

$$3aF = \frac{18}{5}aP,$$

$$F = 6P/5.$$

The system will reduce to a couple of magnitude $4aP$ by adding a force $\sqrt{10}P$ through D at $\tan^{-1}\tfrac{9}{13}$ to AD, and forces $6P/5$ along BA and DC.

4.2 Extension of the parallelogram of vectors

Suppose that two forces can be expressed as multiples of the lengths of two sides of a triangle, where these sides represent the directions of the forces. Let two forces acting at a point O be equivalent in magnitude, direction and position to $a\overrightarrow{OA}$ and $b\overrightarrow{OB}$. Let their resultant cut AB at a point P, and let X be the fourth vertex of the parallelogram OPAX, and Y the fourth vertex of the parallelogram OPBY (Fig. 37).

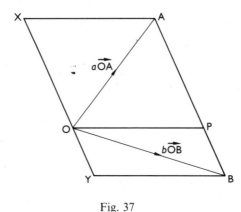

Fig. 37

Applying the converse of the parallelogram of vectors,

$$a\overrightarrow{OA} = a\overrightarrow{OP} + a\overrightarrow{OX},$$

and similarly

$$b\overrightarrow{OB} = b\overrightarrow{OP} + b\overrightarrow{OY}.$$

Adding,

$$a\overrightarrow{OA} + b\overrightarrow{OB} = a\overrightarrow{OP} + b\overrightarrow{OP} + a\overrightarrow{OX} + b\overrightarrow{OY}.$$

But the resultant was defined to lie on OP, and so $a\overrightarrow{OX} + b\overrightarrow{OY}$ must equal zero. Then

$$a\overrightarrow{OA} + b\overrightarrow{OB} = (a+b)\overrightarrow{OP}.$$

Further, since $a\overrightarrow{OX} + b\overrightarrow{OY} = 0$, and OX = AP, OY = PB, it follows that AP:PB = $b:a$. Thus we have the useful extension to the parallelogram of vectors that:

> *if two forces can be represented as $a\overrightarrow{OA}$ and $b\overrightarrow{OB}$ in both magnitude and direction in triangle OAB, then their resultant is $(a+b)\overrightarrow{OP}$ where P lies on AB and divides AB in the ratio $b:a$.*

EXAMPLE 3   P *is a point outside triangle* ABC. *Show that*

$$\overrightarrow{PA} + \overrightarrow{PB} + \overrightarrow{PC} = 3\overrightarrow{PG}$$

where G *is the centroid of triangle* ABC.

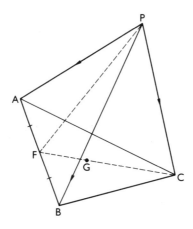

Fig. 38

The reader will be familiar with the fact that the centroid, the intersection of the medians, divides each median in the ratio $1:2$. Let the midpoint of AB be F, then by the parallelogram principle

$$\overrightarrow{PA} + \overrightarrow{PB} = 2\overrightarrow{PF}.$$

But also

$$2\overrightarrow{PF} + \overrightarrow{PC} = 3\overrightarrow{PG}$$

where G divides CF in the ratio $2:1$, i.e. where G is the centroid. Thus

$$\underline{\overrightarrow{PA} + \overrightarrow{PB} + \overrightarrow{PC} = 3\overrightarrow{PG}.}$$

EXAMPLE 4   *Prove that the resultant of four forces represented by*

$2\overrightarrow{OA}$, $3\overrightarrow{OD}$, $2\overrightarrow{OC}$ *and* $\overrightarrow{OB}$ *where* O *is a point lying outside a rectangle*

ABCD *is* $8\overrightarrow{OG}$, *where* G *lies on* BD *and* DG$:$GB $= 3:5$.

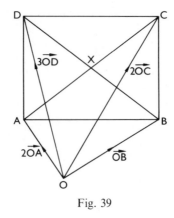

Fig. 39

By the Parallelogram of Vectors

$$2\overrightarrow{OA} + 2\overrightarrow{OC} = 4\overrightarrow{OX}$$

where X is the intersection of the diagonals AC and BD. Similarly

$$3\overrightarrow{OD} + \overrightarrow{OB} = 4\overrightarrow{OY}$$

where Y divides DB in the ratio $1:3$. Thus

$$2\overrightarrow{OA} + \overrightarrow{OB} + 2\overrightarrow{OC} + 3\overrightarrow{OD} = 4\overrightarrow{OX} + 4\overrightarrow{OY}$$

$$= 8\overrightarrow{OZ}$$

where Z is the mid-point of XY. But $XY = \frac{1}{4}DB$, and so Z is the point G

on AD where $DG:GB = 3:5$, and the resultant is $8\overrightarrow{OG}$—Q.E.D.

4.3 Hooke's Law

In all our examples so far the rods have been rigid and our strings in-extensible. We are not going to concern ourselves at this point with non-rigid rods, but we do need to consider the extensible string. Hooke's Law applies in the first instance to rods or bars, and states that:

> *The tension T in a bar when slightly stretched is proportional to the extension per unit length e_u.*

If k is a constant then we can express the Law in the form

$$T = ke_u. \qquad 4.1$$

This form of the Law does not take into account the nature of the material being stretched. Young applied the fact that a given substance must have a fixed resistance to stretching, and this can be measured in terms of Young's Modulus, E. Equation 4.1 is then modified to read

$$T = EAe_u, \qquad\qquad 4.2$$

where A is the cross-sectional area of the bar.

We however are not directly concerned with the characteristics of particular materials, but rather with the mathematics that arise. So, from our point of view we are interested in the form of 4.1. In fact there are a number of highly elastic substances which obey this law over very large extensions, and it is in such strings that we are mainly interested. A string which obeys Hooke's Law over any extension is said to be perfectly elastic.

In practice it is more convenient to write e_u as e/l, where e is the actual extension and l is the natural (i.e. unstretched) length of the string. We also commonly write k as λ. Then the law becomes

$$T = \lambda\frac{e}{l}. \qquad\qquad 4.3$$

We refer to λ as the modulus of elasticity. Notice the distinction between this and Young's modulus: the modulus of elasticity relates to a particular string; Young's modulus relates to a particular material.

Hooke's Law also holds for a compression. For example, the force exerted by a coil spring when compressed is still $\lambda e/l$, but e represents the compression rather than the extension.

EXAMPLE 5   *A uniform rod* AB *of weight W and length 2a is hinged at* A *to a point on a vertical wall. An elastic string of natural length 3a/2 is attached at one end to* B *and at the other to a point* C *on the wall at a height a vertically above* A. *When in equilibrium the rod rests horizontally. Find the modulus of elasticity of the string.*

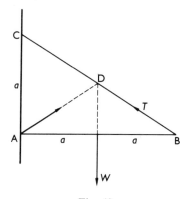

Fig. 40

Let the modulus of elasticity be λ and the tension in the string be T. All the forces act through D, the mid-point of BC, and triangle ADC is the triangle of forces. By Pythagoras, the length of BC is $\sqrt{5}a$, and hence of CD is $\dfrac{\sqrt{5}a}{2}$. Thus

$$T = \frac{\sqrt{5}W}{2}.$$

But by Hooke's Law,

$$T = \lambda\frac{\sqrt{5}a - 3a/2}{3a/2}.$$

$$\therefore \ \sqrt{5}W/2 = \lambda\frac{2\sqrt{5} - 3}{3}$$

giving

$$\lambda = \frac{3\sqrt{5}W}{4\sqrt{5} - 6}.$$

Exercise 8

1 Find the position, magnitude and direction of the resultant of forces $3F$, $2F$, F and $-F$ acting along AB, BC, CD and DA where ABCD is a square.

2 ABCDEF is a regular hexagon. Forces of magnitudes P, P, $2P$, $2P$, X and Y act along AB, BC, DE, EF, AD and AC respectively. Show that if $Y = \sqrt{3}P$ then the resultant has magnitude X and is parallel to AD.

3 Forces of $6P$, $9P$, $10P$, Q and R act along the sides AB, CB, BD, AD and CA in the senses indicated by the order of the letters, ABCD being a rectangle with AB = 4 units and BC = 3 units. Find Q and R in terms of P if the system reduces to a couple, and find the magnitude of this couple.

4 Forces of magnitudes $2P$, P, $3P$ and $4P$ act along the sides AB, BC, CD and DA of a rectangle ABCD. If AB = 3 and BC = 1, find the resultant and where it cuts AB.

Find the magnitude of the couple which if added to the system will cause the resultant to pass through B.

5 ABCD is a rectangle such that AB = $4a$, BC = $3a$. Forces of magnitudes P, $3P$, $3P$ and P act along the sides AB, BC, CD and AD in the directions indicated by the order of the letters. Find the magnitude of the resultant, and where it cuts AB, produced if necessary.

Forces of magnitudes Q and R are now added so as to act along the lines AC and BD respectively, the effect of which is to reduce the system to a couple. Find Q and R, and calculate the moment of this couple.

6 Relative to a Cartesian frame of reference Ox, Oy a system of forces has moments of $+3$, $+20$ and -11 about the points $(3, 2)$, $(-1, 1)$ and $(4, -1)$. Find the magnitude of the resultant and the equation of its line of action.

If the system is reduced to a couple by an equal and opposite force through the general point (x, y), find the moment of the couple in terms of x and y.

7 ABC is a triangle right-angled at B. If the resultant of vectors represented in magnitude, direction and position by $\overrightarrow{AB}$, $2\overrightarrow{CB}$ and $3\overrightarrow{AC}$ cuts AC at D and BC at E, find D and E. If the resultant is $n\overrightarrow{DE}$, what is n?

8 P and Q are two points lying outside a triangle ABC. If X is the mid-point of PQ, show that
$$\overrightarrow{PA}+\overrightarrow{PB}+\overrightarrow{PC}+\overrightarrow{QA}+\overrightarrow{QB}+\overrightarrow{QC} = 2\overrightarrow{XA}+2\overrightarrow{XB}+2\overrightarrow{XC}.$$

9 Given a triangle ABC, forces of $2\overrightarrow{AB}$, $3\overrightarrow{CB}$ and $5\overrightarrow{AC}$ act along the sides as indicated. Their resultant cuts AC in D and BC in E. Find D and E, and express the resultant in terms of $\overrightarrow{DE}$.

10 Show that the resultant of the four vectors $2\overrightarrow{DA}$, $3\overrightarrow{DC}$, $2\overrightarrow{BD}$ and $\overrightarrow{BC}$, where ABCD is a rectangle and each vector is represented by the respective line in magnitude, direction and position, is represented in magnitude and direction by the vector $\overrightarrow{AC}$. Show further, by considering the moment about D or otherwise, that the resultant is also represented in position by $\overrightarrow{AC}$.

11 Find the extension in the length of an elastic string whose modulus of elasticity is 75 N and natural length 200 mm when it supports a mass of 20 kg on a smooth slope inclined at 30° to the horizontal, the string being parallel to the slope. (Take g as 9·81 m/s^2.)

12 A particle of weight W is attached to the mid-point of a light elastic string of natural length l, the ends of which are attached to two fixed points distance $2l$ apart on the same horizontal level. The particle hangs in equilibrium, supported only by the string, at a depth of $7l/24$ below the fixed points. Find the modulus of elasticity of the string in terms of W.

13 A light elastic band of natural length $2a$ is hung round two smooth pegs A and B on the same horizontal level a distance a apart. A particle C of mass m is attached to a point on the elastic band so that when it hangs in equilibrium below AB, angle ACB $= 2 \sin^{-1} \frac{1}{3}$. Find the modulus of elasticity of the band.

14 P and Q are two points in the plane of a triangle ABC. Show that if $\overrightarrow{XY}$ represents a vector in magnitude, position, and direction equivalent to the line XY then
$$\overrightarrow{PA}+\overrightarrow{PB}+\overrightarrow{PC}+\overrightarrow{QA}+\overrightarrow{QB}+\overrightarrow{QC} = 6\overrightarrow{NG}$$
where G is the centroid of the triangle ABC, and N is the mid-point of PQ.

4.4 Friction

Up to this point we have considered systems in which all the components are smooth. Suppose now that two bodies in contact are not smooth, and that there is a force acting so as to prevent them sliding over each other. This force, the force of friction or frictional force, acts at the point of contact tangentially to the surfaces. The magnitude of the force will depend on several factors: the nature of the materials in contact, the magnitude of the normal reaction between them, the magnitude of other forces acting in the line of the frictional force, and on whether or not they are in motion.

Suppose that we want to move a heavy chest by pushing it along the floor. Before we start to push no force of friction will act, but when we begin to push the frictional force will equate to the force we exert—Newton's 3rd Law—until suddenly the chest begins to move. We have reached the point of limiting friction. The reader who has pushed objects around in this way may have noticed that once moving it often becomes easier. This is because the maximum frictional force two objects can exert on each other when sliding is not generally as great as the maximum force they can exert when both are stationary. We therefore have to distinguish between static friction and dynamic friction.

The weight of the chest acts vertically downwards, i.e. normal to the plane of contact with the floor. Assuming that we are pushing horizontally it must be clear that we are not pushing against the weight, but it is also evident that a heavy chest is more difficult to move than a light one. We conclude, and experiment confirms, that the frictional force is proportional to the weight. More specifically, experiment establishes that the frictional force F cannot exceed μR, where R is the normal reaction between the surfaces and μ a constant peculiar to those two surfaces called the **coefficient of friction**.

$$F \leqslant \mu R.$$

In the limiting case, or during motion against the frictional force, $F = \mu R$. Although not impossible, μ is rarely greater than 1. The coefficient of dynamic friction is generally slightly less than the coefficient of static friction.

At the point of contact there are now two forces acting—the frictional force F and the normal reaction R. Suppose their resultant is S, and that the line of action of S makes an angle α with R then

$$\tan \alpha = \mu R/R = \mu.$$

α is called the **angle of friction**. In all these respects static and dynamic friction are the same.

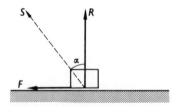

Fig. 41

EXAMPLE 6   *A block of mass m is held stationary on a plane inclined at an angle* $\tan^{-1} \frac{2}{3}$ *to the horizontal by a horizontal force P, the coefficient of friction between the block and the plane being* $\frac{1}{2}$. *Find the two possible values of P if the block is in limiting equilibrium.*

There are two possible values of P since the block might be about to move up the plane, or about to move down. We consider first the case when it is about to slide down.

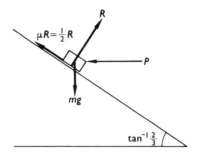

Fig. 42

Let the normal reaction between the block and the plane be R, then

$$R = mg \cos (\tan^{-1} \tfrac{2}{3}) + P \sin (\tan^{-1} \tfrac{2}{3})$$

$$= \frac{3}{\sqrt{13}} mg + \frac{2}{\sqrt{13}} P.$$

Equating forces along the plane,

$$\tfrac{1}{2}R + P \cos (\tan^{-1} \tfrac{2}{3}) = mg \sin (\tan^{-1} \tfrac{2}{3})$$

Substituting for R and multiplying by $\sqrt{13}$,

$$3mg/2 + P + 3P = 2mg$$

$$P = mg/8.$$

If the block is about to slip up the plane, we have the same equation for R as above, but equating forces along the plane gives

$$P \cos (\tan^{-1} \tfrac{2}{3}) = \tfrac{1}{2}R + mg \sin (\tan^{-1} \tfrac{2}{3}).$$

Hence
$$3P = 3mg/2 + P + 2mg,$$

$$P = 7mg/4.$$

When about to slip down, $P = mg/8$; when about to slip up, $P = 7mg/4$.

EXAMPLE 7   *A uniform rod* **AB** *of weight W is placed so as to lean against a step 12 cm high, the foot of the rod,* **A,** *resting on horizontal ground. The angle of the rod to the horizontal is* $\sin^{-1} 4/5$, *and the rod is 20 cm long. Find the coefficient of friction* μ *at the ground and the step (given that they are equal) if the rod is in limiting equilibrium.*

Let the normal reaction at the top of the step be R and at A be N. We note that $\sin^{-1} 4/5$ is $\cos^{-1} 3/5$. Resolving vertically:

$$\frac{3}{5}R + \frac{4}{5}\mu R + N = W. \qquad (1)$$

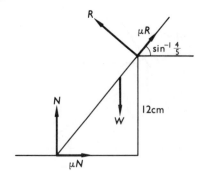

Fig. 43

Resolving horizontally:

$$\frac{4}{5}R = \frac{3}{5}\mu R + \mu N, \tag{2}$$

Taking moments about A:

$$\frac{3}{5} \cdot 10W = 15R,$$

$$2W = 5R. \tag{3}$$

Substituting from (3) into (1):

$$(3+4\mu)\frac{2W}{5} + 5N = 5W,$$

and into (2):

$$(4-3\mu)\frac{2W}{5} = 5\mu N.$$

Hence

$$6W/5 + 8W\mu/5 + 8W/5\mu - 6W/5 = 5W,$$

$$8\mu^2 - 25\mu + 8 = 0.$$

Using the formula

$$\mu = \frac{25 \pm \sqrt{625 - 4 \cdot 64}}{16}$$

$$= \frac{25 \pm \sqrt{369}}{16}.$$

Assuming μ is less than 1,

$$\mu = \frac{25 - 3\sqrt{41}}{16}.$$

The same principles used in these static examples apply to dynamic problems. In effect friction just adds a further force to bring into our problems based on the equations of motion and Newton's Laws. We can also now use our knowledge of how to resolve a force into components to analyse motion on inclined planes, or that of connected particles where the string is not vertical. The following examples present a variety of possibilities.

EXAMPLE 8   *A plank 1 m long is fixed with one end 28 cm above the level of the other. The top half of the plank is smooth, and the bottom half is rough. When a small block of mass m is released at the top end so as to slide down the plank, it just reaches the bottom. Calculate the coefficient of friction between the block and the rough part of the plank.*

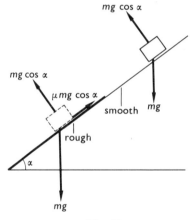

Fig. 44

The inclined plank makes an angle α with the horizontal where

$$\alpha = \sin^{-1} \frac{28}{100}$$

$$= \sin^{-1} \frac{7}{25}.$$

But 7, 24, 25 are a set of Pythagorean numbers, and so

$$\cos \alpha = 24/25.$$

On the smooth part of the plank the force acting on the block down the plank is $mg \sin \alpha = 7mg/25$. Applying the principle, force $=$ mass $\times$ acceleration ($F = ma$), the acceleration a_1 of the mass on the smooth section satisfies

$$7mg/25 = ma_1.$$

$$\therefore \ a_1 = 7g/25.$$

Let the speed of the block at the end of the smooth section be V, then using the equation of motion $v^2 = u^2 + 2as$,

$$V^2 = 2 \cdot \frac{7g}{25} \cdot \frac{1}{2}$$

$$= 7g/25.$$

On the rough portion of the plank the normal reaction is $mg \cos \alpha$, and so the force due to friction is $\mu mg \cos \alpha = 24\mu mg/25$. The decelerating force is then $24\mu mg/25 - 7mg/25$, and if the deceleration is a_2, $F = ma$ gives

$$24\mu mg/25 - 7mg/25 = ma_2,$$

$$a_2 = (24\mu - 7)g/25.$$

But it comes to rest at the bottom, and applying the equation of motion $v^2 = u^2 + 2as$,

$$O = V^2 - 2a_2 \cdot \tfrac{1}{2}.$$

Hence $$(24\mu - 7)g/25 = 7g/25$$

giving $$24\mu - 7 = 7,$$

$$\mu = 7/12.$$

The coefficient of friction is $7/12$.

EXAMPLE 9   *A smooth fixed wedge has one face inclined at $30°$ to the horizontal and a second face at $45°$ to the horizontal—the faces are adjacent to each other at the top of the wedge. Particles of masses $2m$ and $5m$ are held on these respective faces connected by a taut inelastic string passing over a smooth pulley at the top of the wedge. Find the acceleration of the system if the particles are simultaneously released, and show that the force acting on the pulley is*

$$\frac{10}{7}mg(1 + \sqrt{2}) \cos 52\tfrac{1}{2}°.$$

The system is illustrated in Fig. 45. Let the tension in the string be T and the acceleration of the system be a. Applying the principle, force $=$ mass $\times$ acceleration for the $2m$ particle

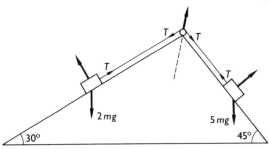

Fig. 45

$$T - 2mg \sin 30° = 2ma,$$

$$T - mg = 2ma, \qquad (1)$$

Similarly for the $5m$ particle

$$5mg \sin 45° - T = 5ma,$$

$$5mg/\sqrt{2} - T = 5ma, \qquad (2)$$

Adding (1) and (2)

$$5mg/\sqrt{2} - mg = 7ma,$$

$$\left(\frac{5}{\sqrt{2}} - 1\right)g = 7a,$$

the acceleration of the system is $\left(\dfrac{5}{\sqrt{2}} - 1\right)g/7.$

From (1) $T = mg + 2ma.$

$$\therefore \ T = mg + 2mg\left(\frac{5}{\sqrt{2}} - 1\right)/7.$$

$$T = mg(7 + 10/\sqrt{2} - 2)/7$$

$$= mg(5 + 5\sqrt{2})/7$$

$$= 5mg(1 + \sqrt{2})/7.$$

The force on the pulley is the resultant of the tension in the string on the two sides. The angle between them is $(60° + 45°) = 105°$. Therefore the force on the pulley is

$$2T \cos (105/2)° = 2T \cos 52\tfrac{1}{2}°$$

$$= \frac{10mg}{7}(1 + \sqrt{2}) \cos 52\tfrac{1}{2}°.$$

EXAMPLE 10   *A block of wood of mass 10m is held on a rough hori-*
zontal table, coefficient of friction μ. An inelastic string connected to the
block passes over a smooth pulley at the end of the table and then passes
under a second smooth pulley of mass 5m vertically below the first (Fig. 46).
The other end of the string is fixed to a point vertically above the second
pulley. The block is released and accelerates at a rate of g/9. Find the value
of μ.

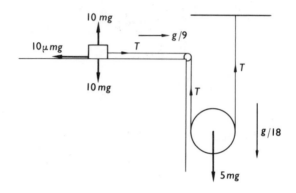

Fig. 46

If the acceleration of the block is $g/9$, the acceleration of the second
pulley is $g/18$. Let the tension in the string be T, then applying the principle: force = mass × acceleration, for the block

$$T - 10\mu mg = 10mg/9, \tag{1}$$

and similarly for the pulley

$$5mg - 2T = 5mg/18, \tag{2}$$

Adding twice (1) to (2)

$$5mg - 20\mu mg = 5mg/18 + 20mg/9,$$
$$1 - 4\mu = 1/18 + 4/9$$
$$= 1/2.$$
$$\therefore\ 4\mu = 1/2,$$
$$\underline{\mu = 1/8.}$$

EXAMPLE 11   *A small block of mass m is held on the smooth face of a*
wedge which is held at rest on a smooth horizontal table. The wedge is of
mass 6m, and the face of the wedge is inclined at an angle of 30° to the

horizontal. If the wedge and block are released simultaneously, calculate the acceleration of the wedge and the reaction between the wedge and the block.

As with pulley systems, we define all the accelerations relative to a fixed background, but since we do not know the precise path of the block we define the acceleration of the block in terms of its horizontal and vertical components. This is quite in order since acceleration is a vector. The similarity with pulley systems persists in the method we then employ to solve the problem. We form our equations on the principle force = mass × acceleration, and also form a relation between the accelerations.

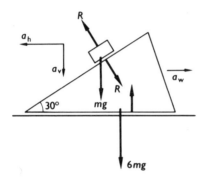

Fig. 47

Let the horizontal and vertical accelerations of the block be a_h and a_v respectively, and the acceleration of the wedge be a_w. Let the reaction between block and wedge be R.

Since the block must stay on the face of the wedge,

$$\frac{a_v}{a_h + a_w} = \tan 30°,$$

i.e.

$$\sqrt{3} a_v = a_h + a_w, \tag{1}$$

Applying the principle, force = mass × acceleration, to the block horizontally

$$R \sin 30° = m a_h,$$

$$R = 2 m a_h, \tag{2}$$

and vertically

$$mg - R \cos 30° = m a_v,$$

$$mg - \sqrt{3} R / 2 = m a_v. \tag{3}$$

Applying the principle to the wedge

$$R \sin 30° = 6ma_w,$$

$$R = 12ma_w. \tag{4}$$

Substituting from (2), (3) and (4) into (1):

$$\sqrt{3}(g - \sqrt{3}R/2m) = R/2m + R/12m,$$

$$12\sqrt{3}mg = 6R + R + 18R$$

$$= 25R.$$

∴ The reaction between the block and the wedge is $12\sqrt{3}mg/25$.

From (4), the acceleration of the wedge is $\sqrt{3}g/25$.

Exercise 9

1 A block of wood rests on a rough plane inclined at an angle α to the horizontal. Show that if it is in limiting equilibrium then α equals the angle of friction.

2 Prove that the least force required to prevent a block of mass m from sliding down a plane of inclination α is

$$mg(\sin \alpha - \mu \cos \alpha)/\sqrt{\mu^2 + 1}$$

where μ is the coefficient of friction, given that $\tan \alpha > \mu$.

3 A uniform rod AB of weight W is supported at an angle of 30° to the horizontal by a string attached at A. The end B rests on a rough plane also at 30° to the horizontal (60° to the rod) with coefficient of friction μ. Find μ if the string is perpendicular to the rod and the system is in limiting equilibrium.

4 A particle is held at the top of a rough plane 1·2 m long which is inclined at an angle $\sin^{-1} \frac{8}{17}$ to the horizontal. Find the coefficient of friction μ if it takes 2 s to reach the bottom when released. (Take g as 9·8 m/s².)

5 A uniform ladder of length l rests against a smooth vertical wall at an angle α to the wall. The weight of the ladder is W and a man of weight $7W$ wishes to climb to the top. Find the least value of the coefficient of friction μ between the ladder and the ground if it is to be safe for him to do so. What difference would it make if a friend of weight $5W$ stands on the bottom rung?

6 A particle is projected along the line of greatest slope up a plane of inclination $\sin^{-1} \frac{1}{3}$ to the horizontal. The coefficient of friction is $1/4$. Show that the ratio of the initial speed to the speed with which it again passes through the starting point is $1 : \sqrt{(3 - 2\sqrt{2})}$.

7 A block of mass $4m$ is held on a plane AB inclined at an angle α to the horizontal. A light inelastic string attached to the block passes up over a smooth pulley at B and is attached to a weight of mass $3m$ which hangs vertically below B. The angle of friction of the slope AB is λ. Show that if the system moves when released then

$$\tan \lambda < \pm\tfrac{1}{4} \sec \alpha(3 - 4 \sin \alpha)$$

explaining the two possibilities.

If $\sin \alpha = \frac{5}{13}$ and $\tan \lambda = \frac{1}{4}$, find the acceleration of the system.

8 A rod rests horizontally with its ends against two perpendicular planes where one of them is inclined at an angle α to the horizontal. The rod is perpendicular

to their line of intersection, and is uniform. If the coefficient of friction between the rod and the planes is μ, show that in limiting equilibrium

$$\tan 2\alpha = \frac{1-\mu^2}{2\mu}.$$

9 The figure illustrates a system consisting of a weight mg hanging freely at one end, connected by a light inextensible string to a block of mass M on a plane of inclination $30°$ to the horizontal. A second inelastic string connects the block over a smooth pulley at the top and under a second smooth pulley of mass $5M$ to a

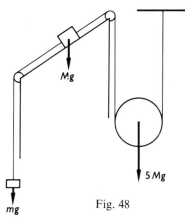

Fig. 48

fixed point vertically above this second pulley. The coefficients of static and dynamic friction are μ_s and μ_d respectively where $11\mu_s/12 = \mu_d = 1/4$. Find m if the system is static in limiting equilibrium with the block about to move up the plane.

Show that in this case if the system is jogged into motion then the acceleration will be

$$\sqrt{3}g/(374 - 12\sqrt{3}).$$

10 A block of mass m is dragged at a constant speed over a rough horizontal floor by a rope inclined at an angle α to the horizontal, the rope and line of motion being in the same vertical plane. Express T, the tension in the rope, in terms of m, g, α and μ_d the coefficient of dynamic friction.

If the block is at rest, the minimum tension in the rope to start the block moving when at the same angle α to the horizontal is $3T/2$. If μ_s is the coefficient of static friction show that

$$\mu_d = \frac{2\mu_s}{3+\mu_s \tan \alpha}.$$

11 A bead is projected with speed 2 m/s up the face of an inclined plane along the line of greatest slope, which is inclined at an angle α to the horizontal, and comes to rest in a distance of 0·5 m. When projected down the face of the plane at the same speed along the line of greatest slope it comes to rest in a distance of 3 m. Find the value of α, and if μ is the coefficient of friction show that

$$\mu = \frac{7}{\sqrt{9g^2 - 25}}.$$

12 A wedge of mass M is held on a smooth horizontal table. A smooth face of the wedge is inclined at an angle $\sin^{-1} \frac{4}{5}$ to the horizontal. A block of mass m is held on this face. When the system is released the actual path of the block makes an angle $\tan^{-1} 2$ to the horizontal. Show that $m:M = 1:2$.

5 Frames

5.1 Jointed rods

Up to this point we have not had to consider in any of our examples the internal forces acting, but if we have a system which is composed of several distinct parts it may become necessary. In particular, how can we analyse a system of jointed rods, finding the reactions at the joints as well as the external forces?

When considering frameworks we must distinguish between two types: those made up of heavy rods (usually referred to simply as jointed rods), and those which are composed only of light rods, which have special techniques associated with them, and are generally referred to as light frameworks. We investigate the light framework later in the chapter; at this point we discuss methods applicable to jointed rods. We do so by reference to two examples.

EXAMPLE 1   *Two uniform rods* AB *and* BC *are smoothly jointed at* B, *and rest in a vertical plane with* A *and* C *on a smooth horizontal plane. They are prevented from sliding apart by an inextensible string attached to each rod a quarter of the way up their lengths. If the rods are both inclined at 60° to the horizontal, and* AB *weighs 2W while* BC *weighs 3W, calculate the reaction at the joint and the tension in the string.*

The method of solution still amounts to resolving and taking moments, but we can do this in three different systems: we can take the system as a whole, we can take just the rod AB, or we can consider just the rod BC. Fig. 49a shows the external forces only that act on the whole system; Fig. 49b splits this up to show the internal forces as well. We normally begin a problem of this kind by drawing this latter figure. Notice that we do not know in which direction the reaction acts at the joint, and so we give it in the form of two components. Also, the forces acting at B on one rod must be equal and opposite to the forces acting on the other (by Newton's 3rd Law).

Let the reaction at B have components X and Y in the senses shown in Fig. 49b. Let the tension in the string be T, and the reactions at A and C be R_a and R_c respectively.

Taking moments about A for the whole system

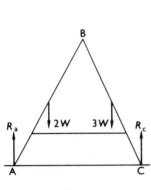

Fig. 49a

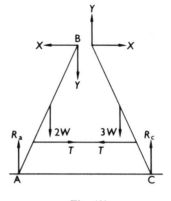

Fig. 49b

$$2W + 3 \times 3W = 4 \times R_c,$$
$$R_c = 11W/4.$$

But resolving for the whole system gives $R_a + R_c = 5W$, and so

$$R_a = 9W/4.$$

Resolving vertically for the rod AB

$$R_a = 2W + Y, \tag{1}$$

and horizontally for AB

$$X = T. \tag{2}$$

Taking moments about B for AB

$$2W \cos 60° + \tfrac{3}{2}T \cos 30° = 2R_a \cos 60°,$$
$$W + 3\sqrt{3}T/4 = 9W/4,$$
$$4W + 3\sqrt{3}T = 9W.$$
$$3\sqrt{3}T = 5W.$$

$\therefore$ The tension in the string is $\dfrac{5W}{3\sqrt{3}}$.

Substituting back in (2)

$$X = 5W/3\sqrt{3}.$$

From (1)
$$Y = R_a - 2W$$
$$= W/4.$$

By Pythagoras, the reaction R_b at B satisfies

$$R_b^2 = X^2 + Y^2$$

$$= \frac{W^2}{16} + \frac{25W^2}{27}$$

$$= \frac{W^2}{16 \cdot 27}(27 + 400).$$

$$\therefore \quad R_b = \frac{W}{12}(427/3)^{\frac{1}{2}}.$$

This acts at an angle $\tan^{-1}\dfrac{Y}{X}$ to the horizontal, $= \tan^{-1}\dfrac{3\sqrt{3}}{20}$.

Reaction at B is $\dfrac{W}{12}(427/3)^{\frac{1}{2}}$ at $\tan^{-1}\dfrac{3\sqrt{3}}{20}$ to the horizontal.

EXAMPLE 2   *Four rods* **AB, BC, CD, DE** *each of length 2a are suspended from points* **A** *and* **E** *on the same horizontal level.* **AB** *and* **DE** *both weigh 2W, and* **BC** *and* **CD** *both weigh W, and they are smoothly hinged at* **B, C** *and* **D.** *Show that if* **AB** *and* **BC** *hang at angles* θ *and* φ *to the vertical respectively, then tan* φ *= 4 tan* θ.

We notice immediately that there is a symmetry about this system, and we take advantage of this as we draw our figure, in at least three ways: (i) we note that the vertical reactions at A and E must both be $3W$ (together they must support $6W$, so they each take $3W$), (ii) the reaction at C must be horizontal, and (iii) we need only fill in the reactions on half the diagram since the other half is identical. Resolving horizontally is so easy a matter too that we see that every component is the same. However, while we may draw this in immediately on our diagram, we should at the same time give some reason for doing so in our solution. The following is a suggested pattern.

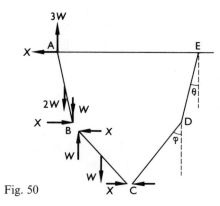

Fig. 50

By symmetry the reaction X at C is horizontal, and the vertical reactions at A and E are equal, both $3W$ by resolving. Resolving horizontally, each horizontal reaction is X as shown. Let the vertical reaction at B be Y, then resolving vertically for BC gives

$$Y = W.$$

Taking moments about A for AB

$$a.2W \sin \theta = 2a.W \sin \theta = 2aX \cos \theta,$$

$$2W \tan \theta = X. \tag{1}$$

Taking moments about B for BC

$$aW \sin \phi = 2aX \cos \phi,$$

$$\tfrac{1}{2}W \tan \phi = X. \tag{2}$$

Equating (1) and (2),

$$2 \tan \theta = \tfrac{1}{2} \tan \phi,$$

$$\tan \phi = 4 \tan \theta. \qquad \text{Q.E.D.}$$

Exercise 10

1 Two uniform rods AB and BC are equal in length but AB has weight $2W$ and BC has weight W. The rods are smoothly hinged at B, and the mid-points are connected by a light inelastic string. The system stands in a vertical plane with A and C on a smooth horizontal table. If angle BAC is $60°$, find the reaction at B and the angle it makes with the vertical.

2 Two uniform rods of equal length are smoothly jointed at B, and are hung by their other ends A and C to points on the same horizontal level. B hangs below AC so that angle ABC is $90°$. If AB has weight $3W$ and BC has weight W, find the reaction at B.

3 Two identical smooth uniform rods AB and BC are smoothly jointed at B. They are both of length $2a$, and they rest symmetrically on a horizontal cylinder of radius a. Show that if angle ABC $= 2\theta$, then

$$\tan^2 \theta (\tan \theta - 1) = 1.$$

4 A framework ABC is made up of three equal rods each of weight W jointed smoothly at their ends. The system is hung from the joint A. Find the reaction at either B or C.

5 A framework ABCD consists of three rods AB, BC, CD smoothly jointed at B and C. AB and CD both are of weight W; BC is of weight $2W$. The system stands in a vertical plane in equilibrium, with A and D resting on a rough horizontal plane, AD > BC. If AB is at an angle θ to the horizontal, and the coefficient of friction at A and D is $3/8$, find the minimum value of θ consistent with equilibrium. Find also the reaction at B in this limiting case.

6 Two rods of the same mass per unit length are smoothly jointed at B. The longer rod, AB of weight $2W$, is twice the length of BC. The system hangs from a smooth pivot at A, and a horizontal force P applied at C is such that AB makes an angle $\tan^{-1} \tfrac{1}{3}$ to the vertical. Determine the value of P, and the angle that BC makes with the horizontal.

5.2 Light frameworks

A framework of light rods demands very different techniques to those just described. The first point that we must make is that when a rod is light the reactions at its ends are equal and act in the line of the rod. A few moments thought will convince the reader of this since the rod must be in equilibrium under just these two forces. Problems concerning frameworks can therefore be solved by considering just the joints, replacing the rods at the joint by forces acting in the directions of the rods, and resolving.

A distinction is often drawn between rods in a state of compression (or thrust) and rods in a state of tension. When no such distinction is made we refer to the force in a rod as a stress. Because we perform calculations on the forces at the joints, we mark in the forces on the rods in our diagram as they act on the joints. Suppose for example rod AB is part of a framework, and that it is pulling on the joints at A and B. It is then in a state of tension, and we mark in the forces on AB pointing inwards (Fig. 51a). If however it is pressing outwards on the joints A and B then it is in a state of compression, and we mark the forces on the rod as acting outwards (Fig. 51b).

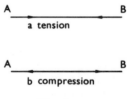

Fig. 51

We should emphasize at this point that our framework must be inherently rigid, but not over rigid. The reader will probably know already that if three rods are jointed to form a triangle then the shape is unique — the framework is rigid. But if we have four rods jointed to form a rectangle, then it is not rigid because we can distort it into the shape of a parallelogram with angles whatever size we please. If we now take two equal rods and add them to these four so as to form the two diagonals of the rectangle the frame will be over rigid. One diagonal is enough to make it rigid; the second is superfluous. A brief study of networks shows us that if we start with a rigid system, e.g. a triangle, then it requires two and just two bars to enlarge the frame and for it to be still rigid but not over rigid. For every two bars we add, we include one extra joint. The simplest rigid framework is a triangle containing three joints and three rods. Hence a system containing n joints contains $3 + 2(n-3) = 2n-3$ rods.

Our framework must be supported externally, and may also have a variety of weights hung from various joints. This gives rise to three possible unknowns which together with the stresses in the rods makes $2n$ in all. Since we can form two equations at each joint, the problem will be determinate.

In practice we distinguish between three different methods of approach. If the framework has not got too many joints then we generally consider each one separately, solving the $2n$ simultaneous equations that result— we refer to this as the method of joints. A systematic extension of this method, particularly useful for larger frameworks or where not every stress is required, is by breaking the frame up into sections, replacing rods by forces—we refer to this as the method of sections. Thirdly, if a graphical method is permissible, then we use a special notation devised by Bow, and referred to as Bow's notation. We outline these methods by one example of each.

EXAMPLE 3   *The framework* ABCDE *(Fig. 52) is composed of seven rods where* $AE = EB = BD = CD,$ *and* $AB = BC = DE,$ *the angles between the rods being 45° and 90° as appropriate. A mass of weight 20 N*

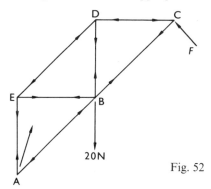

Fig. 52

is fixed at the joint B, *and a force* F N *acts at* C *perpendicularly to* AC. *The frame is hinged smoothly at* A. *Find the value of* F, *and the stresses in all the rods, distinguishing clearly which are in tension and which are in compression.*

We mark the forces on the diagram starting at C. Because we know the direction of F and only three forces act at C we can determine that CD is in compression and BC in tension. Moving round to D, again because only three forces act at D and we know the direction of the force due to DC, we can conclude that ED is under compression, but BD is under tension. So to E, to A, and finally to B. It is not essential to get all these correct at the beginning, but it does eliminate negative signs in later working, and also acts as an intuitive check on our final answers.

Let the stress in each rod XY be S_{xy} N, then taking moments about A for the whole frame gives

$$2F = 20/\sqrt{2}.$$
$$\therefore \ F = 10/\sqrt{2}$$
$$= 5\sqrt{2}.$$

Considering the joint C, resolving perpendicularly to BC,

$$S_{cd}/\sqrt{2} = F$$
$$\Rightarrow S_{cd} = 10.$$

Resolving along BC,

$$S_{cd}/\sqrt{2} = S_{bc}$$
$$\Rightarrow S_{bc} = 5\sqrt{2}.$$

Considering the joint D, resolving horizontally

$$S_{de}/\sqrt{2} = S_{cd}$$
$$\Rightarrow S_{de} = 10\sqrt{2}.$$

Resolving vertically,

$$S_{bd} = S_{de}/\sqrt{2}$$
$$= 10.$$

Considering the joint E, resolving horizontally

$$S_{be} = S_{de}/\sqrt{2}$$
$$= 10.$$

Resolving vertically,

$$S_{ae} = 10.$$

Considering the joint B (avoiding the unknown and unwanted reaction at A), resolving along AC

$$S_{ab} = S_{eb}/\sqrt{2} + 20/\sqrt{2} - S_{bd}/\sqrt{2} - S_{bc}$$
$$= 5\sqrt{2} + 10\sqrt{2} - 5\sqrt{2} - 5\sqrt{2}$$
$$= 5\sqrt{2}.$$

We can summarise these results as follows:

Rod	Stress (newtons)	Nature
AB	$5\sqrt{2}$	Compression
BC	$5\sqrt{2}$	Tension
CD	10	Compression
DE	$10\sqrt{2}$	Compression
EA	10	Compression
BE	10	Tension
BD	10	Tension

EXAMPLE 4   *Fig. 53 illustrates a light framework of rods* AB, BC, CD, DE, EF, FA, FB, FC *and* EC. *Those rods not horizontal or vertical are inclined at 30° to the vertical, the system being in a vertical plane. Masses*

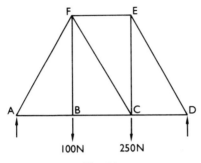

Fig. 53

of weights 100 N and 250 N are hung from joints B *and* C *respectively, and the system is supported by vertical reactions at* A *and* D. *Find the stresses in all the rods, distinguishing clearly their nature.*

Let the reactions at A and D be R_a N and R_d N respectively, and the stresses in each rod XY be S_{xy} N.

Taking moments about A for the whole system,

$$3R_d = 100 + 2 \times 250$$

$$= 600.$$

$$\therefore R_d = 200,$$

and $$R_a = 150.$$

The particular value of the method of sections is that we can start at any part of the frame which can be cut off by a line crossing not more than three of the rods. It is thus most appropriate to a problem in which not all the stresses are required, but for sake of demonstration we shall apply the method here in three separate stages.

Consider the section to the right of a line cutting FE, FC and BC. We replace each of these rods by the corresponding stresses S_{ef}, S_{cf} and S_{bc} as in Fig. 54. The sub-frame CDE must be in equilibrium under these forces together with the weight at C and the reaction at D. Taking moments about C,

$$\sqrt{3}S_{ef} = 200$$

$$\Rightarrow S_{ef} = 200/\sqrt{3}.$$

Resolving vertically,

$$S_{cf} \cos 30° = 250 - 200,$$

$$S_{cf} = 100/\sqrt{3}.$$

Resolving horizontally,

$$S_{bc} = S_{ef} - S_{cf} \cos 60°$$

$$= \frac{200}{\sqrt{3}} - \frac{50}{\sqrt{3}}$$

$$= 50\sqrt{3}.$$

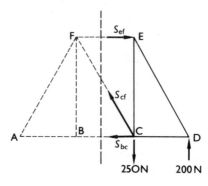

Fig. 54

Consider now the section cut off by a line through EF, EC and CD. Resolving horizontally,

$$S_{cd} = 200/\sqrt{3}.$$

Resolving vertically,

$$S_{ce} = 200.$$

Resolving vertically at the joint D,

$$\sqrt{3}S_{de}/2 = 200$$

$$\Rightarrow S_{de} = 400/\sqrt{3}.$$

Consider the section to the left of a line through AF, BF and BC. Taking moments about A

$$S_{bf} = 100.$$

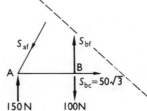

Fig. 55

Taking moments about **B**,

$$S_{af} \cos 30° = 150$$
$$\Rightarrow S_{af} = 100\sqrt{3}.$$

Resolving horizontally at the joint **A**,

$$S_{ab} = 50\sqrt{3}.$$

We summarize these results as follows:

Rod	Stress (newtons)	Nature
AB	$50\sqrt{3}$	Tension
BC	$50\sqrt{3}$	Tension
CD	$200/\sqrt{3}$	Tension
DE	$400/\sqrt{3}$	Compression
EF	$200/\sqrt{3}$	Compression
FA	$100\sqrt{3}$	Compression
BF	100	Tension
CF	$100/\sqrt{3}$	Tension
CE	200	Tension

EXAMPLE 5   *A frame of seven light equal rods* **AB, BC, CD, DE, EA,
EB** *and* **BD** *takes the form illustrated by Fig. 56, all the joints being smooth.
The frame is supported in a vertical plane on a fixed pivot at C and by a
horizontal force at* **E** *of magnitude F N. A load of weight 25 N hangs from
the joint* **A**. *Find the value of F, the reaction at the pivot, and the stresses in
each of the rods, all to the nearest 0·5 N.*

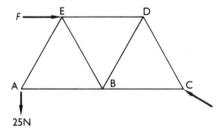

Fig. 56

We choose a relatively simple frame for our illustration. Bow's graphical
method is based on the fact that the forces at each joint are in equilibrium
and can be represented by the sides of a polygon taken in order (an
extension of the Triangle of Vectors). Since the stresses in the rods appear
in two such polygons, corresponding to two joints, these polygons can all

be superimposed. Bow devised a notation which enables us to draw this complete vector diagram from just one known length. We confine ourselves here to describing the method; if the reader is interested he can investigate this further himself. Suffice it to say that each vertex in the vector diagram corresponds to just one space between the forces in the frame itself.

We demonstrate Bow's method step by step as follows. (1) Each region between the forces is labelled with a capital letter: P, Q, R, S, T and U.

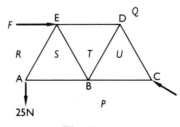

Fig. 57

(2) A line is drawn to an appropriate scale to represent 25 N; it is labelled pr since the weight separates the two regions P and R.

Fig. 58

(3) We observe that S lies next to both R and P. ps is perpendicular to pr, and rs is at 30° to pr. We can therefore construct the point s.

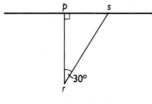

Fig. 59

(4) rq must be perpendicular to pr since F is horizontal. But so is tq perpendicular to pr, and t lies on a line through s at 120° to ps.

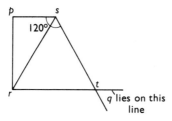

Fig. 60

(5) *tu* is at 120° to *rt*. But *pu* is horizontal—hence we construct *u*.

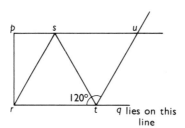

Fig. 61

(6) *uq* is at 120° to *pu*. But we already know that *q* lies on *rt* or *rt* produced. Hence we construct *q*.

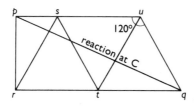

Fig. 62

(7) We now joint *p* to *q* to represent the reaction at the pivot.

Clearly it is advisable to draw the vector diagram in rough first, as it is not clear in which direction it is going to go from the first line, nor how large certain parts will be. Our conclusions are as follows:

Rod	Vector diagram line	Stress (N)	Nature
AB	*ps*	14·5	Compression
BC	*up*	43·5	Compression
CD	*qu*	29·0	Compression
DE	*qt*	29·0	Compression
EA	*rs*	29·0	Tension
EB	*st*	29·0	Compression
DB	*tu*	29·0	Tension
---			---
F	*rq*	58·0	
Reaction	*qp*	63·0	

We can determine the nature of the stresses in two ways. The easiest is generally to fill in the forces on the original diagram by inspection, taking a joint where there is a known force and only two others (as in Example 3). The second possibility is to remember that each triangle or polygon in the vector diagram represents the forces involved, and from the diagram we can deduce the direction of each force in the frame. For example, *prs* is the triangle of forces which act at A. They must act in the sense *p* to *r*, *r* to *s*, and *s* to *p* if it is to correspond with a weight of 25 N acting downwards. Therefore *sp*, i.e. AB, is in compression and *rs*, i.e. AE, is in tension. But consider now the triangle *rst*—it is not complete because we must include *q* if it is to correspond to the joint E. We must also remember that the force represented by *rs* must now be taken as from *s* to *r* (Fig. 63). Generally the former method is quicker and to be preferred.

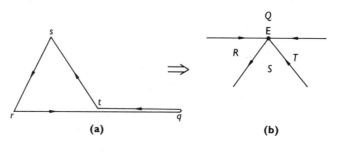

Fig. 63

5.3 Bending moment and shearing force

In considering jointed rods and frameworks we have repeatedly broken down the system into sections of one or more rods. There is no reason why we should confine ourselves to doing this at the joints. There are forces acting at all points along a rod which can be evaluated in a similar way.

Suppose that C is a point on a thin rod AB. If we remove the portion CB, what forces must we apply at C to maintain AC in the same state? These forces we would have to apply must equal the internal forces within the rod itself.

The component of the force at C can be resolved along and perpendicular to the rod. The component along the rod, T, corresponds to the tension in the rod. The force acting perpendicularly to the rod, S, tending to pull the rod apart laterally, is called the **shearing force**. The situation cannot be entirely accounted for by these two forces, and so we must assume a couple of moment M to act there as well. M is called the **bending moment**. We can evaluate T, S and M by resolving and taking moments for AC.

Fig. 64

EXAMPLE 6   *A light rod* **AB** *of length 3a carries a mass of weight W at the point* **C** *distant a from* **A** *and is supported in a horizontal position by vertical forces at* **A** *and* **B**. *Determine the stress and bending moment at a point distant x from* **A**.

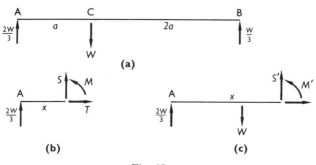

Fig. 65

Resolving and taking moments for the whole rod gives the forces at A and B to be $\dfrac{2W}{3}$ and $\dfrac{W}{3}$ as shown in the figure.

Consider the point distant x from A, $x < a$. Let the tension be T, the shearing force S and the bending moment M in the senses shown. Resolving horizontally

$$T = 0.$$

Resolving vertically

$$S = -\frac{2W}{3}.$$

Taking moments about A,

$$M = -xS$$

$$\Rightarrow M = \frac{2xW}{3}.$$

Now let $x > a$. The tension is still zero. Let the shearing force be S' and the bending moment M'. Resolving vertically

$$S' = \frac{W}{3}.$$

Taking moments about A,

$$xS' + M' = Wa$$

$$\Rightarrow M' = Wa - \frac{xW}{3}.$$

The shearing force at a distance x from A is

$$-\frac{2W}{3}, x < a; \quad \frac{W}{3}, a < x < 3a.$$

The bending moment distance x from A is

$$\frac{2xW}{3}, x < a; \quad \left(a - \frac{x}{3}\right)W, a < x < 3a.$$

These results can be represented graphically as in Fig. 66. It should be noted that there is a particular relation between the shearing force and the bending moment, i.e. the gradient of the line representing the bending moment is equal to the shearing force. This is clear algebraically since taking moments about A in a general case gives

$$xS + M = \text{constant}.$$

Since S is constant between external forces, differentiating with respect to x gives

$$\frac{dM}{dx} = -S.$$

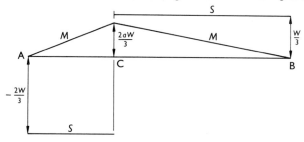

Fig. 66

EXAMPLE 7   *A uniform heavy rod of weight W and length a is supported in a horizontal position by vertical forces applied at the ends. Sketch the bending moment and shearing force diagrams, stating the maximum value of each.*

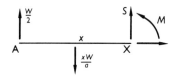

Fig. 67

Let AX be the section of length x measured from A. The weight of this portion is then $\dfrac{xW}{a}$. Let the shearing force and bending moment at X be S and M as shown in Fig. 67. Resolving vertically

$$S = \left(\frac{x}{a} - \frac{1}{2}\right)W.$$

Taking moments about A,

$$xS + M = \frac{x^2}{2a}W.$$

$$M = \frac{x^2}{2a}W - xS$$

$$= \left(\frac{x^2}{2a} - \frac{x^2}{a} + \frac{x}{2}\right)W$$

$$= \frac{x}{2a}(a - x)W.$$

Notice that it is still true that $\dfrac{dM}{dx} = -S$. The maximum value of M occurs when $S = 0$—i.e. when $x = \dfrac{a}{2}$.

Maximum bending moment $= aW/8$;

Maximum shearing force $= W/2$.

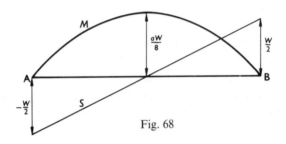

Fig. 68

The relation $\dfrac{dM}{dx} = -S$ is true for all beams, and can be demonstrated by considering a small element of a beam, AB, of length δx. If the tension, shearing force and bending moment at A are T, S and M, and at B are $T+\delta T$, $S+\delta S$ and $M+\delta M$, then the only other force which may be

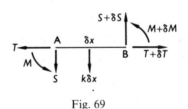

Fig. 69

acting is a gravitational force proportional to δx, and taking moments about A for the element gives

$$S\delta x + (M+\delta M) - M = 0,$$

ignoring terms of order greater than δx. Thus

$$S\delta x + \delta M = 0,$$

$$\frac{\delta M}{\delta x} = -S,$$

which in the limit gives

$$\frac{dM}{dx} = -S.$$

Exercise 11

1 A light framework is in the shape of a square ABCD, composed of five rods AB, BC, CD, DA and BD. It is smoothly pivoted at A and carries a mass of 40 kg at B. It is kept in a vertical plane with AB horizontal, C above B, by an upward force F N applied at C at 45° to the vertical. Calculate the reaction at A and the stresses in the rods, stating clearly their nature.

2 The figure illustrates a light framework ABCDEFGH with weights of 180 N and 120 N hung from B and C. The frame is pivoted at A and is supported with AD

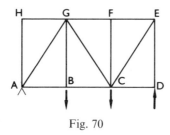

Fig. 70

horizontal by a vertical force at D. Find the stress and its nature in rod GC if each rod not vertical or horizontal makes an angle $\sin^{-1} \frac{8}{17}$ with the vertical.

3 Fig. 71 shows a light framework consisting of seven light rods jointed smoothly at A, B, C, D and E. It stands in a vertical plane with A and D on smooth horizontal ground. Angles CBE, BCE = 30°, and angles BAE, CDE = 25°. Angles DCE, ABE are both 90°. Find graphically the stress in each rod if a weight of mass 200 kg hangs from E.

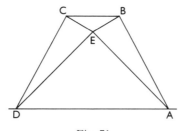

Fig. 71

4 A wheel at a fair is in the shape of a hexagon ABCDEF with light rods joining adjacent vertices and joining each vertex to the centre O where it is smoothly pivoted. It is in a vertical plane, and has seats of mass 100 kg at each vertex. Calculate the stress in each rod when AB is horizontal at the top assuming that when in this position the stress in AB is zero. Why is it necessary to stipulate the stress in AB?

5 A light framework ABCDEF is composed of nine rods: AB, BC, CD, DE, EF, FA, FB, FC and CE. It is in the shape of a trapezium with ABCD a straight line, FE = BC and AF = ED. Angle FAB = angle BFC = $\tan^{-1} \frac{4}{3}$. Weights of 40 N hang from both B and C, and a weight of 20 N hangs from D. The frame is pivoted at A and is supported with AD horizontal in a vertical plane by a force X N acting at F along FC. Find which rod takes the greatest strain.

6 ABCDE is a regular pentagon made up of seven light rods: AB, BC, CD, DE, EA, CA and DA. All the joints are smooth. The frame is in equilibrium in a vertical plane, being smoothly pivoted to a fixed point at A. A particle of weight 30 N is attached at B, and the system is held in equilibrium with CD horizontal below A by a horizontal force acting at E. Determine graphically the stresses in all the rods, the force at E and the reaction at A.

7 A light beam of length $3a$ is supported by vertical forces at the ends, and carries loads of weight W at the points of trisection, the beam being horizontal. Draw the shearing force and bending moment diagrams for the system, stating the maximum value of each.

8 A light beam ABCDE of length 8 m carries loads of masses 20 kg, 40 kg and 30 kg at B, C and D respectively, the beam being smoothly pivoted at A and kept in a horizontal position by a vertical force at B. AB = BC = CD = DE. Draw accurately the bending moment and shearing force diagrams for the system.

9 A uniform rod AB of mass m and length l rests at an angle of 60° to the horizontal with A against a smooth vertical wall, the other end B being on rough horizontal ground. Determine the tension, shearing force and bending moment at a point distant x from A.

10 A certain bridge can be treated as a uniform beam of length $4a$ and weight W supported by vertical forces at the ends. A vehicle of mass $2W$ crosses the bridge. Draw the shearing force and bending moment diagrams for the instant when the vehicle is on the centre of the bridge, and state the maximum bending moment in this case.

11 A light beam ABC is smoothly hinged to a fixed point at C. A mass of weight $8W$ is hung from A, the beam being kept in a horizontal position by a wire attached at B. If BC = a and AB = $2a$, sketch the shear force diagram and bending moment diagram if a bird of weight W stands on AB at D, a distance d from A. If the maximum bending moment that the rod can sustain is $17.2aW$ show that d must not be less than $4a/5$.

12 Project Example.

You are commissioned to design a bridge to span a 20 m gap, to consist of two identical light frameworks supporting between them a roadway 5 m wide made of hardcore 0·4 m thick weighing 1 kN per m³. The maximum load any rod can bear is 5t. Formulate, discuss and compare designs with fellow students, bearing in mind the additional load due to traffic.

Support Exercise A

Miscellaneous examples which may be worked concurrently with Chapters 2–5

1 A, B, C and D are four points in that order on a straight line. A mass of 1 kg at A is attached by a light inextensible string passing through a smooth ring at C and is attached by the other end to a mass of 2 kg at B. The string is just taut. The ring is pulled with a constant force of 20 N towards D. When the lighter mass reaches the heavier mass they coalesce. Find the ratio of the relative acceleration of the two masses before impact to the acceleration of the combined mass.

If AB is 40 cm, find the time interval between the start of the motion and the instant of impact. (Ignore gravity.)

2 An engine drives a car of mass 1·1 t at a maximum speed of 140 km/h against resistances which amount to $(\frac{1}{2}V^2 + 20V + 600)$ N at a speed of V km/h. Assuming the engine exerts the same force at all speeds, calculate the acceleration of the car at 60 km/h.

3 A car seat-belt is designed to spread any load put on it equally to its three anchorage points. In a collision, a car is brought to rest in 1 s from 70 km/h. Calculate the force exerted on the anchorage points by a man of 72 kg to the nearest 10 newtons.

4 A train accelerates from rest at A at a m/s² for t s, maintains a steady speed for T s, and comes to rest at B after being uniformly retarded for a further $2t$ s. Determine the acceleration of a second train which also starts from rest at A and which accelerates uniformly to reach B in the same time. What is the speed of this train as it reaches B?

Find the least time taken by a third train which has a maximum speed of at m/s, maximum acceleration $3a/2$ m/s², and maximum retardation a m/s², to travel from rest at A to rest at B.

5 The engine of a car of mass 810 kg can produce a force of $8(480 + 74v - v^2)$ N, where v is the speed of the car in m/s. The resistance due to wind and other causes is $(v^2 + 16v + 60)$ N. Using the principle that force equals mass × acceleration, determine
   (i) the maximum acceleration (to 2 significant figures), and at what speed it occurs,
   (ii) the maximum speed in km/h.

Illustrate the performance of the car graphically.

6 A particle P of mass m moves on a straight line AOB so that its distance from O after t seconds satisfies the equation $s = t(t-1)(t-2)$, (A to B taken as positive). A second particle Q of mass $2m$ is at rest at A when $t = O$, and is immediately acted on by a constant force so as to strike P when P is at O. If AO is a units, discuss the feasibility that Q can be accelerated at two different rates for this to be achieved. (Hint: A graphical consideration may be helpful initially.)

If on collision the masses coalesce, and $a = 2$, find the velocity of the combined mass immediately after the collision.

7 Assuming the earth to be a perfect sphere of radius 6360 km, calculate the percentage error (to 2 significant figures) made in the acceleration of a mass at a height of 6000 m by taking it as the true value of g at sea level.

8 A train accelerates at a rate of 0·5 m/s² to a speed of 72 km/h and maintains this speed for a period of $2\frac{1}{2}$ min. The train then slows down at a constant rate of $\frac{a}{8}$ m/s² without the brakes, and finally to rest by braking over the last few metres at a rate of a m/s². Find the distance travelled in terms of a if the total time taken was $4\frac{1}{2}$ min.

9 A man stands in a lift which, starting from rest, accelerates at $\frac{1}{2}g$ m/s² downwards or $\frac{1}{3}g$ m/s² upwards. Find the ratio of the reaction between the man's feet and the lift floor in the two cases.

10 A train rolls into a siding in such a way that it passes three points A, B and C distant 60 m, 110 m and 130 m from the beginning of the branch after 5 s, 11 s and 15 s respectively. Show that this is consistent with uniform retardation.

The train must come to a halt approximately 140 m from the beginning of the branch. Discover whether a further retardation will be required, and if so, how much if it is only applied from C.

11 A cable-car accelerates uniformly from rest for $3t$ s, and then travels at a constant speed of $4u$. On approaching the end of its run it decelerates to a speed of u in t s, and then to a standstill in a further $2t$ s. Find expressions for the initial acceleration and for the two retardations (assumed constant) in terms of u and t.

If the total distance is $1000u$ m, and $t = 5$ s, find the total time of the journey in minutes and seconds to the nearest 10 seconds.

12 A boy at A sees his bus leave the stop B and accelerate at 0·6 m/s² down the road towards C. AB is perpendicular to BC, and AB is 50 m. The boy sprints at an angle α to the road at a steady speed to intercept the bus at D, by which time the bus is travelling at 32·4 km/h. Find α and the speed at which the boy runs.

13 An inextensible string passing over a fixed smooth pulley has a mass of M on one end, and a smooth pulley of mass xM on the other. This latter pulley has an inextensible string passing over it with a mass of $\frac{1}{3}M$ on one end and of $\frac{1}{4}M$ on the other. Find the tension in the string passing over the fixed pulley, and deduce the limiting value of x if this tension must not exceed $3Mg/2$.

14 A train is travelling at a speed of 80 km/h. Neglecting resistances due to wind and other causes, find the constant brake resistance in kg wt. per tonne needed to stop the train in 600 m.

(N.B. xg N is equivalent to x kg wt. Take g as 9·8 m/s² and give the answer to 2 significant figures.)

15 Two weights connected by a light inextensible string over a smooth pulley are held at rest at a height of 40 cm above an inelastic horizontal plane. If their masses are 20 g and 50 g, and they are both released simultaneously, find (a) the maximum height attained by the smaller mass, and (b) the velocity with which the heavy mass is jerked off the table the first time. (Take g as 9·8 m/s². Inelastic means that the momentum of any body perpendicular to the plane will be completely destroyed on impact.)

16 Find to two significant figures the acceleration due to gravity on the moon's surface if the mass density of the moon is 2/3 the mass density of the earth. (Take g as 9·8 m/s²; the radius of the earth as 6360 km; the radius of the moon as 1740 km.)

A man weighing 85 kg can jump 1·6 m into the air on earth. How high can he jump on the moon in a space-suit of mass 15 kg? (Assume the initial momentum in each case is the same, and use the two-figure answer of the first part for your calculation.)

17 A light inextensible string, fixed at A, passes under a smooth pulley B of weight 10 kg, and up over a fixed smooth pulley C, and is connected to a weight D of mass 20 kg at its free end. If all the free parts of the string are vertical, determine the tension in the string, and the acceleration of B.

18 A string passing over a fixed smooth pulley A has a mass of $10m$ on one end, and a light smooth pulley B on the other. A second string passing over B has masses of $3m$ and $6m$ on the ends. If the strings are light and inextensible, find the accelerations of the three masses.

19 A car of mass 900 kg pulls a trailer of mass 200 kg. Resistances for both car and trailer amount to MkV^2 where M is the mass, k is a constant and V is the speed in m/s. Find k if the maximum pull of the engine is 3600 N and the maximum speed is 108 km/h. Find also the tension in the coupling when travelling at 20 m/s at full power.

20 Find graphically the resultant of the five vectors acting in directions as given in Fig. 72.

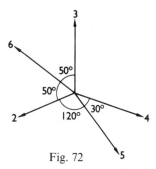

Fig. 72

A vector of magnitude P is added to the system to act in a direction bisecting the angle between the vectors of magnitudes 3 and 4. The resultant then has magnitude 2. Find P graphically.

21 A string passing over a fixed pulley has a particle of mass 5 kg attached at one end and is attached by the other to a second pulley. A further string passes over the second pulley and has particles of masses 2 kg and 3 kg attached to its ends. Both pulleys are smooth and the strings are light and inextensible. Show that if the system is released from rest and if g is taken to be 9·8 m/s² then the 5 kg mass will move downwards with an acceleration of 0·2 m/s².

Find the accelerations of the other two particles.

22 A telegraph pole supports 12 wires from the direction 020°, five wires from 130° and six wires from 300°. Find graphically the magnitude of the resultant force on the pole if each wire exerts a force of 8 N.

Two supporting stays are to be fixed to the pole so that the angle between their horizontal projections is 90°. One stay is only half as strong as the other. Find by any appropriate method how they should be positioned to best advantage.

23 Two particles A and B move in the same groove with speeds v_a and v_b respectively where after time t

$$v_a = u + at, \quad \text{and} \quad v_b = at + \tfrac{1}{2}bt^2$$

(u, a and b constants). A is in front of B and both are at O when $t =$ O. Find at what instant they collide, and sketch the distance-time graph.

If when they collide they coalesce and the forces acting on them continue to act on the combined particle, and if both A and B are of unit mass, show that the velocity v_{ab} after impact is given by the equation

$$4v_{ab} = 2u + 4at + bt^2, \quad t \geqslant \sqrt{\frac{6u}{b}}.$$

24 Two particles A and B of masses m and $2m$ are connected by a light inextensible string over a smooth fixed pulley. They are held both at a height d above an inelastic horizontal table with the string taut, and are released simultaneously. Show that the time that elapses between B's first impact with the table and the instant the whole system finally comes to rest is $2\sqrt{6d/g}$. (Assume that the pulley does not interfere with the motion.)

25 A bolt has to bear a weight of 200 kg together with a horizontal force of 25 kg wt., a force of 50 kg wt. at 30° to the horizontal donwards, and a force of 100 kg wt. at 60° to the horizontal upwards. All these forces act in the same plane, and the latter three all have components acting in the same horizontal direction. Assuming that all four forces begin to act at the same instant, prove whether or not it is safe to use a bolt made to hold a maximum force of 250 kg wt.

26 A non-uniform rod AB has centre of mass at G where BG = 2AG. A string passes from A to B and has length 2AB. The rod is hung by the string over a smooth peg P. Find at what angle the rod will stay in equilibrium.

27 A mass m_1 is connected by a light inextensible string over a smooth pulley to a second light smooth pulley. Masses m_2 and m_3 are connected by a similar string over this second pulley. If m_1 and m_3 both move when free to do so in the same direction with acceleration a (relative to a fixed point), show that

$$m_1 : m_2 : m_3 = 2 : \frac{g+a}{g-3a} : 1.$$

28 A non-uniform rod AB of length 60 cm is supported by two strings AC and BC each of length 40 cm from a peg C. The centre of mass of the rod divides AB in the ratio $1:2$. Find the angle at which the rod will hang in equilibrium, and the tensions in the strings in terms of the weight of the rod W.

29 Forces act radially outwards from the centre O of a regular hexagon ABCDEF: 3 N along OA, 6 N along OB, 10 N along OC, −8 N along OD, 9 N along OE and 3 N along OF. Find their resultant.

Show that if the resultant remains unaltered when the forces along OA, OF remain unchanged, and forces of magnitudes P, Q, R and S act radially from O along OB, OC, OD and OE respectively, then if $O < P < S$, R is negative. Find in this case the minimum value of Q.

30 A smooth bead is held at A, the top of a circular ring centre O of radius a which is fixed in a vertical plane. The bead is released so as to slide down a chord AB from A where angle $OAB = \theta$. Show that the time taken to reach B is independent of θ.

Find θ if a second smooth bead is released at the same instant as the first, but from O along the radius OB (B below O) so that they reach B at the same instant, and find the ratio of their speeds at the instant of impact.

31 A uniform rod OA is hinged at O to a wall, and a string AB supports the rod where B is vertically above O. If OA = $3a$, OB = $2a$ and AB = $2a$, and the weight of the rod is W, find the tension in the string and the reaction at O.

32 A man and a boy are carrying a uniform ladder weighing 40 kg wt.
(i) If the boy cannot carry more than 14 kg wt., find the maximum value of the ratio of the length between them to the length of the ladder.
(ii) Find the value of the ratio in (i) if the boy takes an end and the man takes 4/5 of the weight of the ladder.

33 A bar AB of length 2 m and mass 120 kg has centre of mass C one third of the way along its length. It is to be lifted by a crane using two equal cables DX and EX connected to the main cable FX at X. DX and EX both make an angle of 45° with the bar. Find the positions of D and E on the bar if they are 1 m apart if (i) the tensions in DX and EX are the same, (ii) the tension in DX is twice the tension in EX. What is the tension in EX in the second case? Show that AB makes an angle

$$\frac{\pi}{4} + \tan^{-1}\tfrac{1}{2}$$

with the vertical in the second case.

34 A non-uniform beam AB with centre of mass C is supported in a horizontal position by strings at A and B. The string at A is at 45° to BA produced, and the string at B is at 60° to the horizontal. Find the ratio AC:CB. If the mass of the rod is m, and a weight of mass xm is placed at the mid-point of AC, find the horizontal force P which must be applied at A if the system is to remain in the same position.

35 A uniform rod AB of mass 15 kg smoothly hinged at A is supported at an angle of 60° to the upward vertical through A by a string attached at B. Find the tension in the string if it is (i) perpendicular to the rod, (ii) at 60° to the rod. Show that the angle the string makes with the rod cannot be less than $\sin^{-1}\frac{\sqrt{3}}{8}$ if the breaking tension of the string is $30g$ N.

36 A physicist has set up a pulley system as illustrated in Fig. 73 consisting of two light smooth pulleys X and Y fixed at the ends of a horizontal line on which are marked points O and P 1 m apart. A light inextensible string passes over the pulleys; on one end a mass m hangs freely below Y, and on the other a mass

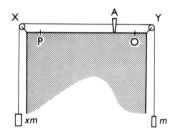

Fig. 73

$xm(x > 1)$, similarly below X. A light marker A is attached to the string so as to pass along the scale OP. Assuming the resistance to motion is constant, show that just two values of x enable the physicist to evaluate g without knowing the values of either the resistance or m.

If when $x = 2$ the time for A to move from rest at O to P is t, and when x is any other value x' the corresponding time is t', show that

$$g = \frac{6t'^2 - 2(1+x')t^2}{(2-x')t'^2t^2}.$$

and find an appropriate value for x' if $t' = \frac{1}{3}t = 1$ s. How practical would this experiment be? (Give your reasons.)

(Take g as 9·8 m/s².)

37 Prove that a system consisting of a force F acting through a point A and a couple of magnitude M can be reduced to a single force, and find where this single force acts relative to A.

ABCD is a square. Forces of magnitudes P, $\sqrt{2}P$ and $2P$ act along BA, DB and DC in the senses indicated by the order of the letters. If forces of magnitudes xP and yP are added along DA and AC respectively then the system reduces to a couple. Find x and y.

38 A heavy uniform metal ring is supported by three equal wires XA, XB, XC at rest hanging freely in a horizontal plane. A, B and C are equally spaced on the ring. Each wire is of length a, and triangle ABC has sides of length a. Find the tension in any wire if the ring has a mass of 10 kg.

A mass of 10 kg is now hung from a point D on the ring diametrically opposite to C. Show that the tensions in XA and XB each increase by an amount

$$5(4-\sqrt{2})g/\sqrt{3} \text{ N.}$$

39 Forces of magnitudes P, $2P$, $2P$, $4P$, xP and yP newtons act along the sides

AB, BC, CD, DE, EF and FA of a regular hexagon in the directions indicated by the order of the letters. Each side of the hexagon is of length a. If the system reduces to a couple, find x and y, and the moment of the couple.

Show that if the forces xP and yP are removed that the remaining forces reduce to a single force cutting AB produced at a point $7a/2$ from A. Find the magnitude and direction of this resultant.

40 A thin rigid uniform rod of mass M and length l has a particle of mass $2M$ attached to one end. The rod rests in equilibrium inside a smooth hemispherical bowl of radius $3l/4$ which is fixed with its rim horizontal. Find the angle of the rod to the horizontal and the magnitudes of the reactions between the rod and the bowl.

41 A uniform ladder $6a$ units long is held at an angle $\tan^{-1}\frac{4}{3}$ to the horizontal on a smooth horizontal floor against a smooth vertical wall by a rope attached to a point on the ladder $2a$ units up its length to a point on the wall on the same horizontal level. Show that the maximum tension in the rope is $99W/16$ if a man weighing $5W$ uses the ladder and if the weight of the ladder is W.

42 State Hooke's Law, and distinguish between the Modulus of Elasticity and Young's Modulus.

Two elastic strings AB, BC are attached at B. The Modulus of Elasticity of AB is λ_1, and of BC is λ_2. A particle of mass m is attached at B, and particles each of mass M are attached at A and C. If the system is first hung freely under gravity from A, and then freely under gravity from C, show that the difference in the length of AC in the two cases is

$$agm\frac{\lambda_2-\lambda_1}{\lambda_1\lambda_2}$$

where the natural length of each string is a.

Find this difference if, when suspended from A, AB $= 5a/4$, and when suspended from C, BC $= 4a/3$.

43 O is a point outside an equilateral triangle ABC of side $3a$, in the same plane as the triangle. Forces are represented in magnitude, direction and position by $2\overrightarrow{OA}$, $3\overrightarrow{OB}$ and $\overrightarrow{OC}$. If their resultant is similarly represented by $6\overrightarrow{OP}$, show that PC $= \sqrt{19}a/2$.

44 C is a point distant $\dfrac{3a}{2}$ from a fixed rough peg P on the same horizontal level as C.

A uniform rod AB of weight W and length $2a$ is supported by an elastic string of natural length a attached at A to C, and it leans against the peg at an angle θ to the vertical in such a way that the string AC is vertical. Show that

$$\frac{3}{4} \leqslant \sin\theta < \frac{3}{\sqrt{13}}.$$

If the modulus of elasticity of the string is λ, the coefficient of friction at the peg μ, find both λ and μ if $\theta = \sin^{-1}\frac{4}{5}$.

45 A is a fixed point on the same horizontal level as a smooth fixed pulley B where AB $= 2a$ units. A weight of mass $4m$ hangs in equilibrium between A and B, being supported by two strings AC and CD: AC is an elastic string of modulus λ and natural length a; CD is a light and inextensible string passing over B, and has a weight of mass $3m$ attached at D. If angle ACB is $90°$, find λ.

46 Forces of magnitudes P, $2P$, $3P$, $4P$ and $2P$ act along the sides AB, BC, CD, DA and diagonal AC of a quadrilateral. AB $= 1$ unit, BC $= 2$ units, AC $= 2$ units, AD $= 4$ units and CD $= 3$ units long. Show that the system reduces to a single force, and find its line of action. Find the couple which must be added to the system if the single force is to act through D.

47 A uniform rod AB rests with the end A on rough horizontal ground and B on a smooth plane of inclination 2ϕ to the horizontal so that AB makes an angle ϕ

with the horizontal. Find μ, the coefficient of friction at A, if it is in limiting equilibrium.

Show that the rod will not slip if any weight is placed on the rod nearer to A than to B.

48 State Lami's Theorem.

A light inextensible string ACD, AC > CD, of length a is attached to two fixed points on the same horizontal level less than a apart by the ends A and D. A particle of weight W is attached at C, and a smooth ring B also of weight W is threaded on the section AC of the string. When the system hangs in equilibrium AB and CD make angles α and β with the vertical. Show that

$$\tan \alpha = 3 \tan \beta.$$

If $\beta = \pi/6$, find the tensions in the string.

49 A vehicle accelerates in such a way that after t s its velocity v (m/s) is given by the equations

$$
\begin{aligned}
v &= t^2 + 6t, && (0 \leqslant t \leqslant 3), \\
v &= 24t - 2t^2 - 27, && (3 < t \leqslant 6), \\
v &= 45, && (t > 6).
\end{aligned}
$$

Show that there is no discontinuity (i.e. sudden change) in acceleration at any time $t > 0$. Sketch the velocity-time graph.

A second vehicle accelerates uniformly for 6 s from rest to 45 m/s, starting at the same time and in the same direction as the first vehicle from the same point. Find

(i) whether one overtakes the other at any time t, $0 < t < 6$, and

(ii) how far apart they are when $t = 6$.

50 An elastic string with Modulus of Elasticity λ is attached to a fixed point A on a rough slope of inclination α to the horizontal. A particle of mass m is attached to the other end of the string, and α is greater than the angle of friction β. If l is the least distance, and L the greatest, that the particle can be from A consistent with equilibrium, show that

$$\frac{l}{L} = \frac{mg \sin (\alpha - \beta) + \lambda \cos \beta}{mg \sin (\alpha + \beta) + \lambda \cos \beta}.$$

51 A smooth hemispherical bowl of radius a and centre O is fixed with the rim horizontal. A is a point on the rim, and a smooth plane AB inclined at 30° to the horizontal is such that A, B and O are in the same vertical plane and B is below A. A weight of $2mg$ is held at rest on the plane at a distance a from A by an elastic string of natural length a and Modulus of Elasticity λ which passes over a smooth pulley at A and is attached at the other end to a particle C of weight $\sqrt{6}mg$. If the string inside the bowl is inclined at an angle β to the vertical show that angle ACO $= \pi/2 - \beta$.

Hence show that $\beta = \cos^{-1} \sqrt{\frac{2}{3}}$, and find the value of λ.

52 A wedge of mass 6 kg rests with one face on a smooth horizontal table. A particle of mass 1 kg is held at the top of another face of the wedge which is inclined at an angle $\sin^{-1} \frac{3}{5}$ to the horizontal and is 0·5 m from the top to the bottom edge. The system is released. Find the maximum speed of the wedge in the ensuing motion.

53 A smooth plane is pivoted at the foot O, and for a given angle of inclination α to the horizontal, A represents the point on the plane from which a particle will slide from rest to O in 1 s. Show that if O is the origin of perpendicular axes x and y, x horizontal and y vertical, then the locus of A is

$$y(g - 2y) = 2x^2.$$

Find the corresponding locus if the plane is rough, the coefficient of friction being μ.

54 A heavy uniform sphere of radius a has a light inextensible string attached to a point on its surface. The other end of the string is fixed to a point on a rough vertical wall. The sphere rests in equilibrium touching the wall at a point distant h below the fixed point. If the point of the sphere in contact with the wall is about to slip downwards and the coefficient of friction between the sphere and the wall is μ, find the inclination of the string to the vertical.

If $\mu = \dfrac{h}{2a}$ and the weight of the sphere is W, show that the tension in the string is $W(1+\mu^2)^{\frac{1}{2}}/2\mu$. (L)

55 Vectors are represented in magnitude, position and direction by $2\overrightarrow{AD}$, $3\overrightarrow{AC}$ and $\overrightarrow{AB}$, where ABCD is a parallelogram. Show that

$$2\overrightarrow{AD}+3\overrightarrow{AC}+\overrightarrow{AB} = 6\overrightarrow{AE}+3\overrightarrow{AF}$$

where E, F are the points of trisection of DB. Hence show that

$$2\overrightarrow{AD}+3\overrightarrow{AC}+\overrightarrow{AB} = 9\overrightarrow{AY}$$

where $DY:YB = 4:5$.

56 A framework ABCD has the shape of a kite; AB = AD and BC = CD. The rods AB, AD each weigh $2W$, and the rods BC, CD each weigh $3W$, and $3AB = 2BC$. The framework is suspended from A, and a light rod $EF = \frac{1}{2}BC$ maintains the shape, where E and F are the mid-points of AB and AD. Find the reaction at D and the stress in EF, assuming all the joints are smooth.

(N.B. The reactions at the ends of a light rod lie along the rod. See p. 70.)

57 A car of mass M kg exerts a maximum force of 5400 N, against which acts a resistance of kMv N where $k = \frac{1}{5}$ and v is the speed in m/s. A trailer of mass m kg which may be attached to the car has a resistance to motion of $\frac{1}{2}mkv$ N. If $M = 850$ and $m = 300$, find the accelerations of the car up an incline of $\sin^{-1}\frac{1}{10}$ at full power when travelling at 54 km/h with and without the trailer. Find the tension in the coupling in the former case. Find also the maximum speed to the nearest km/h up the incline both with and without the trailer.

58 Three uniform rods AB, BC and CD each of length $2a$ have weights W, $2W$ and $3W$ respectively. They are smoothly jointed at B and C, and are hung from A and D so that A and D are on the same horizontal level a distance $4a$ apart. The system is made to hang symmetrically by the attachment of a light inextensible string fastened to the mid-points of AB and BC. Show that the tension in this string is W.

59 Triangle ABC is the vertical cross-section of a fixed wedge where angle ABC $= \theta$, angle A $= 90°$ and BC is horizontal. Blocks P and Q are held at rest on the faces AB and AC respectively; P is of mass $3m$ and Q is of mass m. The coefficients of friction between blocks and wedge are μ_1 and μ_2 on AB and AC respectively. An inextensible light string connects P and Q over a smooth pulley at A and is just taut. The length AQ $= 2x$. The system is released, and is such that Q moves towards A. When Q is a distance x from A, it picks up another block R of mass m, the effect of which is to cause the system to come momentarily to rest just as Q and R reach A. Show that

$$\tan \theta = \frac{14+27\mu_1}{27-14\mu_2}.$$

60 A uniform right circular cylindrical can of radius a and weight W, having no lid, rests with its base on a horizontal plane. A uniform rod of weight kW rests in smooth contact with the rim and the inner curved surface area of the can. The rod is inclined to the horizontal at an angle of $45°$ and the can is about to topple. Draw 3 separate diagrams showing the forces on the whole system, on the rod and on the can.

Find the value of k and the length of the rod. (L)

61 A framework is composed of three uniform rods AB, BC and CA smoothly jointed at A, B and C. It is supported in a vertical plane, BC horizontal and A above BC, by two supports X and Y on BC where BX = XY = YC. AB = AC, and these two rods are each of weight W. BC is of weight $3W$ and angle ABC is 30°. Find the reactions at A and X if an additional weight $2W$ is hung on AB a quarter of the way down AB.

62 ABCD is a square of side a, and forces of magnitudes F, F, $-4F$, $-2F$, P and Q act along the lines AB, BC, CD, DA, CA and DB respectively in the senses indicated by the order of the letters. If the system reduces to a couple, find P and Q.

If P is now reversed in direction find the resultant of the new system, finding where it cuts AD, produced if necessary.

63 A wedge of mass $2m$ is held at rest on a smooth plane inclined at 30° to the horizontal. Another face of the wedge makes an angle of 60° with the plane, being also at 30° to the horizontal. A small block of mass m is placed on this face which is also smooth. When the system is released, show that the acceleration of the wedge is $\dfrac{7g}{11}$ down the plane, and find the reaction between the block and the wedge.

64 A light framework ABCDE consists of seven rods in the shape of a trapezium ACDE. The rods AB, BC, DE are all 1 m long, and ABC is a straight line. AE, EB, BD, DC are all 2 m long. The framework is supported in a vertical plane by vertical forces at A and C, AC being horizontal, and ED above ABC. F is a point vertically above B, midway between AC and ED. A mass of $4t$ is supported at F by two equal light wires from E and D. If all the joints are smooth, find the nature and magnitude of the stresses in every rod.

65 A mass is drawn up a smooth inclined plane by a light inextensible string which passes over a small smooth pulley at the top of the plane and carries an equal mass at the other end. If the string is cut at any time, the mass travels thereafter half as far up the plane as it has already travelled from rest. Find the inclination of the plane.   (O)

66 Fig. 74 illustrates a light framework ABCDEF pivoted smoothly at E. A horizontal force acts at A and a weight of 2 tonne hangs from F. CBA is horizontal; CDFB forms a square, and angles EFD, BFA are both 72°. Find graphically the tension in every rod and the reaction at E.

(Hint: Find the direction of the reaction at E using the fact that three forces in equilibrium act through a point.)

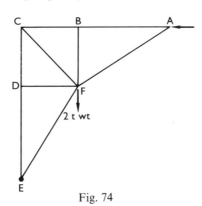

Fig. 74

6 Vectors (2)

6.1 Position vectors and unit vectors

The reader will by now appreciate the value of being able to split a vector up into components at right-angles. To make more effective use of this we note a similarity with the cartesian coordinate geometry with which we are already familiar.

Cartesian coordinates in two dimensions refer to two perpendicular axes. When we refer to the point (4,7) for example we know that we can find this point by looking at its 'components' separately. The first 'component' is 4, and refers to the x-direction; the second 'component' is 7, and refers to the y-direction. Each 'component' is measured from a fixed point, the origin, and if we draw a straight line from the origin O to the point (4,7) then this line is unique, and has both magnitude and direction —it is therefore a vector! Of course, the representation of this vector by the number pair (4,7) has been quite satisfactory up to this point, and you may have been using this notation for several years without knowing anything about vectors.

This vector represented by OP is called the position vector of P, and we see that it can be represented as the sum of two components at right-angles—one of four units in the x-direction, and one of seven units in the y-direction. The bracket notation however can be a little clumsy when

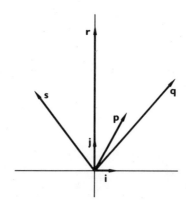

Fig. 75

applied to vector problems, and so we modify it a little by introducing unit vectors.

A **unit vector** is just what its name implies—a vector with magnitude 1 unit. It is common notation to let **i** be a unit vector acting at O in the x-direction, **j** a unit vector acting in the y-direction, and when we work in three dimensions we take **k** to be a unit vector in the z-direction. Then if the position vector of P is **p** we have

$$\mathbf{p} = 4\mathbf{i} + 7\mathbf{j}.$$

Similarly the position vector of Q(7,11) is

$$\mathbf{q} = 7\mathbf{i} + 11\mathbf{j},$$

of R(0,17) is

$$\mathbf{r} = 17\mathbf{j},$$

and of S(-6,10) is

$$\mathbf{s} = -6\mathbf{i} + 10\mathbf{j}.$$

6.2 Relative position vectors

Consider the relative positions of the two points P and Q as defined by **p** and **q** above. Suppose that the unit vectors each have magnitude 1 metre and that the axes are drawn out on a large horizontal floor. If I am standing at P, how far am I from Q, and what is the direction of Q from the point where I am standing?

The line joining P to Q is a vector by the same argument as before—it has both magnitude and direction—and this vector tells me all I want to know. If we call this vector **t**, then since the parallelogram of vectors must apply

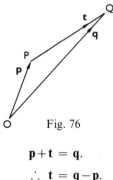

Fig. 76

$$\mathbf{p} + \mathbf{t} = \mathbf{q}.$$
$$\therefore \ \mathbf{t} = \mathbf{q} - \mathbf{p}.$$

Substituting for **p** and **q**,

$$\mathbf{t} = (7\mathbf{i} + 11\mathbf{j}) - (4\mathbf{i} + 7\mathbf{j})$$
$$= 3\mathbf{i} + 4\mathbf{j}.$$

By Pythagoras the magnitude of t is $\sqrt{(3^2+4^2)} = 5$, and so I am standing 5 metres from Q, and Q lies in a direction $\tan^{-1}\frac{4}{3}$ with the direction of $\mathbf{i}$.

We shall from this point refer to the magnitude of a vector quite frequently, and we shall use what is called the modulus notation: we shall take the expression '$|\mathbf{t}|$' to mean the magnitude of $\mathbf{t}$. In speech this is referred to as 'the modulus of $\mathbf{t}$' or loosely as just 'Mod-$\mathbf{t}$'.*

We must at this point make a careful distinction between the vectors $\mathbf{p}$ and $\mathbf{q}$ and the vector $\mathbf{t}$. The lines $\mathbf{p}$ and $\mathbf{q}$ are both positioned at O, and because of this we tend to refer to $\mathbf{p}$ and $\mathbf{q}$ as **the** position vectors of P and Q; the fact that they are relative to O is taken for granted. But the vector $\mathbf{t}$ is **not** represented by a line at O, and so it is essential that we refer to $\mathbf{t}$ as a **relative position vector** and to say to which point it is relative. In this case, $\mathbf{t}$ is the position vector of Q relative to P.

Readers who have already studied complex numbers may note the similarity between complex numbers (particularly as represented in the Argand diagram) and this representation of vectors. The similarity is quite extensive, but it is not entirely isomorphic. The project example in Exercise 14 is drawn to your attention in this connection.

EXAMPLE 1   *The three vertices of a triangle* ABC *are given by the position vectors* $\mathbf{a} = -3\mathbf{i}-5\mathbf{j}$, $\mathbf{b} = 4\mathbf{i}+7\mathbf{j}$ *and* $\mathbf{c} = -2\mathbf{i}+9\mathbf{j}$ *respectively. Find the position vector of the centroid* G *and state the position of* B *relative to* G.

Let the mid-point of the side BC be given by the position vector $\mathbf{d}$, then

$$\mathbf{d} = \tfrac{1}{2}(\mathbf{b}+\mathbf{c}).$$

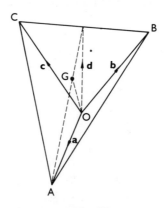

Fig. 77

---

* The reader will come across this notation in other branches of Mathematics, if he has not done so already, e.g. with scalars: $|a|$ meaning $|a| = a$ if $a > 0$, but $|a| = -a$ if $a < 0$; also with complex numbers.

We can argue the truth of this equation by considering the method we would use to find the mid-point of a line in coordinate geometry. But a more direct method based on vector principles is possible. We established an extension of the Parallelogram of Vectors (pp. 49–50), and in this context it tells us that $\mathbf{b}+\mathbf{c} = 2\mathbf{d}$ where $\mathbf{d}$ is the position vector of the mid-point of BC—hence the equation above.

From this equation

$$\mathbf{d} = \tfrac{1}{2}(4\mathbf{i}+7\mathbf{j}-2\mathbf{i}+9\mathbf{j})$$
$$= \mathbf{i}+8\mathbf{j}.$$

By the same principle, since G divides the median in the ratio 2:1,

$$2\mathbf{d}+\mathbf{a} = 3\mathbf{m}$$
$$\therefore \ \mathbf{m} = \tfrac{1}{3}(2\mathbf{d}+\mathbf{a})$$
$$= \tfrac{1}{3}(2\mathbf{i}+16\mathbf{j}-3\mathbf{i}-5\mathbf{j})$$
$$= -\tfrac{1}{3}\mathbf{i}+3\tfrac{2}{3}\mathbf{j}.$$

$\therefore$ The centroid has position vector $-\tfrac{1}{3}\mathbf{i}+3\tfrac{2}{3}\mathbf{j}$,

and the position of B relative to G is $\mathbf{b}-\mathbf{m} = 4\tfrac{1}{3}\mathbf{i}+3\tfrac{1}{3}\mathbf{j}$.

The above example could be solved even more simply by using the result of Example 3 on p. 51. In this context that result reads

$$\overrightarrow{OA}+\overrightarrow{OB}+\overrightarrow{OC} = 3\overrightarrow{OG}.$$

(This result is independent of whether O lies inside or outside the triangle.) Thus

$$\mathbf{m} = \tfrac{1}{3}(\mathbf{a}+\mathbf{b}+\mathbf{c}).$$

We use this fact in Example 2.

One important advantage of the notation we have now established is that it extends to three dimensions without any modification being required. Example 2 is principally the same as Example 1, but extended to three dimensions.

EXAMPLE 2   *Find the centroid of the triangle* ABC *if the position vectors of* A, B *and* C *are* $\mathbf{a}$, $\mathbf{b}$ *and* $\mathbf{c}$ *respectively where* $\mathbf{a} = 3\mathbf{i}-5\mathbf{j}+2\mathbf{k}$, $\mathbf{b} = 4\mathbf{i}+7\mathbf{j}$ *and* $\mathbf{c} = -2\mathbf{i}+9\mathbf{j}-6\mathbf{k}$.

Let the centroid have position vector $\mathbf{m}$, then

$$\mathbf{m} = \tfrac{1}{3}(\mathbf{a}+\mathbf{b}+\mathbf{c})$$
$$= \tfrac{1}{3}(-3\mathbf{i}-5\mathbf{j}+2\mathbf{k}+4\mathbf{i}+7\mathbf{j}-2\mathbf{i}+9\mathbf{j}-6\mathbf{k})$$
$$= \tfrac{1}{3}(-\mathbf{i}+11\mathbf{j}-4\mathbf{k}).$$

The position vector of the centroid is $-\tfrac{1}{3}\mathbf{i}+3\tfrac{2}{3}\mathbf{j}-\tfrac{4}{3}\mathbf{k}$.

Exercise 12

1 Write down the position vectors for the points A(6,2), B(1,−3), C(7,−1) and D(−2,4).
Find the relative position vectors of A from B, D from A and C from D.
Which point is nearest to A?

2 Draw in the position vectors **a**, **b** and **c** relative to unit vectors **i** and **j** for the points A(4,2), B(9,−10) and C(12,−6). Find the positions of B and C relative to A in vector form. Which point is nearer to A?

3 ABCD is a parallelogram, the vertices of which have position vectors **a**, **b**, **c** and **d** respectively.
    (i) Express **d** in terms of **a**, **b** and **c**,
    (ii) find the position vector for the intersection of the diagonals, and
    (iii) deduce whether or not the following points form a parallelogram:

$$\mathbf{a} = 3\mathbf{i}-2\mathbf{j}, \quad \mathbf{b} = 6\mathbf{i}+2\mathbf{j}, \quad \mathbf{c} = 8\mathbf{i}+\mathbf{j} \quad \text{and} \quad \mathbf{d} = 5\mathbf{i}-3\mathbf{j}.$$

    Sketch this quadrilateral, and find the lengths of its sides.

4 Three points P, Q and R with position vectors **p**, **q** and **r** respectively form an equilateral triangle. If $\mathbf{p} = 6\mathbf{i}+4\mathbf{j}$ and $\mathbf{p}-\mathbf{q} = 3\mathbf{i}+3\mathbf{j}$, find
    (i) **q**, and
    (ii) the two possible positions of R.

5 A square WXYZ has centre $\mathbf{r} = 5\mathbf{i}-5\mathbf{j}$. If the vertices have position vectors **w**, **x**, **y** and **z**, and $\mathbf{z} = 2\mathbf{i}-\mathbf{j}$, find **w**, **x** and **y**.

6 Find the position of the centroid of a triangle ABC if the vertices A, B and C have position vectors $\mathbf{a} = 2\mathbf{i}-\mathbf{j}+3\mathbf{k}$, $\mathbf{b} = 7\mathbf{i}-4\mathbf{j}-\mathbf{k}$ and $\mathbf{c} = 3\mathbf{i}-\mathbf{j}+7\mathbf{k}$.
    Another triangle DEF has the same centroid, and vertices D and E have positions $\mathbf{d} = 7\mathbf{i}+3\mathbf{j}-\mathbf{k}$ and $\mathbf{e} = -10\mathbf{k}$. Find **f**, the position vector of F.

7 ABC is a triangle with vertices A, B and C defined by the vectors $\mathbf{a} = 3\mathbf{i}+2\mathbf{j}+\mathbf{k}$, $\mathbf{b} = 6\mathbf{i}-\mathbf{j}-5\mathbf{k}$ and $\mathbf{c} = -4\mathbf{i}-\mathbf{j}+10\mathbf{k}$, respectively. D is a point on AB such that AD:DB = 1:2; E is a point on BC such that BE:EC = 2:3; F is a point on DE such that DF:FE = 3:5. Find the position vectors of D, E and F.

8 If $\mathbf{a} = \mathbf{j}$, $\mathbf{b} = \mathbf{i}+2\mathbf{j}$ and $\mathbf{c} = 3\mathbf{i}+4\mathbf{j}$, form expressions for $\mathbf{b}-\mathbf{a}$, $\mathbf{c}-\mathbf{a}$ and $\mathbf{c}-\mathbf{b}$.
    These three points lie in a straight line. Form its cartesian equation. If t is a scalar variable, write down an expression in vector form for any point on the line in terms of t. What conclusions can you draw about the gradient of any line when represented in this vector form?

6.3 Centre of mass

Consider a system consisting of three particles A, B and C of masses m_a, m_b and m_c respectively, Fig. 78. Let O be a point such that the position

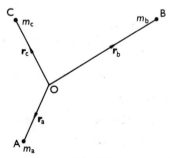

Fig. 78

vectors of A, B and C relative to O are $\mathbf{r}_a$, $\mathbf{r}_b$ and $\mathbf{r}_c$, then we say that the **linear moment** of the system about O is the sum

$$m_a\mathbf{r}_a + m_b\mathbf{r}_b + m_c\mathbf{r}_c.$$

If we choose O so that the linear moment is zero, then we call O the Centre of Mass (or Mass Centre).

We have already made reference to the terms Centre of Gravity, Centre of Mass, and Centroid. While these terms generally amount to the same thing, there is a distinction to be drawn between them. The **Centre of Gravity** can only be defined within the context of a gravitational field, and is that point through which the force due to gravity acting on a body can be taken to act. The **Centre of Mass** is defined as that point about which the linear moment of the body is zero. The **Centroid**, while it means in effect the mass centre, is used more specifically in relation to curves and surfaces which do not necessarily have mass as such at all, and in effect means their centre. It is however normally found by assuming that the curve or surface has got a mass, and by finding its mass centre.

Consider again the system of particles A, B and C, but now add $n-3$ further particles giving us n particles all together. Relabel the masses as $m_1, m_2, m_3, \ldots, m_n$ instead of m_a, m_b, m_c, etc. Similarly read $\mathbf{r}_1, \mathbf{r}_2, \mathbf{r}_3, \ldots, \mathbf{r}_n$ for $\mathbf{r}_a, \mathbf{r}_b, \mathbf{r}_c$, etc. The linear moment of the system about O is then

$$m_1\mathbf{r}_1 + m_2\mathbf{r}_2 + \ldots + m_n\mathbf{r}_n = \sum_{i=1}^{n} m_i\mathbf{r}_i.$$

Suppose that O is the origin, and that G is the mass centre, and that the position vector of G is $\mathbf{m}$, then by the definition of G

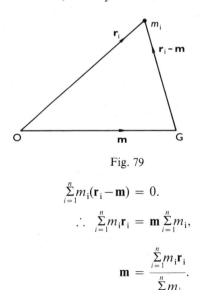

Fig. 79

$$\sum_{i=1}^{n} m_i(\mathbf{r}_i - \mathbf{m}) = 0.$$

$$\therefore \ \sum_{i=1}^{n} m_i\mathbf{r}_i = \mathbf{m} \sum_{i=1}^{n} m_i,$$

$$\mathbf{m} = \frac{\sum_{i=1}^{n} m_i\mathbf{r}_i}{\sum_{i=1}^{n} m_i}.$$

In a two dimensional system we may take $\mathbf{r}_i$ as $x_i\mathbf{i}+y_i\mathbf{j}$,* and it is customary to write $\mathbf{m}$ as $\bar{x}\mathbf{i}+\bar{y}\mathbf{j}$,* then

$$\mathbf{m} = \bar{x}\mathbf{i}+\bar{y}\mathbf{j}$$

$$= \frac{\sum\limits_{i=1}^{n}m_i x_i}{\sum\limits_{i=1}^{n}m_i}\mathbf{i}+\frac{\sum\limits_{i=1}^{n}m_i y_i}{\sum\limits_{i=1}^{n}m_i}\mathbf{j}. \qquad 6.1$$

From this equation we can find the centre of mass as illustrated in the examples that follow. It should be noted that we have made no attempt to show that the Centre of Mass and the Centre of Gravity coincide. This would not strictly be in the confines of this text, but we assume that they do so from this point on.

EXAMPLE 3   *A uniform lamina ABCD has the shape of a trapezium, AB parallel to DC, AB = 10 cm and DC = 4 cm. EFCD is a square with E and F points on AB such that AE = 2 cm and FB = 4 cm. Find the position of the centre of mass of the lamina.*

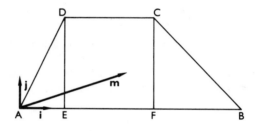

Fig. 80

Let $\mathbf{i}$ and $\mathbf{j}$ be perpendicular unit vectors through A, $\mathbf{i}$ along AB, and let the mass centre have position vector relative to A given by
$$\mathbf{m} = \bar{x}\mathbf{i}+\bar{y}\mathbf{j}.$$

We consider the trapezium to be made up of three parts: triangles AED, FBC, and the square EFCD. Their masses are proportional to their areas which are 4 cm², 8 cm², and 16 cm² respectively.

The mass centre of triangle AED has position

$$(\tfrac{2}{3}\times 2)\mathbf{i}+(\tfrac{1}{3}\times 4)\mathbf{j} = \tfrac{4}{3}\mathbf{i}+\tfrac{4}{3}\mathbf{j}$$

(the position of the centroid).

Similarly the mass centre of triangle FBC has position

$$(6+\tfrac{1}{3}\times 4)\mathbf{i}+(\tfrac{1}{3}\times 4)\mathbf{j} = \tfrac{22}{3}\mathbf{i}+\tfrac{4}{3}\mathbf{j}.$$

* In a three dimensional system, add $z_i\mathbf{k}$ and $\bar{z}\mathbf{k}$ respectively.

The centre of mass of the square EFCD has position $4\mathbf{i}+2\mathbf{j}$. Thus by *6.1*,

$$\mathbf{m} = ((4\times\tfrac{4}{3}+8\times\tfrac{22}{3}+16\times4)\mathbf{i}+(4\times\tfrac{4}{3}+8\times\tfrac{4}{3}+16\times2)\mathbf{j})/(4+8+16)$$

$$= ((\tfrac{16}{3}+\tfrac{176}{3}+64)\mathbf{i}+(\tfrac{16}{3}+\tfrac{32}{3}+32)\mathbf{j})/28$$

$$= \tfrac{128}{28}\mathbf{i}+\tfrac{48}{28}\mathbf{j}$$

$$= 4\tfrac{4}{7}\mathbf{i}+1\tfrac{5}{7}\mathbf{j}.$$

∴ The mass centre has position $4\tfrac{4}{7}\mathbf{i}+1\tfrac{5}{7}\mathbf{j}$ relative to A, with usual vector notation, $\mathbf{i}$ acting along AB and of magnitude 1 cm.

In this example we have used the fact that the mass centre of a triangle is at the intersection of the medians. We can establish this by supposing that a triangle ABC is made up of a large number of thin strips parallel to BC. The centre of mass of each strip is at its mid-point, but by similar triangles the median from A passes through all these mid-points, and so the mass centre lies on the median from A. Similarly it lies on the other medians. Thus the mass centre is at the centroid, the intersection of the medians.

From this result a useful corollary follows. If G is the centroid of a triangle ABC, and $\mathbf{a}$, $\mathbf{b}$ and $\mathbf{c}$ are the position vectors of A, B and C from G, then we already know that

$$\mathbf{a}+\mathbf{b}+\mathbf{c} = 0.$$

(See p. 97 and also Example 3, p. 51.)

Hence it must be true that

$$\frac{m}{3}\mathbf{a}+\frac{m}{3}\mathbf{b}+\frac{m}{3}\mathbf{c} = 0.$$

But this is the linear moment of three equal masses each of $m/3$ at A, B and C, and so G is also their mass centre. Thus a triangle of mass m, and a system having weights of mass $m/3$ at the vertices of the triangle are linearly equivalent. This means that in examples on equilibrium and when taking moments we may use either system with the same result.

EXAMPLE 4   *A uniform rectangular lamina measuring 12 cm by 20 cm has a small square cut out from it measuring 4 cm by 4 cm. The sides of the square are parallel to the sides of the rectangle and two adjacent sides of the square are both 1 cm from their nearest side of the rectangle. Find the centre of mass of the lamina.*

We find the centre of mass of the lamina by saying that the linear moment of the lamina plus the linear moment of the square equals the linear moment of the complete rectangle.

Suppose that unit vectors $\mathbf{i}$ and $\mathbf{j}$ each of magnitude 1 cm act along the sides of the rectangle closest to the square, Fig. 81.

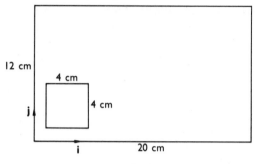

Fig. 81

The masses of the rectangle, square and lamina are proportional to their areas which are 240 cm², 16 cm² and 224 cm² respectively. Their centres of mass have position vectors $10\mathbf{i}+6\mathbf{j}$, $3\mathbf{i}+3\mathbf{j}$ and $\bar{x}\mathbf{i}+\bar{y}\mathbf{j}$ say, respectively. Equating the linear moment about the origin,

$$224(\bar{x}\mathbf{i}+\bar{y}\mathbf{j})+16(3\mathbf{i}+3\mathbf{j}) = 240(10\mathbf{i}+6\mathbf{j}),$$

$$14(\bar{x}\mathbf{i}+\bar{y}\mathbf{j}) = -3\mathbf{i}-3\mathbf{j}+150\mathbf{i}+90\mathbf{j}$$

$$= 147\mathbf{i}+87\mathbf{j}.$$

∴ The position of the mass centre is given by the vector $\frac{21}{2}\mathbf{i}+\frac{87}{14}\mathbf{j}$.

6.4 Centre of mass by integration

In the previous section we arrived at the equation *6.1* by making the assumption that we could represent a system by a finite number of masses located at clearly distinct points. We can however apply the theory to continuous systems by making use of Calculus. This way we are able to establish a number of important results—the positions of the mass centres of cones, hemispheres (both solid and hollow), sectors, arcs, etc. We illustrate by means of two examples.

EXAMPLE 5   *Find the mass centre of a solid hemisphere of radius a.*

Let **i**, **j**, and **k** be mutually perpendicular unit vectors, **j** and **k** lying in the plane face of the hemisphere and **i** lying along the axis of symmetry. By symmetry, the mass centre lies on this axis and has position $\bar{x}\mathbf{i}$, say. Consider the hemisphere as a series of discs, thickness δx, each disc being parallel to the **j**,**k**-plane. Then a disc with centre at $x\mathbf{i}$ has radius

$$\sqrt{(a^2-x^2)},$$

and its volume is

$$\pi(a^2-x^2)\delta x.$$

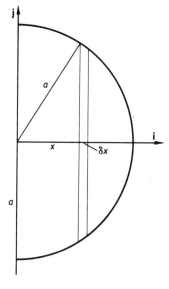

Fig. 82

Since mass is proportional to volume, Equation *6.1* gives

$$\bar{x} = \frac{\sum \pi x(a^2 - x^2)\delta x}{\sum \pi(a^2 - x^2)\delta x}.$$

But as $\delta x \to 0, \sum \pi x(a^2 - x^2)\delta x \to \int_0^a \pi x(a^2 - x^2)dx$, and similarly

$$\sum \pi(a^2 - x^2)\delta x \to \int_0^a \pi(a^2 - x^2)dx.$$

$$\therefore \ \bar{x} = \pi \int_0^a (a^2 x - x^3)dx / \pi \int_0^a (a^2 - x^2)dx$$

$$= \left[\frac{a^2 x^2}{2} - \frac{x^4}{4}\right]_0^a \bigg/ \left[a^2 x - \frac{x^3}{3}\right]_0^a$$

$$= (\tfrac{1}{2}a^4 - \tfrac{1}{4}a^4)/(a^3 - \tfrac{1}{3}a^3)$$

$$= \frac{3a}{8}.$$

$\therefore$ The centre of mass of a solid hemisphere of radius a is $3a/8$ from the plane face.

It is important to realise that the method of cutting up into discs is too clumsy for certain shapes, particularly hollow objects, and in such cases we frequently use an angle as the variable of integration rather than x. We illustrate this in the case of a hemispherical shell.

EXAMPLE 6   *Find the position of the mass centre of a thin hemispherical shell radius a (i) in the form of an open bowl, and (ii) when completely enclosed.*

We define unit vectors **i**, **j** and **k** as in Example 5, and take the centre of mass in case (i) as $\bar{x}_1\mathbf{i}$, and in case (ii) as $\bar{x}_2\mathbf{i}$.

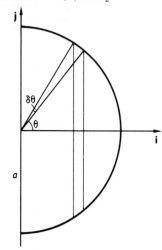

Fig. 83

We consider a thin ring formed by the shell cut off by two planes a very small distance apart parallel to the **j,k**-plane. Let the width of the ring subtend an angle $\delta\theta$ at the origin O of unit vectors, then its width is $a\delta\theta$. If the angle of any position vector of a point on the ring to **i** is θ, then the radius of the ring is $a \sin\theta$, and the area of the ring is

$$2\pi a \sin\theta . a\delta\theta.$$

Since mass is proportional to area, equation 6.1 gives

$$\bar{x}_1 = \underset{\delta\theta\to0}{\text{Lim}}\frac{\sum 2\pi a \sin\theta . a \cos\theta . a\delta\theta}{\sum 2\pi a \sin\theta . a\delta\theta}$$

$$= \int_0^{\pi/2} 2\pi a^3 \sin\theta . \cos\theta d\theta \bigg/ \int_0^{\pi/2} 2\pi a^2 \sin\theta d\theta$$

$$= \left[\tfrac{1}{2}a \sin^2\theta\right]_0^{\pi/2} \bigg/ \left[-\cos\theta\right]_0^{\pi/2}$$

$$= (a/2)/1$$

$$= \frac{a}{2}.$$

∴ The centre of mass of an open hemispherical bowl is half-way along the symmetric radius.

We use this result for case (ii). The area of the lid is πa^2, and since mass is proportional to area, equation 6.1 gives

$$\bar{x}_2 = ((2\pi a^2 . \bar{x}_1) + (\pi a^2 . 0))/(2\pi a^2 + \pi a^2)$$
$$= \pi a^3/3\pi a^2$$
$$= a/3.$$

∴ The centre of mass of a closed hemispherical shell is 1/3 the way along the symmetric radius from the plane face.

It is possible to deduce similar formulae for other common shapes, and the reader is encouraged to establish these for himself in the Exercise that follows. It is not recommended that all these should be memorized, but those deduced in Examples 5 and 6 are frequently used and are worth remembering, together with the corresponding results for the cone. For a solid cone of height h the mass centre is a distance $h/4$ from the base; for the corresponding cone, hollow and open at the base, the centre of mass is a distance $h/3$ from the base.

Exercise 13

1 A system consists of five particles of masses m, $2m$, $2m$, $5m$ and $6m$ at points given by vectors **a**, **b**, **c**, **d** and **e** relative to a point O. Find the centre of mass relative to O if **a** $= 4\mathbf{i} - \mathbf{j}$, **b** $= 3\mathbf{i} + 2\mathbf{j}$, **c** $= 3\mathbf{i} - 3\mathbf{j}$, **d** $= 7\mathbf{j}$ and **e** $= -2\mathbf{i} - 3\mathbf{j}$.

2 Find the centre of mass of particles of masses $2m$, $6m$, $3m$ and $5m$ situated at points $4\mathbf{i}$, $2\mathbf{i} - 3\mathbf{k}$, $6\mathbf{i} - 3\mathbf{j} - \mathbf{k}$ and $\mathbf{j} + \mathbf{k}$ respectively.

3 A uniform circular disc of radius 6 cm has a circular hole of radius 2 cm cut with the centre of the hole 2 cm from the centre of the disc. Find the centre of mass of the disc.

4 A uniform rectangular sheet of metal, 30 cm by 20 cm, has a cut 5 cm long made in a longer side parallel to the shorter sides and 10 cm from a corner. The rectangle on this corner measuring 5 cm by 10 cm is folded back to lie flat against the adjacent sheeting. Find how far the centre of mass has been moved by this operation.

5 A uniform lamina in the form of an equilateral triangle ABC has mass $4m$. E and F are the mid-points of AC and AB respectively, and the triangle AEF is cut off. The remainder is suspended freely under gravity by a thread at B. Find the angle BC makes with the vertical.

6 Show that the centre of gravity of a solid circular cone of height h is distant $h/4$ from the base.

7 Show that the centre of mass of a uniform right circular conical shell of height h and base radius r is at a distance $2h/3$ from the vertex if it has an open base. Hence find the centre of mass of a similar hollow conical shell with a base made of the same material, giving your answer as the distance from the base.

8 A square lamina ABCD has sides of length 12 cm. A semi-circle with diameter

CD is cut from the lamina. Find the distance of the centre of mass of the remainder from the line AB.

(Hint: To find the centre of mass of a sector, consider the sector to be composed of triangles of height equal to the radius, and vertical angle $\delta\theta$.)

9 A lamina in the shape of a sector of a circle radius a angle 2α is cut from a complete circle. Show that the mass centre of this sector is a distance $(2a \sin \alpha)/3\alpha$ from the vertex, $\alpha < \dfrac{\pi}{2}$.

If $\alpha = \dfrac{\pi}{3}$, find the centre of mass of the other portion of the original disc.

10 A uniform wire of length $3a$ is bent into a circular arc of radius $2a$. Show that the centre of mass is a distance $\dfrac{8a}{3} \sin \dfrac{3}{4}$ from the centre of the circle.

6.5 Velocity and relative velocity vectors

Velocity has already been defined as a vector, and any vector can be split into its components whatever its nature. It is particularly useful to use the **i,j** unit vector notation for velocities, but we should remember that a vector normally has position, and since it is not easy to describe velocity in terms of the origin the velocity vector is positioned on the body itself.

Suppose we have two objects P and Q moving with velocities **v** and **w** respectively. To find the velocity of P relative to Q we 'add' a velocity to both so that their relative velocity remains unchanged but so that Q is 'brought to rest'. In other words we add ' $-\mathbf{w}$' to both velocities; that of P becomes $\mathbf{v}-\mathbf{w}$, and that of Q is O. Because Q is now at rest, $\mathbf{v}-\mathbf{w}$ is the relative velocity of P to Q. In words we can summarize this simple result: the velocity of one body to a second is the velocity of the first minus the velocity of the second.

EXAMPLE 7   *A boy cycles along a flat straight road at 15 km/h. There is a wind blowing at right-angles to the road at 10 km/h. Where does the wind appear to come from to the boy, and how strong does it feel to him?*

Let the road be in the direction of the unit vector **i**, and the wind blow in the direction of **j**, then the velocity of the boy is

$$\mathbf{b} = 15\mathbf{i},$$

and the wind's velocity is

$$\mathbf{w} = 10\mathbf{j}.$$

Thus the velocity of the wind relative to the boy is

$$\mathbf{w} - \mathbf{b} = -15\mathbf{i} + 10\mathbf{j}.$$

The apparent strength of the wind is $|\mathbf{w} - \mathbf{b}|$ and is

$$\sqrt{(15^2 + 10^2)} \doteqdot 18 \text{ km/h.,}$$

and it appears to come from a direction $\tan^{-1} \frac{2}{3}$ to the line of the road.

EXAMPLE 8   *An officer on board a ship travelling due north at 28 km/h estimates the wind velocity to be 15 km/h from a direction 040° (N 40° E) relative to the ship. Find the true wind velocity.*

Let **i** and **j** be unit vectors due east and north respectively. Then the ship has velocity

$$\mathbf{s} = 28\mathbf{j},$$

and the velocity of the wind, **w**, satisfies

$$\mathbf{w} - \mathbf{s} = -15 \sin 40°\mathbf{i} - 15 \cos 40°\mathbf{j}$$
$$= -9{\cdot}65\mathbf{i} - 11{\cdot}49\mathbf{j}.$$
$$\therefore \ \mathbf{w} = -9{\cdot}65\mathbf{i} + 16{\cdot}51\mathbf{j}.$$

Hence
$$|\mathbf{w}| = \sqrt{(9{\cdot}65^2 + 16{\cdot}51^2)}$$
$$= \sqrt{(93 + 272)}$$
$$= \sqrt{365} = 19{\cdot}1.$$

The direction of **w** is $\tan^{-1} \dfrac{9{\cdot}65}{16{\cdot}51}$ east of south,

$$= \tan^{-1} 0{\cdot}595$$
$$= 30{\cdot}35°.$$

∴ The wind is blowing at 19 km/h from the direction 149·6° (S 30·4° E).

Because of the theme of this chapter we have approached the subject of relative velocity through the method of vectors. However, some such problems are more quickly solved either by using trigonometry or graphically. The theory we have outlined is still the basis for these methods since both require the drawing of the triangle of vectors. The triangle of vectors in Example 8 is illustrated in Fig. 84. To solve this example trigonometric-

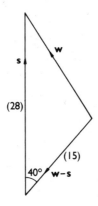

Fig. 84

ally involves sketching this figure and applying the Sine or Cosine Rule to it as appropriate. In this case if the wind-speed is w km/h, then by the Cosine Rule

$$w^2 = 28^2 + 15^2 - 2.28.15 \cos 40°,$$

giving $w \doteq 19$. Then by the Sine Rule

$$\frac{\sin \theta}{15} = \frac{\sin 40°}{w}$$

where θ is the wind direction east of south. There is probably little difference in this instance in the length of the solution, and any particular example must be taken on its own merit. The vector method is however more methodical and is possibly less likely to cause accidental error for this reason.

A graphical method involves drawing Fig. 84 to scale, and is clearly the quickest where great accuracy is not required, and is generally used in practical navigation.

Exercise 14

1 Two cars on different straight roads are converging on a junction, the first at 48 km/h and the second at 36 km/h. The angle between the roads is 60°. Find the magnitude and direction of their relative velocity.

2 A cargo ship is sailing due east at 16 km/h, and a wind of 32 km/h is blowing from 240° (W 30° S). In what direction does the smoke move relative to the ship?

3 Two ships are approaching a harbour entrance, one at 20 km/h on a course of 135°, the other at 15 km/h on a course of 240°. Find the magnitude and direction of their relative velocity.

4 A hovercraft travels from Dover to Calais in 27 min. in the face of a 20 km/h wind from a bearing of 160°. If the bearing of Calais from Dover is 112° and the distance 40 km, find the time for the return journey under similar conditions.

5 A navigator wishes to reach a small island 18 km distant on a bearing of 300° from his present position. The current flows at 6 km/h in the direction 105°. Find graphically the course he must set and his estimated time of arrival if the ship can make 15 km/h and he leaves at 0100 hours (1 a.m.).

6 Two ships A and B are on a collision course. A is sailing at 15 km/h on a course of 270°, and B is sailing at 25 km/h on a course of 240°. An officer on the bridge of ship A runs from the port to the starboard side (i.e. towards B) at 10 km/h. Find the speed of the officer relative to B!

7 Rain drops are falling with a vertical velocity of 3 m/s, and a south-westerly wind is blowing at 12 km/h. Find at what angle to the horizontal the rain appears to fall to a man driving a car travelling at 48 km/h and with what speed the drops hit the windscreen of the car (i) if he is travelling north-east, and (ii) if he is travelling north-west.

(Use unit vectors in three dimensions.)

8 Project Example.
Investigate the extent of the similarity of vectors and complex numbers as represented in the Argand diagram. Compare vector addition with addition of complex numbers. Can you find a property of vectors to correspond to multiplication in the Argand diagram? If time permits compare the scalar and vector products of vectors (sometimes called dot and cross products) with complex numbers. See pp. 141, 249 for definitions of scalar and vector products, and make reference to other books on vector algebra.

6.6 Vector equation of a straight line

We began this chapter by comparing vectors and cartesian coordinates. We found that the bracket notation in the latter was equivalent to a position vector expressed in terms of its components. But lines can also be expressed in both systems, and we hinted at this in Exercise 12, No. 8.

Consider the cartesian equation of a straight line, $y = 2x + 3$. Suppose that Q is a point on the line and that it has an x-coordinate of t, then it is the point $(t, 2t+3)$. But the position vector of Q is

$$\mathbf{q} = t\mathbf{i} + (2t+3)\mathbf{j}.$$

Since Q represents any point on the line this is the vector equation of the line in terms of the scalar variable t.

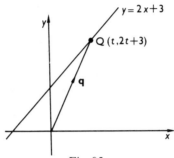

Fig. 85

In the cartesian form we would refer to t as a parameter, and so the vector equation is just another way of writing the parametric form. This does not only apply to straight lines, but to all curves including those in three dimensions.

In practice we rarely need to convert an equation from one form to another in this way. Suppose that P and Q are points on a straight line with position vectors $\mathbf{p}$ and $\mathbf{q}$. The position of Q relative to P is $\mathbf{q} - \mathbf{p}$, and any other point on the line has position vector $m(\mathbf{q} - \mathbf{p})$ relative to P. Thus the position of a general point on the line is given by the equation

$$\mathbf{r} = \mathbf{p} + m(\mathbf{q} - \mathbf{p}).$$

Let $\mathbf{q} - \mathbf{p} = \mathbf{s}$, then the line has equation

$$\mathbf{r} = \mathbf{p} + m\mathbf{s}.$$

EXAMPLE 9   *Find the equation of the line passing through the point given by* $\mathbf{p} = 3\mathbf{i} + 2\mathbf{j}$ *with the direction of* $2\mathbf{i} - 5\mathbf{j}$.

Let the equation be of the form

$$\mathbf{r} = \mathbf{p} + m\mathbf{s}$$

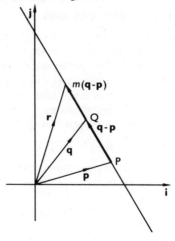

Fig. 86

·where m is a scalar variable, then $\mathbf{p}$ is as above, and

$$s = 2\mathbf{i} - 5\mathbf{j}.$$

∴ Equation is

$$\mathbf{r} = (3\mathbf{i} + 2\mathbf{j}) + m(2\mathbf{i} - 5j),$$

i.e. $$r = (3 + 2m)\mathbf{i} + (2 - 5m)\mathbf{j}.$$

There are an infinite number of parameters to choose from as our scalar variable, and there are often several that are equally obvious choices in a particular problem. Do not be surprised therefore if your solution in a given problem does not appear to be the same at first glance as someone else's. For example, the equation for Example 9 could equally well read

$$\mathbf{r} = n\mathbf{i} + \tfrac{1}{2}(19 - 5n)\mathbf{j}.$$

The new parameter n is related to the former m by the expression

$$n = 2m + 3.$$

EXAMPLE 10   *Two ships* A *and* B *are sighted at 1000 hours from a lighthouse, their respective position vectors being given by*

$$\mathbf{a} = 6\mathbf{i} + 4\mathbf{j}$$

and $$\mathbf{b} = -3\mathbf{i} + 6\mathbf{j},$$

where $\mathbf{i}$ *and* $\mathbf{j}$ *are unit vectors each of magnitude 1 km in directions north and west respectively. The velocity of* A *is given by*

$$\mathbf{v_a} = -10\mathbf{i} + 8\mathbf{j},$$

and the velocity of B *is*

$$\mathbf{v}_b = 15\mathbf{i} + 6\mathbf{j}.$$

Find (*i*) *their positions at 1045 hours,*
  (*ii*) *how far apart they are at 1045 hours,*
  (*iii*) *when they are nearest together, and*
  (*iv*) *where their paths cross.*

Since $\mathbf{v}_a$ implies the course that A sails and at a certain time it is at the point **a**, the equation of its path is

$$\mathbf{p}_a = \mathbf{a} + t\mathbf{v}_a.$$

But when $t = 0$ the ship is at A, and when $t = 1, \mathbf{p}_a$ gives the position of A an hour later. t is therefore the time in hours after 1000 hours.

The reader will already be familiar with the function notation used for scalar expressions $-f(x)$ meaning a function of the variable x. We sometimes use a similar notation for vector functions, and in this instance we shall take $\mathbf{p}_a(t)$ to mean the function $\mathbf{a} + t\mathbf{v}_a$ which is a vector function of the scalar variable t.

The position of A at 1045 hours is $\mathbf{p}_a(\tfrac{3}{4})$ where

$$\mathbf{p}_a(t) = (6 - 10t)\mathbf{i} + (4 + 8t)\mathbf{j},$$

i.e. $$\mathbf{p}_a(\tfrac{3}{4}) = -1\tfrac{1}{2}\mathbf{i} + 10\mathbf{j}.$$

Similarly the position of B after t hours is

$$\mathbf{p}_b(t) = \mathbf{b} + t\mathbf{v}_b$$

$$= (15t - 3)\mathbf{i} + (6 + 6t)\mathbf{j}.$$

$$\therefore \ \mathbf{p}_b(\tfrac{3}{4}) = 8\tfrac{1}{4}\mathbf{i} + 10\tfrac{1}{2}\mathbf{j}.$$

Positions of A and B at 1045 hours are $-1\tfrac{1}{2}\mathbf{i} + 10\mathbf{j}$ and $8\tfrac{1}{4}\mathbf{i} + 10\tfrac{1}{2}\mathbf{j}$ respectively.

The position of B relative to A at 1045 hours is

$$\mathbf{p}_b(\tfrac{3}{4}) - \mathbf{p}_a(\tfrac{3}{4}) = 9\tfrac{3}{4}\mathbf{i} + \tfrac{1}{2}\mathbf{j}.$$

Thus their distance apart at this time is

$$\left|9\tfrac{3}{4}\mathbf{i} + \tfrac{1}{2}\mathbf{j}\right| = \sqrt{(9 \cdot 75^2 + 0 \cdot 5^2)}$$

$$\doteqdot 9 \cdot 8.$$

They are 9·8 km apart (to 2 significant figures) at 1045 hours.

The position of B relative to A after t hours is

$$\mathbf{p}_b(t) - \mathbf{p}_a(t) = (25t - 9)\mathbf{i} + (2 - 2t)\mathbf{j}.$$

Now $|\mathbf{p}_b - \mathbf{p}_a|$ is a minimum when $|\mathbf{p}_b - \mathbf{p}_a|^2$ is a minimum, and to avoid unnecessary complication we use the derivative of the latter to find when this relative distance is least. Thus the ships are closest together when

$$\frac{d}{dt}((25t-9)^2 + (2-2t)^2) = 0.$$

i.e. when $2(25t-9) \times 25 + 2(2-2t) \times (-2) = 0,$

$$629t - 229 = 0,$$

$$t = \frac{229}{629},$$

$$\equiv 22 \text{ min.}$$

The ships are closest together at 1022 hours.

In order to find where the paths cross we need to change the variable—the path is not dependent on t. The equations of the two paths in terms of the independent variables r and s are

$$\mathbf{p_a} = (6-10r)\mathbf{i} + (4+8r)\mathbf{j}$$

and

$$\mathbf{p_b} = (15s-3)\mathbf{i} + (6+6s)\mathbf{j}.$$

When the paths cross, $\mathbf{p_a} = \mathbf{p_b}$, and if two vectors are equal then their corresponding components are equal. Therefore

$$6 - 10r = 15s - 3,$$

i.e.

$$15s + 10r = 9, \tag{1}$$

and

$$4 + 8r = 6 + 6s,$$

i.e.

$$3s - 4r = -1. \tag{2}$$

Subtracting $5 \times (2)$ from (1)

$$30r = 14,$$

$$r = \tfrac{7}{15}.$$

Substituting back in $\mathbf{p_a}$,

$$\mathbf{p_a} = (6-\tfrac{14}{3})\mathbf{i} + (4+\tfrac{56}{15})\mathbf{j}$$

Their paths cross at the point $\tfrac{4}{3}\mathbf{i} + 7\tfrac{11}{15}\mathbf{j}$.

We can summarize the fundamental ideas behind the solution of this and similar examples as follows. Suppose we have two moving objects with positions after time t given by the equations

$$\mathbf{p}(t) = \mathbf{p}(0) + t\mathbf{v}$$

and

$$\mathbf{q}(t) = \mathbf{q}(0) + t\mathbf{w}.$$

From these equations the conditions for certain events to happen are

(i) to collide after an unspecified time t:

$$\mathbf{p}(t) = \mathbf{q}(t),$$

(ii) to collide after a particular time t':

$$\mathbf{p}(t') = \mathbf{q}(t'),$$

(iii) their paths cross at the point where

$$\mathbf{p}(t_1) = \mathbf{q}(t_2), \quad \text{and}$$

(iv) they are closest together (or furthest apart) when

$$\frac{d}{dt}|\mathbf{p}(t) - \mathbf{q}(t)|^2 = 0,$$

and if this equation has the solution $t = T$ then the shortest distance apart is

$$|\mathbf{p}(T) - \mathbf{q}(T)|.$$

It is possible to solve some of these problems graphically by drawing the relative velocity vector to scale. If the objects A and B have velocity vectors $\mathbf{v}_a$ and $\mathbf{v}_b$ then the vector $\mathbf{v}_a - \mathbf{v}_b$ would be drawn from the position

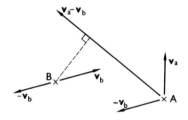

Fig. 87

of A when time $t = 0$. The shortest distance between them would then be the distance of this line from the position of B when $t = 0$ (Fig. 87). The condition for them to collide becomes $\mathbf{v}_a - \mathbf{v}_b$ must pass through B.

EXAMPLE 11   *Find the magnitude and line of action of the resultant of the three forces*

$$\mathbf{F}_1 = 2\mathbf{i} + 3\mathbf{j},$$
$$\mathbf{F}_2 = 3\mathbf{i} - 2\mathbf{j},$$
$$\mathbf{F}_3 = 4\mathbf{j},$$

which act through the points $\mathbf{i}$, $2\mathbf{j}$ *and* $3\mathbf{i} - \mathbf{j}$ *respectively.*

Let the resultant be **R** and act through the point $a\mathbf{i}+b\mathbf{j}$. Then

$$\mathbf{R} = \mathbf{F}_1+\mathbf{F}_2+\mathbf{F}_3$$
$$= 5\mathbf{i}+5\mathbf{j}.$$

By Pythagoras,

$$|\mathbf{R}| = \sqrt{25+25}$$
$$= 5\sqrt{2}.$$

The magnitude of the resultant is $5\sqrt{2}$.

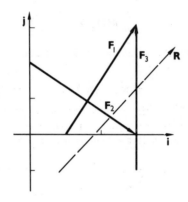

Fig. 88

Since **R** is not parallel to either axis, it must cut both, and so we take the point $a\mathbf{i}+b\mathbf{j}$ to be where **R** will cut the **j**-axis—i.e. take $b = 0$.

Taking moments about the origin, we note that if we consider each force at the point where it cuts an axis, then only one component has a moment about the origin. For example, the moment of $\mathbf{F}_1$ taken to act at **i** is $1 \times$ the **j**-component $= 3$. Thus equating moments,

$$1 \times 3-2 \times 3+3 \times 4 = a \times 5,$$
$$5a = 3-6+12$$
$$= 9.$$
$$a = 1\tfrac{4}{5}.$$

The line of action has the direction of **R**, i.e. that of $5\mathbf{i}+5\mathbf{j}$. But this is the same as that of $\mathbf{i}+\mathbf{j}$.

The line of action is $\mathbf{r} = (1\tfrac{4}{5}+s)\mathbf{i}+s\mathbf{j}$.

Exercise 15

1 Taking **i** and **j** as unit vectors along the x- and y-axes, rewrite the following as
(a) vector equations:

(i) $y = 3x-1$, (ii) $2y = 5x+3$, (iii) $x = 5$, (iv) $\dfrac{x-1}{2} = \dfrac{y+1}{3}$.

(b) cartesian equations:
   (i) $\mathbf{r} = t\mathbf{i}+(2t-1)\mathbf{j}$,   (ii) $\mathbf{r} = (3t+2)\mathbf{i}-3t\mathbf{j}$,
   (iii) $\mathbf{r} = 3\mathbf{i}+2s\mathbf{j}$,   (iv) $\mathbf{r} = 3t\mathbf{j}$.

2 Write down the equations of the lines passing through **P** parallel to **q**:
   (i) $\mathbf{P} = 7\mathbf{i}+2\mathbf{j}$; $\mathbf{q} = \mathbf{i}-\mathbf{j}$, (ii) $\mathbf{P} = 10\mathbf{j}$; $\mathbf{q} = 4\mathbf{i}$.
   (iii) $\mathbf{P} = (13+a)\mathbf{i}+(14-a)\mathbf{j}$; $\mathbf{q} = 7\mathbf{i}+\mathbf{j}$.

3 Find the intersections of the following pairs of lines:
   (a) $\mathbf{r} = 2s\mathbf{i}-(s+1)\mathbf{j}$; $\mathbf{p} = t\mathbf{i}+(t+1)\mathbf{j}$,
   (b) $\mathbf{r} = (2s-1)\mathbf{i}+(3-s)\mathbf{j}$; $\mathbf{p} = (4t+1)\mathbf{i}+(t-3)\mathbf{j}$.

4 Three vertices of a parallelogram are given to be
$$\mathbf{a} = 2\mathbf{i}+4\mathbf{j}, \quad \mathbf{b} = -2\mathbf{i}+\mathbf{j}, \quad \text{and} \quad \mathbf{c} = \mathbf{i}-2\mathbf{j}.$$
Find the position of the fourth vertex, and the equations of the sides.

5 If two opposite vertices of a rhombus have position vectors $\mathbf{r}_1 = 2\mathbf{i}$ and
$\mathbf{r}_2 = (2+2\sqrt{3})\mathbf{i}$, and the angles at each of these vertices are $120°$, find the other
two vertices, and the equations of the sides.

6 A square has sides 13 units long, and two of the sides have equations
$$\mathbf{r} = (2+5t)\mathbf{i}+(2+12t)\mathbf{j} \quad \text{and} \quad \mathbf{r} = (2+12t)\mathbf{i}+(2-5t)\mathbf{j}.$$
If one vertex is given by $14\mathbf{i}-3\mathbf{j}$, find the other three vertices and the equations
of the other two sides. What is the equation of the diagonal from the point
$14\mathbf{i}-3\mathbf{j}$?

7 Two straight roads intersect at O, and with reference to O as origin their vector
equations are $\mathbf{r}_1 = t\mathbf{i}$ and $\mathbf{r}_2 = 2s\mathbf{i}+s\mathbf{j}$. Two cars A and B have position vectors
$\mathbf{a} = -3\mathbf{i}$ and $\mathbf{b} = -4\mathbf{i}-2\mathbf{j}$ at a given instant respectively. A is travelling with
velocity $\mathbf{v}_a = 6\mathbf{i}$. Find the velocity $\mathbf{v}_b$ of B if, assuming all speeds are constant, a
collision takes place at O.

8 The vertices A, B, C of a rhombus ABCD have position vectors $-2\mathbf{i}+5\mathbf{j}$,
$2\mathbf{i}+2\mathbf{j}$, and $-\mathbf{i}-2\mathbf{j}$ respectively. P and Q are two particles and when time $t = 0$,
P is at A and Q is at B. P moves with constant speed along the diagonal AC
arriving at C when $t = 2$. Q moves with constant speed along the diagonal BD
arriving at D when $t = 1$. Find when they are closest together and their distance
apart at this instant.

9 Find the resultant and the line of action of the four forces:
$$\begin{aligned} \mathbf{F}_1 &= 3\mathbf{i}+2\mathbf{j}, \\ \mathbf{F}_2 &= 6\mathbf{i}-3\mathbf{j}, \\ \mathbf{F}_3 &= 3\mathbf{i}-5\mathbf{j}, \\ \text{and} \quad \mathbf{F}_4 &= -5\mathbf{j} \end{aligned}$$
acting through points $2\mathbf{i}$, $3\mathbf{j}$, $-4\mathbf{i}$ and $-5\mathbf{j}$ respectively.

10 A ship has position vector $-6\mathbf{i}+8\mathbf{j}$ relative to the end of a jetty, and is sailing with
velocity $\mathbf{v} = 12\mathbf{i}+9\mathbf{j}$ where the magnitude of $\mathbf{v}$ is in km/h. A launch sets out
from the jetty at a speed of 39 km/h to intercept the ship at the earliest possible
moment. Find
   (i) the time taken by the launch,
   (ii) the point of interception, and
   (iii) the velocity vector of the launch.
(Position vectors are in kilometres.)

11 A ship A is sailing due north at 25 km/h and ship B is sailing on a course of $105°$
at 35 km/h. At 1100 hours A just sights B on a bearing of $325°$, visibility being
12 km. Find graphically their least distance apart, and at what time they lose
sight of each other.

12 A rifleman on firing practice has to hit a target 200 m away which is moving at a constant speed of 10 m/s in a direction perpendicular to the line of the man and the target. If the bullet travels at 150 m/s, find how far in front of the target he must aim.

7 Projectiles

7.1 Differentiation of a vector

In Chapter 1 (p. 5) we wrote Newton's 2nd Law as a vector equation:

$$m\frac{d\mathbf{v}}{dt} = \mathbf{F},$$

but we did not at that stage investigate the true meaning of the derivative of **v**. In Chapter 2 we assumed that differentiation of a scalar was adequate because we were working in only one dimension, but we shall now define the derivative of a vector more carefully.

The symbol $\dfrac{d\mathbf{r}}{dt}$ represents the rate of change of the vector **r** with respect to the scalar variable t. If the change in **r** is $\delta\mathbf{r}$ in a small time δt, then we define

$$\frac{d\mathbf{r}}{dt} = \lim_{\delta t \to 0} \frac{\delta\mathbf{r}}{\delta t}$$

$$= \lim_{\delta t \to 0} \frac{\mathbf{r}(t+\delta t) - \mathbf{r}(t)}{\delta t}.$$

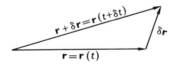

Fig. 89

But if $\mathbf{r} = x\mathbf{i} + y\mathbf{j} + z\mathbf{k}$ at time t, **i**, **j** and **k** being mutually perpendicular unit vectors, and if at time $t + \delta t$

$$\mathbf{r} = (x+\delta x)\mathbf{i} + (y+\delta y)\mathbf{j} + (z+\delta z)\mathbf{k},$$

then

$$\frac{d\mathbf{r}}{dt} = \lim_{\delta t \to 0} \frac{\delta x\mathbf{i} + \delta y\mathbf{j} + \delta z\mathbf{k}}{\delta t}$$

$$= \operatorname*{Lim}_{\delta t \to 0} \left(\frac{\delta x}{\delta t}\mathbf{i} + \frac{\delta y}{\delta t}\mathbf{j} + \frac{\delta z}{\delta t}\mathbf{k} \right)$$

$$= \frac{dx}{dt}\mathbf{i} + \frac{dy}{dt}\mathbf{j} + \frac{dz}{dt}\mathbf{k}.$$

If the acceleration of a body is constant and is equal to $\mathbf{a}$ where

$$\mathbf{a} = a_1\mathbf{i} + a_2\mathbf{j} + a_3\mathbf{k},$$

then we can integrate $\mathbf{a}$ to obtain the velocity $\mathbf{v}$.

$$\begin{aligned} \mathbf{v} &= \int (a_1\mathbf{i} + a_2\mathbf{j} + a_3\mathbf{k})dt \\ &= (u_1 + a_1 t)\mathbf{i} + (u_2 + a_2 t)\mathbf{j} + (u_3 + a_3 t)\mathbf{k} \\ &= \mathbf{u} + \mathbf{a}t, \end{aligned}$$

where $\mathbf{u} = u_1\mathbf{i} + u_2\mathbf{j} + u_3\mathbf{k}$ and is the initial velocity vector; the velocity when $t = 0$. Similarly we can deduce that

$$\mathbf{s} = \mathbf{u}t + \tfrac{1}{2}\mathbf{a}t^2.$$

While these two equations correspond directly with equations *2.1* and *2.2*, it should be noted that equation *2.3* is not basically a vector equation and cannot be deduced in this way.

7.2 Path and horizontal range of a projectile

Consider the motion of a body moving freely under gravity. Components in the horizontal plane have the same characteristics, and so we shall take the motion to be in the $\mathbf{i},\mathbf{j}$-plane where $\mathbf{i}$ is horizontal and $\mathbf{j}$ is vertically upwards. To extend the theory to three dimensions is straightforward and is illustrated later in Example 7.

The acceleration of the body is

$$\mathbf{a} = -g\mathbf{j}.$$

By integration the velocity and position vectors $\mathbf{v}$ and $\mathbf{s}$ are

$$\mathbf{v} = u_h\mathbf{i} + (u_v - gt)\mathbf{j}$$

and
$$\mathbf{s} = u_h t\mathbf{i} + (u_v t - \tfrac{1}{2}gt^2)\mathbf{j},$$

where $\mathbf{s}$ is relative to the position when $t = 0$ (usually the point of projection), and the initial velocity is $\mathbf{u} = u_h\mathbf{i} + u_v\mathbf{j}$.

The equation for $\mathbf{s}$ is that of a parabola, and by writing $\mathbf{s} = x\mathbf{i} + y\mathbf{j}$ we can find the cartesian equation of the path. Thus

$$x = u_h t,$$

and
$$y = u_v t - \tfrac{1}{2}gt^2.$$

Eliminating t, the parabola has equation

$$y = \frac{u_v}{u_h}x - \frac{g}{2u_h^2}x^2.$$

EXAMPLE 1   *Find the maximum horizontal range of a projectile fired with an initial speed of 200 m/s. Find also the maximum height attained for this range, and the time of flight.*

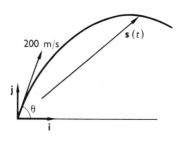

200 m/s   s(t)

Fig. 90

We define **i** and **j** to be unit vectors through the point of projection, **i** being horizontal and **j** vertical. Let the projectile be fired at an angle θ to the horizontal, and the velocity and position vectors after time t be $\mathbf{v}(t)$ and $\mathbf{s}(t)$ respectively, then

$$\mathbf{v}(0) = 200 \cos \theta \mathbf{i} + 200 \sin \theta \mathbf{j},$$

and so

$$\mathbf{v}(t) = 200 \cos \theta \mathbf{i} + (200 \sin \theta - gt)\mathbf{j},$$

and

$$\mathbf{s}(t) = 200t \cos \theta \mathbf{i} + (200t \sin \theta - \tfrac{1}{2}gt^2)\mathbf{j}.$$

When the projectile strikes the horizontal plane, the **j**-component of **s** is zero, i.e.

$$200t \sin \theta = \tfrac{1}{2}gt^2.$$

The solution $t = 0$ refers to the instant of projection, and so when it strikes the plane

$$t = \frac{400}{g} \sin \theta.$$

If this value of t is T say, then the range is given by $\mathbf{s}(T)$ and is of magnitude

$$200 \cos \theta . \frac{400}{g} \sin \theta.$$

But $2 \sin \theta \cos \theta = \sin 2\theta$, and so the range is

$$200^2 \sin 2\theta/g.$$

This is greatest when $\sin 2\theta = 1$, i.e. when $\theta = 45°$.

$\therefore$ Maximum range $= 200^2/g$ m $\doteq 4080$ m.

For $\theta = 45°$, $T = 400/\sqrt{2g}$

$\doteq 29\cdot4$.

$\therefore$ Time of flight is $29\cdot4$ s (to 3 significant figures).

N.B. The angle of projection giving the maximum range is not dependent on the initial speed—the horizontal range is always a maximum for an angle of projection of $45°$.

The projectile is at a maximum height when the **j**-component of **v** is zero. Putting $\theta = 45°$, we get

$$200/\sqrt{2} - gt = 0,$$

$$t = \frac{100\sqrt{2}}{g}.$$

(We could alternatively argue that since the path is a parabola it is symmetrical about the maximum point. Thus it reaches the maximum height when $t = T/2$. This method however is only appropriate if T has already been evaluated.)

Substituting for t in the **j**-component of **s**, the maximum height is

$$\frac{200}{\sqrt{2}} \cdot \frac{100\sqrt{2}}{g} - \tfrac{1}{2}g \cdot \frac{100^2 \cdot 2}{g^2} = (20\,000 - 10\,000)/g$$

$$= 10\,000/g.$$

The maximum height attained is 1020 m (to 3 significant figures).

EXAMPLE 2   *A cricketer can throw a ball with an initial speed of 25 m/s. If he has to throw to the wicket-keeper 50 m away, show that there are two possible angles of projection if the ball first strikes the ground at the feet of the wicket-keeper, and find the two corresponding times of flight.*

We define **i** and **j** as in Example 1. The position vector of the ball after t seconds is then

$$\mathbf{s}(t) = 25t \cos \theta \mathbf{i} + (25t \sin \theta - \tfrac{1}{2}gt^2)\mathbf{j},$$

where θ is the angle of projection to the horizontal. When it strikes the ground, the **j**-component is zero, and if $t = T$,

$$\mathbf{s}(T) = 50\mathbf{i}.$$

Thus equating components we get

$$25t \cos \theta = 50,$$

i.e. $T \cos \theta = 2,$ (1)

and $\qquad\qquad 25t \sin \theta - \frac{1}{2}gt^2 = 0,$

i.e. $\qquad\qquad\qquad T = \frac{50}{g} \sin \theta.$ $\qquad\qquad$ (2)

Substituting from (2) into (1),

$$50 \sin \theta \cos \theta = 2g.$$
$$\therefore \ 25 \sin 2\theta = 2g,$$

and $\qquad\qquad\qquad 2\theta = \sin^{-1} \frac{2g}{25}$

$$= 51° \ 38' \quad \text{or} \quad 128° \ 22'.$$
$$\therefore \ \theta = 25° \ 49' \quad \text{or} \quad 64° \ 11',$$

and <u>there are two possible angles of projection</u>.

From (1),

$$T = 2 \sec \theta.$$

Thus the times of flight are

$$2 \sec 25° \ 49' \doteqdot 2 \times 1\cdot111$$
$$= 2\cdot222,$$

and $\qquad\qquad 2 \sec 64° \ 11' \doteqdot 2 \times 2\cdot296$

$$= 4\cdot592.$$

<u>The time of flight is 2·2 s or 4·6 s (to nearest 0·1 s).</u>

Exercise 16

(Take g as 9·8 m/s² when necessary.)

1 Find the horizontal range and the maximum height achieved by an object thrown with an initial speed of 20 m/s at an angle of 30° to the horizontal.

2 Calculate the maximum horizontal range of a projectile fired with an initial speed of 50 m/s. Find also the velocity vector of the projectile after 2 and after 4 seconds on this trajectory.

3 The acceleration vector of a particle after t s is

$$10t\mathbf{i} + (30t - 40)\mathbf{j},$$

time being measured from the instant it is at the origin of unit vectors $\mathbf{i}, \mathbf{j}, \mathbf{k}$ moving with velocity $-30\mathbf{i} + 20\mathbf{k}$. Find its position and velocity vectors after 2 s. Show that the speed has two stationary values for $t > 0$, and find the acceleration vector at these instants. Explain why $|\mathbf{a}| \neq 0$ at these two times.

4 Find the velocity of projection of a ball which is thrown from a point 18 m from the foot of a tree 14 m high so as just to clear the top of the tree.

(Avoid the angle of projection by letting the initial velocity be $u\mathbf{i} + v\mathbf{j}$.)

5 A stone is thrown horizontally over the sea from the top of a vertical cliff 200 m high at a speed of 24 m/s. Find how far from the foot of the cliff the stone strikes the sea.

6 An artillery crew are maintaining a bombardment of an enemy gun emplacement believed to be 3200 m away by the map but on ground 360 m higher than the crew. Their gun fires shells with a muzzle velocity of 240 m/s. Determine the angle of elevation of the gun.

7 A young boy standing 6 m from the foot of a telegraph pole 6 m high is trying to disturb a seagull perched on the top by hitting it with a stone. If he can throw a stone at a speed of 10 m/s from a height of 1·2 m, determine whether or not he can succeed.

8 A tennis ball is served from a height of 2·8 m at a speed of 36 m/s and just clears the net 1 m high at a distance 12 m from the server. Determine the initial angle of flight of the ball to the horizontal (assuming it to be small) to the nearest degree, and find how far beyond the net the ball strikes the ground.

7.3 Projectiles and the inclined plane

It is not always appropriate to take the unit vectors as being vertical and horizontal. In many examples the plane from which a projectile is fired is not horizontal, and yet the information given or required is closely allied to this inclined plane. In such cases it is often more suitable to define **i** and **j** as being along the line of greatest slope and perpendicular to the plane respectively. The main difference this makes is to bring the effect of gravity into both the components.

EXAMPLE 3   *A projectile is fired from a point* A *on a plane inclined at an angle* $\sin^{-1}\frac{2}{5}$ *to the horizontal so as to strike the plane at a point* B *above* A *on the plane,* AB *being the line of greatest slope. If it is fired with speed 50 m/s at an angle* θ *to* AB *and strikes the plane perpendicularly at* B, *find* (i) *the angle* θ, (ii) *the distance* AB, *and* (iii) *the range if fired down the plane with the same speed at an angle* θ *to* BA.

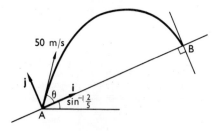

Fig. 91

Let **i** and **j** be unit vectors, **i** along AB and **j** perpendicular to the plane through A. The acceleration due to gravity will then have components $-g \sin (\sin^{-1}\frac{2}{5})$**i** and $-g \cos (\sin^{-1}\frac{2}{5})$**j**. Thus the acceleration vector of the projectile is

$$-\frac{2}{5}g\mathbf{i} - \frac{\sqrt{21}}{5}g\mathbf{j}.$$

The velocity vector after t s is

$$\mathbf{v}(t) = \left(50 \cos\theta - \frac{2}{5}gt\right)\mathbf{i} + \left(50 \sin\theta - \frac{\sqrt{21}}{5}gt\right)\mathbf{j}.$$

The position vector at this time is

$$\mathbf{s}(t) = \left(50t \cos\theta - \frac{g}{5}t^2\right)\mathbf{i} + \left(50t \sin\theta - \frac{\sqrt{21}}{10}gt^2\right)\mathbf{j}.$$

At B the $\mathbf{i}$-component of $\mathbf{v}$ is zero since it strikes the plane perpendicularly. Thus

$$50 \cos\theta - \tfrac{2}{5}gt = 0,$$

$$t = 250 \cos\theta/2g. \tag{1}$$

Also at B, the $\mathbf{j}$-component of $\mathbf{s}$ is zero. Thus

$$50t \sin\theta - \frac{\sqrt{21}}{10}gt^2 = 0,$$

$$t = 500 \sin\theta/\sqrt{21}g. \tag{2}$$

Equating (1) and (2)

$$\frac{500 \sin\theta}{\sqrt{21}g} = \frac{250 \cos\theta}{2g},$$

$$\tan\theta = \frac{\sqrt{21}}{4}.$$

$$\therefore \ \theta = \tan^{-1}\frac{\sqrt{21}}{4}.$$

Since

$$\tan\theta = \frac{\sqrt{21}}{4},$$

$$\cos\theta = \frac{4}{\sqrt{37}}, \quad \text{and}$$

$$\sin\theta = \frac{\sqrt{21}}{\sqrt{37}}.$$

When the projectile strikes B,

$$\mathbf{s} = \left(50t \cos\theta - \frac{g}{5}t^2\right)\mathbf{i}$$

where

$$t = 250 \cos\theta/2g.$$

Substituting in both these expressions for $\cos\theta$,

$$\mathbf{s} = \left(\frac{200}{\sqrt{37}}t - \frac{g}{5}t^2\right)\mathbf{i},$$

and $$t = 500/\sqrt{37g}.$$

Substituting for t in $\mathbf{s}$:

$$\mathbf{s} = \left(\frac{200 \times 500}{37g} - \frac{500^2}{5 \times 37g}\right)\mathbf{i}$$

$$= \frac{50\,000}{37g}\mathbf{i}$$

$$\doteq 138\mathbf{i}.$$

The distance AB is 138 m (to 3 significant figures).

If the particle is fired down the plane instead of up, the position vector of the projectile after time t becomes

$$\mathbf{s}'(t) = \left(50t\cos\theta + \frac{g}{5}t^2\right)\mathbf{i} + \left(50t\sin\theta - \frac{\sqrt{21}}{10}gt^2\right)\mathbf{j}.$$

When it strikes the plane the $\mathbf{j}$-component is zero, giving

$$50t\sin\theta - \frac{\sqrt{21}}{10}gt^2 = 0,$$

$$t = \frac{500\sin\theta}{\sqrt{21}g}$$

(since $t \neq 0$). At this moment,

$$t = 500/\sqrt{37g},$$

and $$\mathbf{s}' = \left(\frac{50 \times 500 \times 4}{37g} + \frac{g}{5} \times \frac{500^2}{37g^2}\right)\mathbf{i}$$

$$= \frac{500}{37g}(200 + 100)\mathbf{i}$$

$$= \frac{150\,000}{37g}\mathbf{i}$$

$$\doteq 414\mathbf{i}.$$

The range down the plane is 414 m (to nearest metre).

In Example 1 we found that the maximum range over a horizontal plane was obtained by making the angle of projection 45° to the horizontal. There is a corresponding result for the maximum range up or down an inclined plane as we show in Example 4.

EXAMPLE 4   *Find expressions for the maximum range of a projectile fired with initial speed 15 m/s from a point on a plane inclined at an angle α to the horizontal (i) up the plane, and (ii) down the plane.*

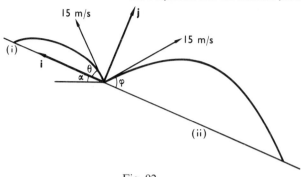

Fig. 92

Case (i): up the plane.

Let the projectile be launched at an angle θ to the plane. Let $\mathbf{i}$ be a unit vector in the line of greatest slope, and $\mathbf{j}$ a unit vector perpendicular to the plane, both passing through the launching point. The position vector for the projectile after t s is then

$$\mathbf{s} = (15t \cos \theta - \tfrac{1}{2}gt^2 \sin \alpha)\mathbf{i} + (15t \sin \theta - \tfrac{1}{2}gt^2 \cos \alpha)\mathbf{j}.$$

When it strikes the plane the $\mathbf{j}$-component is zero.

$$\therefore \quad 15t \sin \theta - \tfrac{1}{2}gt^2 \cos \alpha = 0.$$

Hence when it strikes the plane

$$t = \frac{30 \sin \theta}{g \cos \alpha}.$$

The range is then given by the $\mathbf{i}$-component, and is

$$15t \cos \theta - \tfrac{1}{2}gt^2 \sin \alpha = 15t \cos \theta . \frac{30 \sin \theta}{g \cos \alpha} - \frac{g}{2} \sin \alpha . \frac{30^2 \sin^2 \theta}{g^2 \cos^2 \alpha}$$

$$= \frac{30^2}{2g} \sin \theta \left(\frac{\cos \theta}{\cos \alpha} - \frac{\sin \alpha \sin \theta}{\cos^2 \alpha} \right)$$

$$= \frac{450}{g \cos^2 \alpha} \sin \theta (\cos \theta \cos \alpha - \sin \theta \sin \alpha)$$

$$= \frac{450}{g \cos^2 \alpha} \sin \theta \cos (\theta + \alpha).$$

Since $\dfrac{450}{g \cos^2 \alpha}$ is constant the range is greatest when $\sin \theta \cos (\theta + \alpha)$ is at a maximum. But

$$2 \sin \theta \cos (\theta + \alpha) = \sin (2\theta + \alpha) - \sin \alpha,$$

and this is maximum when $\sin (2\theta + \alpha) = 1$. Therefore the maximum range occurs when

$$2\theta + \alpha = \frac{\pi}{2},$$

$$\theta = \tfrac{1}{2}\left(\frac{\pi}{2} - \alpha\right).$$

But $\left(\dfrac{\pi}{2} - \alpha\right)$ is the angle between the plane and the vertical, and so the maximum range corresponds to an angle of projection bisecting the angle between the vertical and the plane. The maximum range is

$$\frac{450}{g \cos^2 \alpha} \cdot \tfrac{1}{2}(1 - \sin \alpha).$$

But $\cos^2 \alpha = 1 - \sin^2 \alpha = (1 - \sin \alpha)(1 + \sin \alpha)$.

$\therefore$ Maximum range up the plane is $\dfrac{225}{g(1 + \sin \alpha)}$ m.

Case (ii): down the plane.

We define $\mathbf{i}$ and $\mathbf{j}$ as for case (i), and let ϕ be the angle of projection to the plane. The position vector after t s is

$$\mathbf{s} = -(15t \cos \phi + \tfrac{1}{2}gt^2 \sin \alpha)\mathbf{i} + (15t \sin \phi - \tfrac{1}{2}gt^2 \cos \alpha)\mathbf{j}.$$

As before, it strikes the plane when

$$t = \frac{30 \sin \phi}{g \cos \alpha},$$

and the range is

$$15t \cos \phi + \tfrac{1}{2}gt^2 \sin \alpha = 15 \cos \phi \cdot \frac{30 \sin \phi}{g \cos^2 \alpha} + \frac{g \sin \alpha}{2} \cdot \frac{30^2 \sin^2 \phi}{g^2 \cos^2 \alpha}$$

$$= \frac{450}{g \cos^2 \alpha} \sin \phi \, (\cos \phi \cos \alpha + \sin \phi \sin \alpha)$$

$$= \frac{450}{g \cos^2 \alpha} \sin \phi \cos (\phi - \alpha).$$

This is a maximum when $\sin \phi \cos (\phi - \alpha)$ is greatest. But $2 \sin \phi \cos (\phi - \alpha) = \sin (2\phi - \alpha) + \sin \alpha$. This is a maximum when

$$2\phi - \alpha = \frac{\pi}{2},$$

i.e. when

$$\phi = \tfrac{1}{2}\left(\frac{\pi}{2} + \alpha\right).$$

But as in case (i), $\left(\dfrac{\pi}{2}+\alpha\right)$ is the angle between the plane and the vertical.

Thus irrespective of whether it is fired up or down the plane, the maximum range corresponds to an angle of projection bisecting the angle between the plane and the vertical.

The range in this case is

$$\frac{450}{g\cos^2\alpha}\cdot\tfrac{1}{2}(1+\sin\alpha).$$

Maximum range down the plane is $\dfrac{225}{g(1-\sin\alpha)}$ m.

7.4 Harder examples

The methods outlined so far in Examples 1 to 4 lend themselves very easily to more complex situations, and we conclude this chapter with three more difficult examples to show how these techniques can be used.

EXAMPLE 5   *Particles A and B are projected in the same vertical plane from points* $h\mathbf{j}$ *and* $2h\mathbf{i}$ *respectively relative to the origin of unit vectors* $\mathbf{i}$ *and* $\mathbf{j}$, $\mathbf{i}$ *being horizontal and* $\mathbf{j}$ *vertical. They are projected at angles* α *and* β *to the direction of* $\mathbf{i}$ *respectively. If they collide, show that the ratio of the initial speeds of A and B is*

$$\frac{2\sin\beta+\cos\beta}{2\sin\alpha+\cos\alpha}.$$

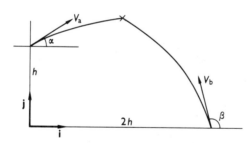

Fig. 93

Let the initial speeds of A and B be V_a and V_b respectively. The position of A at time t after launching **relative to the point** $h\mathbf{j}$ is

$$V_a t\cos\alpha\,\mathbf{i}+(V_a t\sin\alpha-\tfrac{1}{2}gt^2)\mathbf{j}.$$

If s_a is the position at time t relative to the origin of unit vectors then this is $s_a-h\mathbf{j}$.

$$\therefore\quad s_a = V_a t\cos\alpha\,\mathbf{i}+(h+V_a t\sin\alpha-\tfrac{1}{2}gt^2)\mathbf{j}.$$

Similarly the position of B after the same time relative to the origin is

$$s_b = (2h + V_b t \cos \beta)i + (V_b t \sin \beta - \tfrac{1}{2}gt^2)j.$$

When they collide $s_a = s_b$, and equating components

$$V_a t \cos \alpha = 2h + V_b t \cos \beta, \tag{1}$$

and
$$V_b t \sin \beta - \tfrac{1}{2}gt^2 = h + V_a t \sin \alpha - \tfrac{1}{2}gt^2,$$

$$V_b t \sin \beta = h + V_a t \sin \alpha. \tag{2}$$

Subtracting twice (2) from (1),

$$V_a t \cos \alpha - 2 V_b t \sin \beta = V_b t \cos \beta - 2 V_a t \sin \alpha.$$

$$V_a(2 \sin \alpha + \cos \alpha) = V_b(2 \sin \beta + \cos \beta),$$

$$\frac{V_a}{V_b} = \frac{2 \sin \beta + \cos \beta}{2 \sin \alpha + \cos \alpha}, \qquad \text{Q.E.D.}$$

EXAMPLE 6   *A smooth bead is projected with an initial speed of 15 m/s up the face of a plane inclined at an angle α to the horizontal, the initial path of the bead making an angle of $\left(\dfrac{\pi}{2} - \theta\right)$ to the line of greatest slope. Show that if i and j are unit vectors through the point of projection such that j is horizontal and i is along the line of greatest slope, then the highest point on the plane reached by the bead has position*

$$\frac{15^2}{2g \sin \alpha}(\sin^2 \theta i + \sin 2\theta j)$$

relative to the point of projection O.

Show also that if s is the position vector of the particle after time t relative to O, then if $|s|$ reaches a maximum during the motion, $\sin \theta \geqslant 2\sqrt{2}/3$.

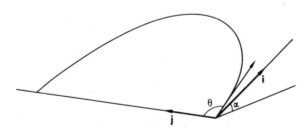

Fig. 94

The bead is subject to an acceleration of $-g \sin \alpha i$, and so the velocity vector of the bead after time t is given by

$$v = (15 \sin \theta - gt \sin \alpha)i + 15 \cos \theta j.$$

Similarly

$$\mathbf{s} = (15t \sin \theta - \tfrac{1}{2}gt^2 \sin \alpha)\mathbf{i} + 15t \cos \theta\mathbf{j}.$$

When at a maximum height up the plane the $\mathbf{i}$-component of $\mathbf{v}$ is zero, giving

$$t = \frac{15 \sin \theta}{g \sin \alpha}.$$

Thus the highest point up the plane has position relative to O given by

$$\mathbf{s} = \left(15 \sin \theta . \frac{15 \sin \theta}{g \sin \alpha} - \frac{g \sin \alpha}{2} . \frac{15^2 \sin^2 \theta}{g^2 \sin^2 \alpha}\right)\mathbf{i} + 15 \cos \theta . \frac{15 \sin \theta}{g \sin \alpha}\mathbf{j}$$

$$= \frac{15^2 \sin^2 \theta}{2g \sin \alpha}\mathbf{i} + \frac{15^2 . 2 \sin \theta \cos \theta}{2g \sin \alpha}\mathbf{j}$$

$$= \frac{15^2}{2g \sin \alpha}(\sin^2 \theta\mathbf{i} + \sin 2\theta\mathbf{j}). \qquad\qquad \text{Q.E.D.}$$

If $|\mathbf{s}|$ reaches a maximum then $\dfrac{d}{dt}|\mathbf{s}|^2 = 0$.

$$|\mathbf{s}|^2 = (15t \sin \theta - \tfrac{1}{2}gt^2 \sin \alpha)^2 + (15t \cos \theta)^2,$$

$$= 15^2 t^2(\sin^2 \theta + \cos^2 \theta) - 15gt^3 \sin \theta \sin \alpha + \tfrac{1}{4}g^2 t^4 \sin^2 \alpha$$

$$= 15^2 t^2 - 15gt^3 \sin \theta \sin \alpha + \tfrac{1}{4}g^2 t^4 \sin^2 \alpha.$$

$$\therefore \frac{d}{dt}|\mathbf{s}|^2 = 2.15^2 t - 45gt^2 \sin \theta \sin \alpha + g^2 t^3 \sin^2 \alpha.$$

Putting $\dfrac{d}{dt}|\mathbf{s}|^2 = 0$, and discounting the solution $t = 0$,

$$g^2 t^2 \sin^2 \alpha - 45gt \sin \theta \sin \alpha + 2.15^2 = 0.$$

This equation has real roots if

$$45^2 g^2 \sin^2 \theta \sin^2 \alpha \geqslant 4.g^2 \sin^2 \alpha.2.15^2,$$

$$9 \sin^2 \theta \geqslant 8,$$

$$\sin \theta \geqslant \frac{2\sqrt{2}}{3}. \qquad\qquad \text{Q.E.D.}$$

EXAMPLE 7   *Two projectiles are fired, the first from the origin of perpendicular unit vectors $\mathbf{i}$, $\mathbf{j}$ and $\mathbf{k}$ where $\mathbf{i}$ and $\mathbf{j}$ are horizontal and $\mathbf{k}$ is vertical, with speed V_1, and the second from the point $200\mathbf{i}$ with speed V_2. The first is projected at an elevation θ in a direction of $30°$ to $\mathbf{i}$, and the second at an elevation ϕ in a direction $45°$ to $-\mathbf{i}$. They collide at a point P whose $\mathbf{k}$-component is $+50$ and whose $\mathbf{i}$ and $\mathbf{j}$ components are both positive. Distances are in metres and speeds in metres per second. Show that*

$$\tan \phi = \sqrt{2} \tan \theta.$$

If $\phi = \dfrac{\pi}{4}$, find θ, V_1 and V_2.

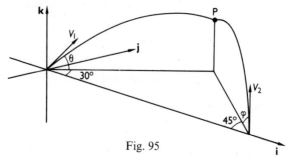

Fig. 95

Let the positions after time t of the first and second particles be $\mathbf{s}_1$ and $\mathbf{s}_2$ respectively, then

$$\mathbf{s}_1 = V_1 \cos \theta \cos 30° t\mathbf{i} + V_1 \cos \theta \sin 30° t\mathbf{j} + (V_1 t \sin \theta - \tfrac{1}{2}gt^2)\mathbf{k}$$

$$= \frac{\sqrt{3}}{2}V_1 t \cos \theta \mathbf{i} + \tfrac{1}{2}V_1 t \cos \theta \mathbf{j} + (V_1 t \sin \theta - \tfrac{1}{2}gt^2)\mathbf{k},$$

and similarly

$$s_2 = (200 - V_2 \cos \phi \cos 45° t)\mathbf{i} + V_2 \cos \phi \sin 45° t\mathbf{j} + (V_2 t \sin \phi - \tfrac{1}{2}gt^2)\mathbf{k}$$

$$= (200 - V_2 t \cos \phi/\sqrt{2})\mathbf{i} + V_2 t \cos \phi/\sqrt{2}\mathbf{j} + (V_2 t \sin \phi - \tfrac{1}{2}gt^2)\mathbf{k}.$$

Putting $\mathbf{s}_1 = \mathbf{s}_2$, $\mathbf{i}$-components give

$$\frac{\sqrt{3}}{2}V_1 t \cos \theta = 200 - V_2 t \cos \phi/\sqrt{2}. \tag{1}$$

$\mathbf{j}$-components give

$$\tfrac{1}{2}V_1 t \cos \theta = \frac{1}{\sqrt{2}}V_2 t \cos \phi,$$

$$V_1 \cos \theta = \sqrt{2}V_2 \cos \phi. \tag{2}$$

$\mathbf{k}$-components give

$$V_1 t \sin \theta = V_2 t \sin \phi = 50 + \tfrac{1}{2}gt^2. \tag{3}$$

From (3)

$$\frac{V_1}{V_2} = \frac{\sin \phi}{\sin \theta},$$

and from (2)

$$\frac{V_1}{V_2} = \frac{\sqrt{2} \cos \phi}{\cos \theta}.$$

$$\therefore \ \tan \phi = \sqrt{2} \tan \theta.$$ Q.E.D.

If $\phi = \dfrac{\pi}{4}$, then $\tan \phi = 1$ and $\tan \theta = \dfrac{1}{\sqrt{2}}$.

$\therefore \ \underline{\theta = 35^\circ \ 16'.}$

It also follows that $\sin \theta = \dfrac{1}{\sqrt{3}}$ and $\cos \theta = \dfrac{\sqrt{2}}{\sqrt{3}}$. Equations (1), (2) and (3) then become

$$\frac{1}{\sqrt{2}}V_1 t = 200 - \tfrac{1}{2}V_2 t, \tag{1a}$$

$$\sqrt{2}V_1 = \sqrt{3}V_2, \tag{2a}$$

and $$\frac{1}{\sqrt{3}}V_1 t = \frac{1}{\sqrt{2}}V_2 t = 50 + \tfrac{1}{2}gt^2. \tag{3a}$$

Eliminating V_1 from (1a) and (2a)

$$\frac{\sqrt{3}}{2}V_2 t = 200 - \tfrac{1}{2}V_2 t,$$

$$(\sqrt{3}+1)V_2 t = 400,$$

$$V_2 t = 400/(\sqrt{3}+1). \tag{4}$$

Substituting for $V_2 t$ in (3a),

$$\frac{400}{\sqrt{2}(\sqrt{3}+1)} = 50 + \tfrac{1}{2}gt^2.$$

$$\tfrac{1}{2}gt^2 = \frac{400}{1 \cdot 414 \times 2 \cdot 732} - 50$$

$$\doteqdot \cdot 103 \cdot 7 - 50.$$

$$\therefore \ t^2 \doteqdot 53 \cdot 7/4 \cdot 9,$$

giving $t \doteqdot 3 \cdot 305.$

Now from (4)

$$V_2 = 400/2 \cdot 732t$$

$$\doteqdot 44 \cdot 2.$$

From (2a)

$$V_1 = \sqrt{3}V_2/\sqrt{2}$$

$$\doteqdot 54 \cdot 2.$$

Speeds of projection are 54 m/s and 44 m/s (to nearest m/s).

Exercise 17

(Take g as 9.8 m/s^2 when necessary.)

1 Find how far up a plane of inclination $40°$ a boy can throw a ball if the greatest speed of projection he can manage is 14.7 m/s.

2 A stone is thrown down a slope of $30°$ to the horizontal at an angle of $30°$ above the horizontal with an initial speed of 14 m/s. Determine where and at what angle it strikes the plane.

3 Show that the range up a plane of inclination α to the horizontal of a particle fired at an angle θ to the horizontal at an initial speed of 20 m/s is

$$800 \sin (\theta - \alpha) \cos \theta / g \cos^2 \alpha,$$

and hence show that the maximum range up the plane is

$$400/g(1 + \sin \alpha).$$

4 Find the maximum distance a boy can throw a ball along a corridor before it bounces without hitting the ceiling if he can throw with a maximum speed of 12 m/s, the corridor is 3 m high, and he cannot throw effectively from a point less than 1 m from the floor.

5 A particle is fired with velocity V at an angle α to $\mathbf{i}$ from the origin of unit vectors $\mathbf{i}$ and $\mathbf{j}$, $\mathbf{i}$ horizontal and $\mathbf{j}$ vertical, to strike a plane the equation of which in the $\mathbf{i},\mathbf{j}$-plane is

$$\mathbf{r} = (a + n \cos \alpha)\mathbf{i} + n \sin \alpha \mathbf{j}.$$

If it strikes this plane perpendicularly, find V in terms of α, g and a.

6 A girl throwing a ball on an open hillside for her dog is able to throw the ball approximately 60 m directly down hill or 35 m directly uphill. Assuming that in each case she throws the ball at the same angle of elevation β to the horizontal show that

$$5 \tan \beta = 19 \tan \alpha$$

where α is the angle of inclination of the ground to the horizontal.

Hence find α to the nearest degree if she throws the ball at $45°$ to the horizontal.

7 A and B are two points in the same horizontal line on a plane inclined at an angle α to the horizontal. $\mathbf{i}$ and $\mathbf{j}$ are unit vectors both passing through A, $\mathbf{i}$ along AB, and $\mathbf{j}$ perpendicular to AB in the plane. A smooth bead is projected up the plane with speed V at an angle θ to AB. If the bead can just pass through B, show that AB is $V^2/g \sin \alpha$.

8 A particle A is thrown from horizontal ground from the origin of unit vectors, $\mathbf{i}$ and $\mathbf{j}$, $\mathbf{i}$ being horizontal and $\mathbf{j}$ vertical, with velocity $2V$ at an angle α to $\mathbf{i}$. A particle B is thrown at the same instant with velocity V at an angle below the horizontal from the point $h\mathbf{j}$ to hit A in flight. Show that it hits A after a time h/VR where $R = \sqrt{1 - 4 \cos^2 \alpha + 2 \sin \alpha}$.

Find where they hit each other, and deduce that if $V^2 \sin \alpha$ is less than $gh/4R$ then they will not in fact be able to collide.

9 A and B are two points on a smooth plane inclined at an angle α to the horizontal. $\mathbf{i}$ and $\mathbf{j}$ are unit vectors through A in the plane, $\mathbf{i}$ being horizontal and $\mathbf{j}$ along the line of greatest slope. The straight line AB makes an angle α with $\mathbf{i}$, and is d units long. Particles are projected simultaneously from A and B, both with speed V, the one from A at an angle θ to $\mathbf{i}$, and the one from B at an angle ϕ to $-\mathbf{i}$, both in the plane. If they do not collide, show that they are closest together when

$$t = \frac{d}{2V}\left[\frac{\cos (\alpha - \theta) + \cos (\alpha + \phi)}{1 + \cos (\theta + \phi)}\right].$$

If however they do collide, show that they do so when

$$t = d/(V\sqrt{2 + 2 \cos (\theta + \phi)}.$$

10 Project Example:

Investigate the dynamics of a tiddly-wink, giving due attention to shape, the projecting force, and the nature of the surface from which it is shot.

Support Exercise B

Miscellaneous examples which may be worked concurrently with Chapters 6 and 7

1 If the position vectors of two points P and Q, with respect to a fixed origin, are **p** and **q**, show that the position vector of any point on PQ is of the form

$$\lambda\mathbf{p}+(1-\lambda)\mathbf{q}.$$

A parallelogram ABCD is given, and A is chosen as origin. The position vectors of B and D are denoted by **b** and **d**. If E is the mid-point of BC, find, in terms of **b** and **d**, the position vector of E.

If AE meets BD at F, find the position vector of F, and show that F is a point of trisection of BD.   (O & C)

2 An equilateral triangular lamina ABC of weight W is in equilibrium in a vertical plane with C on rough horizontal ground and AC making an angle α with the horizontal, $\alpha < 60°$. It is supported in this position by a force F applied at A. Prove that if F is a minimum then F is perpendicular to AC. Hence show that this minimal value is

$$\frac{W}{\sqrt{3}}\cos{(\alpha+30°)}.$$

Find also the coefficient of friction μ at C if this is in limiting equilibrium.

3 Prove by vector theory that the lines joining the mid-points of adjacent sides of a quadrilateral form a parallelogram.

4 Two uniform rods AB, BC each of length $4a$ and weight W are smoothly hinged together at B. The rods rest in a vertical plane on a smooth cylinder of radius a fixed with its axis horizontal. Find the reaction at B and the angle ABC.

If now the cylinder is rough, and the rods can just be made to rest symmetrically as before but with angle ABC $= 2\tan^{-1}(3/2)$ find the coefficient of friction μ.

5 A plane light lamina in the shape of a square ABCD has masses each of weight W attached to each corner and is smoothly pivoted at a point P so that it can turn freely in a vertical plane. If O is the centre of ABCD, OP produced cuts CB at an angle α, and OP $= a$, write down the position vector of O relative to P when AB makes an angle θ with the upward drawn vertical, taking **i** and **j** as unit vectors, **i** horizontal and **j** vertical.

The pivot P is now replaced by an upward vertical force of $4W$ at P. Show that the system reduces to a couple of magnitude M such that $-4aP \leqslant M \leqslant 4aP$, and find the values of θ in terms of α which give the extreme values.

6 If $\mathbf{r} = a\mathbf{i}+b\mathbf{j}+c\mathbf{k}$, prove that $|\mathbf{r}| = \sqrt{(a^2+b^2+c^2)}$, **i**, **j** and **k** being mutually perpendicular unit vectors.

Given that

$$\begin{aligned}
\mathbf{r}_1 &= 3\mathbf{i}+2\mathbf{j}-6\mathbf{k}, \\
\mathbf{r}_2 &= 4\mathbf{i}-2\mathbf{j}+4\mathbf{k}, \text{ and} \\
\mathbf{r}_3 &= -3\mathbf{i}+4\mathbf{k},
\end{aligned}$$

find the magnitudes of $\mathbf{r}_2$, $\mathbf{r}_1+\mathbf{r}_2+\mathbf{r}_3$, and $3\mathbf{r}_1+2\mathbf{r}_2-\mathbf{r}_3$.

7 Relative to perpendicular unit vectors $\mathbf{i}$ and $\mathbf{j}$, the corners of a quadrilateral lamina have positions $\mathbf{a} = \mathbf{i}+2\mathbf{j}$, $\mathbf{b} = \mathbf{i}-4\mathbf{j}$, $\mathbf{c} = 3\mathbf{i}+3\mathbf{j}$, and $\mathbf{d} = 4\mathbf{i}-\mathbf{j}$. Find the position of the centre of mass assuming the lamina to be uniform.

8 A particle accelerates uniformly from rest at a m/s^2 for T s, travels at constant speed v m/s for the next $2T$ s, and comes to rest uniformly retarded in a further $3T$ s. A second particle starting from rest covers the same distance in $11T/2$ s; the first half in $3T$ s and the second half in $5T/2$ s, but does not exceed v m/s. Find the acceleration and deceleration if both are constant, in terms of a.

9 ABCD is a regular hollow tetrahedron made of uniform material such that the positions of the vertices A, B and C are given by the vectors $\mathbf{i}$, $-\mathbf{i}+2\mathbf{j}$ and $-\mathbf{i}-2\mathbf{k}$ respectively. Find the position of D if the origin and D are on opposite sides of the plane ABC. Find the position vector of the centre of mass of the tetrahedron. ($\mathbf{i}$, $\mathbf{j}$ and $\mathbf{k}$ are mutually perpendicular unit vectors.)

10 Two smooth uniform circular cylinders, each of radius a and weight W_1, rest in contact inside a fixed smooth cylinder of radius $4a$. A third smooth uniform cylinder of radius a and weight W_2 rests in equilibrium upon the other two cylinders. All the generators are horizontal and parallel and the centres of gravity of the three uniform cylinders are in a plane perpendicular to the generators. If the two lower cylinders are on the point of separating, show that

$$\frac{W_1}{W_2} = \frac{2\sqrt{6}-3}{6}.$$
(L)

11 Two particles of masses $3m$ and m are connected by a light inextensible string of length h over a smooth pulley fixed at the top edge of a smooth wedge. The $3m$ mass is on the face of the wedge inclined at an angle of $30°$ to the horizontal, and the m mass hangs freely. The wedge is fixed to a horizontal table, and the pulley is a height h above the table. The system is held with the lighter mass just touching the table, and then released. After moving a distance x the string breaks, and the ensuing motion is such that the two masses strike the table at the same instant. Show that $x = 2h/3$ and find the ratio of the momenta of the masses at the time they hit the table.

12 A frustum of a solid cone has two parallel circular faces, one of radius 12 cm, the other of radius 24 cm, at a distance of 15 cm apart. The solid is cut in half by a plane cut through the centre perpendicular to the plane faces. $\mathbf{i}$ and $\mathbf{j}$ are unit vectors, $\mathbf{i}$ along the axis of the cone, and $\mathbf{j}$ in the plane of the smaller face perpendicular to the cut. Find the centre of mass of the semi-frustum in the form $\bar{x}\mathbf{i}+\bar{y}\mathbf{j}$.
(The mass centre of a semi-circular disc radius r is $4r/3\pi$ from the straight edge.)

13 With usual notation, the vertices of a triangle ABC have position vectors $\mathbf{a} = 4\mathbf{i}+3\mathbf{j}+3\mathbf{k}$, $\mathbf{b} = \mathbf{i}+\mathbf{j}+\mathbf{k}$ and $\mathbf{c} = 5\mathbf{i}-2\mathbf{j}-2\mathbf{k}$ respectively. Show that the triangle is right-angled.

A particle P moves from B to A with speed $\frac{\sqrt{17}}{3}$ units/s and a particle Q moves from C to B with speed $\sqrt{\frac{17}{2}}$ units/s, P being at B at the same instant that Q is at C. Find the velocity of P relative to Q and angle PQB t s after P is at B ($t < 2$).

14 Two rods AB, BC are smoothly jointed at B, and rest in limiting equilibrium in a vertical plane with A and C on rough horizontal ground, coefficient of friction μ. AB = 2BC, angle ABC = $90°$ and the rods are made of identical uniform material. Show that BA will slip first, and find μ.

15 Three vectors acting at a point O are represented in magnitude and direction by the multiples of the lengths; $l\overrightarrow{OA}$, $m\overrightarrow{OB}$ and $n\overrightarrow{OC}$ where A, B and C are three points in order on a straight line. Show that their resultant is

$$(l+m+n)\overrightarrow{OZ}$$

where $AZ = \dfrac{m\mathbf{AB}+n\mathbf{AC}}{l+m+n}$.

Hence find the ratio of AB:BC if Z is the mid-point of AC.

16 Two aircraft are flying to Eastleigh. The first flies from Bristol 100 km away, the bearing of Eastleigh from Bristol being 125°. The second flies from Jersey 165 km distant, the bearing of Eastleigh from Jersey being 012°. If the flight from Bristol leaves at 1300 hours and the flight from Jersey at 1230 hours, find the difference in their estimated times of arrival if both have an air-speed of 300 km/h and a south-easterly wind is blowing at 25 km/h. What would this difference be if there were no wind?

(A graphical solution will be acceptable.)

17 A uniform rod AB of length $2a$ and mass $2m$ is fixed in a hemispherical bowl of radius a with its end B at the point in the bowl furthest from the rim and so that the rod touches the rim. The bowl has mass $3m$. The system is placed with the curved surface of the bowl on a smooth horizontal table. Find the angle of the rod to the horizontal in the equilibrium position.

18 A train travelling at v km/h passes a warning signal at which it begins to decelerate at a uniform rate of $\dfrac{v}{90}$ km/h/s until it reaches a speed of $\dfrac{v}{6}$ km/h. At this stage it passes a second signal indicating the line is clear, and the train accelerates back to its former speed at a uniform rate of $\dfrac{v}{45}$ km/h/s. Calculate (a) the distance in metres between the two signals, and (b) the total delay caused to the train assuming it would have maintained a speed of v km/h but for the signals.

19 Find the condition that two vectors $a\mathbf{i}+b\mathbf{j}$ and $c\mathbf{i}+d\mathbf{j}$ are perpendicular. Hence or otherwise find the orthocentre of triangle ABC if the position vectors of A, B and C are $\mathbf{a} = 4\mathbf{i}+4\mathbf{j}$, $\mathbf{b} = -4\mathbf{i}+2\mathbf{j}$ and $\mathbf{c} = -\mathbf{i}-3\mathbf{j}$ respectively.

20 WXYZ is a rectangle such that $XY = 1\cdot5$ m, $WX = 0\cdot8$ m. Forces of 1 N, 2 N, 2 N and 3 N act along WX, XZ, ZY and YX respectively in the directions indicated by the order of the letters. Find the resultant, and show that it cuts XY internally in the ratio 34:1. Find the magnitude of the couple formed by adding to the system at W a force equal and opposite to this resultant.

21 At 1400 hours a ship lying 6 km north and 4 km east of a port P is sailing at 24 km/h towards P. A launch 2 km west and 10 km north of P capable of 48 km/h makes to intercept the ship at the earliest opportunity. Find

(a) the course it must set to the nearest degree,

(b) the time of interception to the nearest minute,

(c) the distance of the point of interception from P to the nearest 100 m.

22 A uniform right circular cone, of weight W_1, base radius 8 cm and vertical height 15 cm, stands with its axis vertical on a fixed horizontal table. A uniform sphere of weight W_2 and radius 5 cm, rests in equilibrium against the curved surface of the cone, being held clear of the table by a light inextensible string of length 8 cm, one end of which is attached to the vertex of the cone and the other end to a point on the surface of the sphere. There is no friction between the cone and the sphere. Find the greatest possible value of $\dfrac{W_2}{W_1}$.   (O)

23 Show that the resultant $\mathbf{R}$ of $\mathbf{F}_1$ and $\mathbf{F}_2$ acting at A: $\mathbf{i}-2\mathbf{j}+\mathbf{k}$, and the resultant $\mathbf{S}$ of $\mathbf{F}_3$, $\mathbf{F}_4$ and $\mathbf{F}_5$ acting at B: $-\mathbf{i}+2\mathbf{j}+\mathbf{k}$ lie in the same plane if $\mathbf{i}$, $\mathbf{j}$ and $\mathbf{k}$ are mutually perpendicular unit vectors and

$$\mathbf{F}_1 = 3\mathbf{j}+3\mathbf{k},$$
$$\mathbf{F}_2 = \mathbf{i}-\mathbf{j}-6\mathbf{k},$$
$$\mathbf{F}_3 = \mathbf{i}-\mathbf{j}+2\mathbf{k},$$
$$\mathbf{F}_4 = 2\mathbf{i}-3\mathbf{j}+\mathbf{k},$$
and
$$\mathbf{F}_5 = 6\mathbf{j}-9\mathbf{k}.$$

Find their common point of action, and the equation of the line of action of **R**+**S**. Find the point at which it cuts AB.

24 A light frame composed of three rigid rods AB, BC, CA is smoothly jointed at A, B and C in the form of a triangle ABC right-angled at A and is such that AB = 2AC = a. The frame is in a vertical plane with AB horizontal and C above A. It is smoothly pivoted to a fixed point at A and carries loads of weight 10 N at the mid-point of AB and 10 N at B, the system being maintained in position by a rope CD, D lying on BA produced so that CA = AD. Find the stresses in the rods BC and AC, and calculate the tension, bending moment and shearing force at any point X distant x from A along AB.

25 A particle is held at rest on the smooth face of a wedge. This face is inclined at an angle α to the horizontal. The particle is released just as the wedge is given a constant acceleration $f(< g \cot \alpha)$ horizontally away from the particle. Show that after T s the particle has moved a distance

$$(g \sin \alpha + f \cos \alpha)T^2/2$$

relative to the wedge.

When the experiment is repeated, but with the wedge having an acceleration f horizontally towards the particle, the distance moved by the particle relative to the wedge is $\frac{1}{3}$ of what it was before in the same interval of time. Show that

$$\alpha = \tan^{-1} \frac{2f}{g}.$$

26 A stationary submarine fires a torpedo to hit a ship moving north-east at 20 km/h on a bearing of 330°. The torpedo travels at 55 km/h. If the ship is 800 m distant, find graphically the bearing on which the torpedo should be fired. Find also the number of seconds between firing and explosion.

27 A wooden toy is in the shape of a solid cone with a solid hemispherical base. Its total mass is m and the semi-vertical angle of the cone is $\tan^{-1} \frac{5}{12}$. A small lead weight of mass M is fixed symmetrically into the surface of the hemisphere so that the toy will always assume an upright position when placed on a horizontal plane. Find the minimum value of the ratio $\dfrac{M}{m}$ if the toy is to work properly.

(You may assume that the mass centres of a solid hemisphere and a solid cone are 3/8 radius and 1/4 height from their plane faces respectively.)

28 A particle is projected from a point on the upper surface of a fixed sphere of radius a, the direction of projection being along a tangent to the sphere and in a vertical plane through the centre. Prove that, if the particle does not meet the sphere again, the velocity of projection must be greater than $\sqrt{(ag \sec \alpha)}$, where α is the acute angle which the radius to the point of projection makes with the vertical. (O)

29 A uniform rod AB of weight W and length $4a$ lies with A on a horizontal table and leaning against a hemisphere of radius a such that the vertical plane through AB passes through the centre of its plane face. The hemisphere is fixed with the plane face in contact with the table. The coefficient of friction at all points of contact is $\frac{1}{4}$. Show that if AB makes an angle θ with the table then $\theta \leqslant \sin^{-1} \sqrt{\frac{2}{17}}$ if it is to remain in equilibrium.

30 Fig. 96 illustrates a light framework ABCDEF of 9 rods smoothly jointed at each

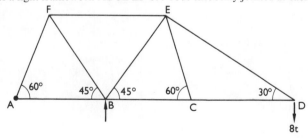

Fig. 96

of these points. It is smoothly pivoted at A and is supported by a vertical force at B. A load of 8 t is hung from D. Find the reactions at A and B, and find the stresses in the rods AF, FE and ED.

31 An apple-core is thrown out of the window of a train travelling at 60 km/h, perpendicularly to the motion of the train. It is projected just as the window is at the beginning of a bridge over a river 20 m wide, 5 m below the level of the window, and it is observed to strike the opposite bank 15 m from the bridge. Find the velocity of projection.

32 A solid sphere of radius r is cut into two parts by a plane distant $\frac{1}{2}r$ from its centre. The larger section is then placed with its plane face in contact with a plane rough enough to prevent slipping. Find the maximum inclination of the plane consistent with equilibrium.

33 Define what is meant by the angle of friction.

AB, BC are two identical uniform rods of weight W and length $2a$ smoothly hinged together at B. A is fixed by a smooth pivot to a vertical wall so as to be free to move in a vertical plane, and AB is inclined at an angle of 60° to the downward vertical. C is in contact with the floor and CB makes an angle of 60° with the floor such that angle ABC is 150°. The floor is just rough enough to prevent slipping. Find the reactions at A, B and C, and deduce the angle of friction at C.

34 The position of a particle P at time t is given by

$$\mathbf{p} = (2-t^2)\mathbf{i}+t\mathbf{j}$$

relative to the origin of perpendicular unit vectors $\mathbf{i}$ and $\mathbf{j}$. A second particle Q has constant acceleration $2\mathbf{i}$, and at time $t = 0$ it has position $-\mathbf{i}$. If the velocity of Q relative to P when $t = 0$ is $\mathbf{j}$ find the position of Q at time t. Sketch the loci of P and Q.

Find the time (>0) when P and Q are closest together, and the velocity of Q relative to P at this instant.

35 Three forces, $\mathbf{F}_1 = 3\mathbf{i}+3\mathbf{j}-2\mathbf{k}$ acting through the point $-2\mathbf{i}-\mathbf{j}-\mathbf{k}$, $\mathbf{F}_2 = 3\mathbf{i}-\mathbf{j}+\mathbf{k}$ acting through the point $7\mathbf{i}-\mathbf{k}$, and $\mathbf{F}_3$ are in equilibrium. Find $\mathbf{F}_3$ and the equation of its line of action.

36 Two particles P and Q are projected from the same point at the same instant, P vertically upwards with velocity u_1, and Q with horizontal and vertical components of velocity v and u_2 respectively. Show that the line joining P and Q is at a constant inclination to the horizontal.

Show further that the distances apart when P is at its greatest height and Q is at its greatest height are in the ratio $u_1:u_2$.

37 The vertices of a rectangle RSTU are given by the vectors $\mathbf{r}$, $\mathbf{s}$, $\mathbf{t}$ and $\mathbf{u}$. Prove that $\mathbf{r}+\mathbf{t} = \mathbf{s}+\mathbf{u}$.

If $\mathbf{r}-\mathbf{s} = 6\mathbf{i}+2\mathbf{j}$ and $\mathbf{u} = 2\mathbf{i}+4\mathbf{j}$, form expressions for $\mathbf{r}$, $\mathbf{s}$ and $\mathbf{t}$ using one scalar variable v.

38 If a man can throw a maximum distance of 64 m on Earth, show that his greatest speed of projection is approximately 25 m/s.

The same man goes on a mission to the moon, and while there is asked to throw a piece of equipment to a fellow astronaut 200 m away on horizontal ground. If he throws at his maximum initial speed, find the angle of projection giving the quickest delivery.

(Take g as 9·8 m/s², and the acceleration due to gravity on the moon as $g_m = 1\cdot8$ m/s².)

39 Fig. 97 (which is not to scale) shows a uniform rod AB of length 65 cm and mass 50 g, which is freely hinged at A to a point of a fixed vertical pole. The end C of a light elastic string CD of natural length 25 cm is attached to the pole at a point 55 cm above A, and the end D is attached to a particle of mass 80 g. A second light elastic string DB of natural length 12·5 cm joins the particle to the end B of the

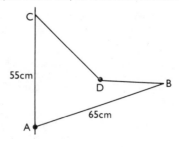

Fig. 97

rod. The system rests in equilibrium with DB horizontal and CD inclined at an angle $\tan^{-1} \frac{4}{3}$ to the horizontal. Find
  (a) the inclination of AB to the horizontal,
  (b) the modulus of each elastic string.   (C, Adapted)

40 Prove that if A, B and C are the points $\mathbf{i}+\mathbf{j}-\mathbf{k}$, $-\mathbf{i}+3\mathbf{k}$ and $-2\mathbf{i}+3\mathbf{j}-2\mathbf{k}$, then triangle ABC is right-angled. ($\mathbf{i},\mathbf{j},\mathbf{k}$ are mutually perpendicular unit vectors.)

A particle P starts from A and moves with constant speed $\frac{\sqrt{21}}{2}$ units/s along AB. Find angle APC at time t s.

A second particle Q also starts from A but one second after P and moves with constant speed along the minor arc of the circumcircle ABC. If Q is at C when P is at B, find the speed of Q.

41 A uniform solid is formed by revolving the curve $y^2 = 4x$ about the x-axis between $x = 0$ and $x = 4$. Find the position of the centre of mass, and show that if the solid is placed on a smooth horizontal table with its curved surface in contact with the table, the axis not being vertical, then the point of contact when in equilibrium lies on a circle on the solid of radius $2\sqrt{\frac{2}{3}}$, corresponding to $x = \frac{2}{3}$.

42 Prove that if two vectors can be represented in magnitude and direction as $m\overrightarrow{OA}$ and $n\overrightarrow{OB}$, then their resultant is $(m+n)\overrightarrow{OP}$ where P lies on AB and

$$AP:PB = n:m.$$

Forces are represented in magnitude, position and direction by $2\overrightarrow{AB}$, $4\overrightarrow{AD}$ and $3\overrightarrow{BC}$, where ABC is a triangle and D is the mid-point of BC. If the resultant is $p\overrightarrow{FE}$ where E lies on BC and F on AB, find p and the positions of E and F.

8 Work and Energy

8.1 Theory of dimensions

All the quantities that we are using in this book which are not purely numerical are made up from three basic concepts—mass, length and time. We refer to these three concepts as **dimensions**, and the quantities we refer to are made up as combinations of one or more of these. If we use letters M, L and T to refer to mass, length and time respectively, then we have for example that velocity always takes the form L/T, distance divided by time, and we say that the dimensions of velocity are $[LT^{-1}]$.

The dimensions of the quantities that we have used so far are as follows:

Distance	$[L]$
Area	$[L^2]$
Volume	$[L^3]$
Density	$[ML^{-3}]$
Velocity	$[LT^{-1}]$
Acceleration	$[LT^{-2}]$
Momentum	$[MLT^{-1}]$
Force	$[MLT^{-2}]$
Couple	$[ML^2T^{-2}]$

We can add to this list **Pressure** which is force per unit area and has dimensions $[ML^{-1}T^{-2}]$.

Notice that we can form these by using conventional algebra. Momentum is mass × velocity, and so its dimensions must be $[M] \times [LT^{-1}]$, giving $[MLT^{-1}]$. Similarly we can deduce the nature of force by thinking of it as mass × acceleration.

It is an important principle that:

Any equation in mechanics must be dimensionally consistent.

This means that every term in the equation must have the same dimensions. Consider for example the equation of motion 2.2:

$$s = ut + \tfrac{1}{2}gt^2.$$

The dimension of the left-hand side is $[L]$. The dimensions of ut are
$$[LT^{-1}][T] \equiv [L],$$
and of $\tfrac{1}{2}gt^2$ are

$$[LT^{-2}][T^2] \equiv [L].$$

The following equation however is not dimensionally consistent:

$$\tfrac{1}{2}mv^2 = ms(v-u)+\tfrac{1}{2}gt$$

where m is mass, and u, v, s and t are defined as for equations 2.1–2.3. The dimensions of $\tfrac{1}{2}mv^2$ are $[ML^2T^{-2}]$, but the dimensions of msv and msu are

$$[M][L][LT^{-1}] \equiv [ML^2T^{-1}]$$

and of $\tfrac{1}{2}gt$ are

$$[LT^{-2}][T] \equiv [LT^{-1}].$$

We conclude that the equation is not valid.

It follows that we have a simple and convenient method for checking the form of an equation, although we cannot find the coefficients this way since these will not have dimensions. In this connection we should notice that the unit vectors $\mathbf{i}$, $\mathbf{j}$ and $\mathbf{k}$ do not have dimensions.

The method of dimensions can help us to express units correctly. A unit is an arbitrary measure of a particular dimension or combination of dimensions. In S.I. units the dimension length $[L]$ is measured in the unit metres, mass $[M]$ in the unit kilogrammes, etc. The newton is a unit of force, and because force has dimensions $[MLT^{-2}]$, we could quite correctly say that force is measured in kg m/s². It is only because this is clumsy, and force of such importance as a quantity, that we use the special unit of the newton.

EXAMPLE 1   *A straight wire of length l and mass m under a tension T vibrates at a rate of f cycles/s. Find an expression for f in terms of l, m and T and a constant assuming that no other factors are involved.*

A cycle is a complete vibration and has no dimension. It follows therefore that the dimension of f is $[T^{-1}]$. Let

$$f = cl^x m^y T^z,$$

where c is a constant, then the dimensions of the right-hand side are given by

$$[L^x][M^y][M^z L^z T^{-2z}] \equiv [L^{x+z}M^{y+z}T^{-2z}].$$

Since this must be equivalent to $[T^{-1}]$, we have

$$x+z = 0,$$
$$y+z = 0,$$

and

$$-2z = -1.$$

Hence $z = \tfrac{1}{2}$, $y = -\tfrac{1}{2}$ and $x = -\tfrac{1}{2}$.

$$\therefore f = c\sqrt{\frac{T}{ml}}.$$

8.2 The scalar product

In our use of vectors so far we have confined ourselves to their addition and subtraction. There are two ways in which we can usefully define the multiplication of two vectors; one of these results in a scalar quantity and is called the scalar product, the other in a vector quantity, which is called the vector product. At this point we shall consider only the former.

Fig. 98

Given two vectors, **r** and **s**, their **scalar product**, written **r.s**, is defined to be the scalar quantity

$$|\mathbf{r}||\mathbf{s}|\cos\theta$$

where θ is the angle between them (Fig. 98). Because of the way in which it is written this is sometimes referred to as the dot product, but as this does not emphasize its nature the term scalar product is adhered to in this text.

We should note that scalar multiplication of two vectors is both ways distributive over addition; i.e.

$$\mathbf{a}.(\mathbf{b}+\mathbf{c}) = \mathbf{a}.\mathbf{b}+\mathbf{a}.\mathbf{c},$$

and
$$(\mathbf{b}+\mathbf{c}).\mathbf{a} = \mathbf{b}.\mathbf{a}+\mathbf{c}.\mathbf{a}.$$

It is also evident from the definition that it is commutative:

$$\mathbf{a}.\mathbf{b} = \mathbf{b}.\mathbf{a}.$$

A particular case occurs when two vectors **p** and **q** are perpendicular, viz:

$$\mathbf{p}.\mathbf{q} = 0.$$

This leads to a useful corollary that

$$(a\mathbf{i}+b\mathbf{j}+c\mathbf{k}).(x\mathbf{i}+y\mathbf{j}+z\mathbf{k}) = ax+by+cz.$$

8.3 Work and power

The effect of a force acting on a body can be measured by the acceleration it produces, or by the change in momentum that it brings about. Measuring the effect by the acceleration does not take account of how long the force acts however, and while the change in momentum is a more relevant measure it does not take direct account of the nature of the force itself. A third way to measure the effect is by the work done by the force. The **work** done by a force **F** is the magnitude of the force times the distance through which its point of application moves in the direction of the force (Fig. 99). More simply, the work done by a force **F** in causing a displacement **s** is W where

$$W = \mathbf{F}.\mathbf{s}. \qquad 8.1$$

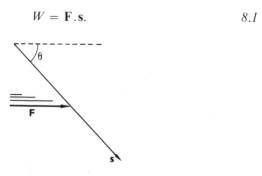

Fig. 99

Work is the product of a force and a displacement. It follows that the dimensions of work are $[ML^2T^{-2}]$. From this we can deduce that appropriate units for measuring work would be kg. m^2/s^2, which is obviously very clumsy. Slightly better would be to measure it in Nm, but because work is so important a concept we define a unit of work in its own right called the joule, symbol 'J'. The **joule** is defined to be the work done when the point of application of a force of one newton is displaced through a distance of one metre in the direction of the force.

The suitability of a particular machine to do a job is sometimes measured by the rate at which it can do work. The speed at which a car can climb a particular hill is a measure of its power. **Power** is a technical term, and is the rate at which work is done. Thus if power is P we deduce from 8.1 that

$$P = \frac{dW}{dt} = \frac{d}{dt}(\mathbf{F}.\mathbf{s}),$$

and if the force happens to be constant then

$$P = \mathbf{F}.\frac{d\mathbf{s}}{dt}$$

$$= \mathbf{F}.\mathbf{v}. \qquad 8.2$$

While it is possible to refer to power in terms of joules per second, we define a unit of power called the watt, symbol 'W'. One **watt** is a rate of work equivalent to one joule per second.

EXAMPLE 2   *Find the work done by a force* $\mathbf{F} = 3\mathbf{i} + 2\mathbf{j} + 4\mathbf{k}$ *(measured in newtons) required to move a particle slowly along a straight groove given by*

$$\mathbf{r}(t) = (3-t)\mathbf{i} + (2+2t)\mathbf{j} + (t-1)\mathbf{k}$$

(measured in metres) from the point $\mathbf{r}(1)$ *to the point* $\mathbf{r}(3)$.

The work done is

$$\begin{aligned}
\mathbf{F}.(\mathbf{r}(3)-\mathbf{r}(1))\ \text{J} &= (3\mathbf{i}+2\mathbf{j}+4\mathbf{k}).(0\mathbf{i}+8\mathbf{j}+2\mathbf{k}-2\mathbf{i}-4\mathbf{j}-0\mathbf{k}) \\
&= (3\mathbf{i}+2\mathbf{j}+4\mathbf{k}).(-2\mathbf{i}+4\mathbf{j}+2\mathbf{k}) \\
&= -6+8+8 \\
&= 10.
\end{aligned}$$

The work done is 10 J.

EXAMPLE 3   *A car of mass 1176 kg can climb a hill of slope* $\sin^{-1}\frac{1}{6}$ *to the horizontal at a maximum speed of 45 km/h. Assuming frictional resistance to be proportional to speed, and the maximum speed on the level to be 126 km/h, find the power of the car assuming this to be the same at all speeds, and find the acceleration of the car up an incline of* $\sin^{-1}\frac{1}{8}$ *when travelling at 36 km/h.*

Fig. 100 shows the forces acting on the car when climbing the incline of $\sin^{-1}\frac{1}{6}$, P being the force exerted by the engine.

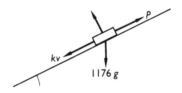

Fig. 100

$$45 \text{ km/h} \equiv \frac{10}{36} \times 45$$

$$= 12\tfrac{1}{2} \text{ m/s}.$$

Let the frictional force be kv N where k is a constant and v the speed in m/s, then

$$P = 1176g \times \tfrac{1}{6} + 12\tfrac{1}{2}k \text{ N}.$$

From *8.2* the rate of working is Pv W,

$$= (196g + 12\tfrac{1}{2}k) \times 12\tfrac{1}{2} \text{ W}. \qquad (1)$$

Consider now the car on the level.

$$126 \text{ km/h} \equiv \frac{10}{36} \times 126$$

$$= 35 \text{ m/s}.$$

Thus the force exerted by the car is F N, where

$$F = 35k,$$

and the rate of working is Fv W,

$$= 35^2 k \text{ W}. \tag{2}$$

Equating (1) and (2)

$$(196g + 12\tfrac{1}{2}k) \times 12\tfrac{1}{2} = 35^2 k,$$

$$98 \times 25g = (35^2 - 12\tfrac{1}{2}^2)k,$$

$$2450g = 47\tfrac{1}{2} \times 22\tfrac{1}{2} \times k,$$

$$k \doteqdot 22 \cdot 47.$$

Thus the car works at a rate of

$$35^2 \times 22 \cdot 47 \doteqdot \underline{27\,500 \text{ W}}.$$

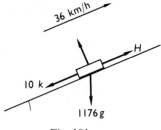

Fig. 101

Let the force exerted by the car at 36 km/h be H N. Fig. 101 illustrates the forces acting on the incline of $\sin^{-1} \tfrac{1}{8}$.

$$36 \text{ km/h} \equiv 10 \text{ m/s}.$$

The accelerating force up the plane is

$$H - (1176g \times \tfrac{1}{8} + 22 \cdot 47 \times 10) = H - 147g - 224 \cdot 7$$

$$= H - 1440 \cdot 6 - 224 \cdot 7$$

$$= H - 1665 \cdot 3 \text{ N}.$$

But $Hv = 35^2 k$, giving

$$H = 2752 \cdot 6.$$

Thus the accelerating force is

$$2752 \cdot 6 - 1665 \cdot 3 = 1087 \cdot 3 \text{ N.}$$

Applying the principle, force = mass × acceleration, if the acceleration is a m/s²,

$$1087 \cdot 3 = 1176a,$$

$$a \doteqdot 0 \cdot 925.$$

The acceleration of the car up incline of $\sin^{-1} \frac{1}{8}$ is $0 \cdot 925$ m/s².

Exercise 18

(Take g as $9 \cdot 8$ m/s² where required.)

1 Investigate the dimensional consistency of the following:

(a) $\frac{1}{2}mv^2 + \frac{1}{2}mu^2 = M\theta$,

where u and v are velocities, m is mass, M the moment of a couple, and θ an angle,

(b) $V = kmp/F$,

where k is a numerical constant, m is a mass, ρ a density, F a force and V a velocity,

(c) $T = 2\pi \sqrt{\dfrac{l}{g} - \dfrac{\pi a}{v}}$,

where T is time, l and a are lengths, and v is a velocity.

2 Use Hooke's Law to deduce the dimensions of λ, the modulus of elasticity of a string.

If the work done in stretching a string of natural length a through an extension x is proportional to $\lambda^p x^q / a$, find p and q.

3 (a) Show that the following vectors are mutually perpendicular:

$$3\mathbf{i} + 2\mathbf{j} + 4\mathbf{k}; \quad 2\mathbf{i} + \mathbf{j} - 2\mathbf{k}; \quad 8\mathbf{i} - 14\mathbf{j} + \mathbf{k}.$$

(b) Find the angles between the lines

$$3\mathbf{i} + 4\mathbf{j} + 5\mathbf{k}; \quad 2\mathbf{i} - 4\mathbf{j} - 2\mathbf{k}; \quad -\mathbf{i} + \mathbf{j} + 2\mathbf{k}.$$

4 A bead of mass 100 g lying in a rough horizontal straight groove, coefficient of friction $\frac{3}{4}$, and equation

$$\mathbf{r}(t) = (1 + t)\mathbf{i} + 2t\mathbf{j}$$

(distances measured in metres), is **slowly** drawn along the groove from the point $\mathbf{r}(0)$ to the point $\mathbf{r}(3)$ by a force which acts parallel to $3\mathbf{i} + \mathbf{j}$. Find the magnitude of this force and the work done.

5 A canal barge requires a steady pull of 20 kg wt. in the line of the boat to be drawn at a steady speed of $0 \cdot 75$ m/s into a lock. A man exerts this force by using a rope 3 m long which he pulls on from a point 2 m laterally from the line of the boat and at a height of 1 m above the boat. Find the force he must exert on the rope, and his rate of working.

6 A bead of mass m is being pulled at a constant speed v m/s up a rough straight wire by a steady horizontal force F. The wire is inclined at an angle of 60° to the horizontal and F acts in the vertical plane of the wire. If the coefficient of friction is μ, prove that the rate at which F is doing work is

$$mgv \frac{\sqrt{3} + \mu}{2(1 - \sqrt{3}\mu)}.$$

7 A locomotive working at 0·5 MW pulls a train of total mass 220 t up a slope of inclination $\sin^{-1} \frac{1}{150}$ at a steady speed of 54 km/h. Calculate the frictional resistance to motion in newtons per tonne.

8 A boy cycles up a hill 200 m long at a steady speed of 9 km/h. The gradient is 10% ($\sin^{-1} \frac{1}{10}$), he himself weighs 52 kg and his bicycle weighs 14 kg. Calculate the total work done and the rate of working, assuming that friction and wind resistance are negligible.

9 When a given locomotive of 50 t draws a train the frictional resistance is $(5000+800n)$ N where n is the number of coaches, each weighing 10 t. When working at maximum power it draws a train of 10 coaches at a maximum speed of 90 km/h up a certain incline. When working at the same rate, but with a train of 12 coaches, the maximum speed down the same incline is 120 km/h. Find the power of the locomotive in megawatts, and the maximum speed on the level when drawing 8 coaches.

10 A super-tanker of 100 000 t has engines of total effective power 100 MW, and the resistance to motion at v km/h is $0·9v^2$ t wt. Find the maximum speed of the tanker. Find also the acceleration of the tanker when sailing at full power at 20 km/h.

8.4 The conservation of energy

We consider the equation 2.3 already deduced from the laws of motion:

$$v^2 = u^2 + 2as.$$

As we would expect, it is dimensionally consistent, its dimensions being $[L^2 T^{-2}]$. If we apply the equation to a body of mass m, then it might equally well be written as

$$mv^2 = mu^2 + 2mas,$$

which has dimensions $[ML^2 T^{-2}]$—the same as those of work. This is significant in that a body has a certain capacity to do work according to its speed, its position, or both. The capacity to do work is called **energy**—i.e. energy is 'stored' work.

First consider the ability of a body to do work due to its position. The simplest example is that of a body of mass m in a gravitational field. If it is allowed to fall freely under gravity through a distance of h m, the force acting on it is mg N, and so the work done by the force is

$$mgh \text{ J.}$$

Thus a body h m above a given (arbitrary) point of reference has energy of magnitude mgh. Energy of this kind which is due to position is called **potential energy**.

By contrast, consider a ball thrown vertically upwards with an initial speed of v m/s under gravity. From the equation of motion 2.3 it will rise a distance $\frac{v^2}{2g}$ m against a force of mg N before it comes instantaneously to rest. The work done by the force through this distance is

$$mg \times \frac{v^2}{2g} = \tfrac{1}{2}mv^2 \text{ J.}$$

in this case the body had energy because of its speed; energy due to motion is called **kinetic energy**.

Returning to the equation 2.3, we write it in the gravitational context:

$$v^2 = u^2 - 2gh.$$

Multiplying by $\frac{1}{2}m$,

$$\tfrac{1}{2}mv^2 = \tfrac{1}{2}mu^2 - mgh.$$

This result, which can be summarized in words as 'the total of kinetic energy and potential energy is constant', is a particular case of a much wider principle, the **Principle of Conservation of Energy**. It states that:

Energy can neither be created nor destroyed.

When the body which we threw into the air comes down again it loses kinetic energy as soon as it strikes the ground (unless it is perfectly elastic), and this is not converted into potential energy. This is because there are other forms of energy which include heat and sound, electricity and forms of molecular energy, and so the principle is not violated, although it might be very difficult to measure the forms into which it is converted. In mechanics we are primarily concerned with those forms of energy which are essentially mechanical in their nature—viz. kinetic and potential energy. If K is the total kinetic energy and P the total potential energy of a system, then we shall generally be using the principle in the form

$$E = K + P, \qquad\qquad 8.3$$

where E is the total energy, a constant. We should note that we must never use this form of the principle where other forms of energy are involved. We can however measure a change in E if we can find the work done by the lost energy (see Example 5).

Note that a body under gravity does not give the only example of kinetic and potential energies. A rotating body has kinetic energy, which we consider in Chapter 11. A body under a magnetic or electrical force has a potential energy, as do also compressed springs and stretched elastic strings.

The calculation of the potential energy of a stretched string requires integration—a summation of work done in stretching the string through a series of infinitesimal distances. Suppose we have a string of natural length a and modulus of elasticity λ. When it has been stretched through a distance x the tension in the string, by Hooke's Law, is

$$\lambda x / a.$$

Suppose the tension remains at this value while it is stretched through a further distance δx, then the work done is

$$\frac{\lambda x}{a}\delta x.$$

Hence the work done in stretching the string from its natural length a to a stretched length of $a+x$ is

$$\int_0^x \frac{\lambda x}{a} dx = \tfrac{1}{2}\lambda x^2/a \text{ J}.$$

Since the tension in the string is $\lambda x/a$, we conclude that the potential energy stored in a stretched elastic string is

$$\tfrac{1}{2} \text{ tension} \times \text{extension}.$$

EXAMPLE 4   *A pump is used to lift water from a depth of 42 m through a pipe with a cross-sectional area of 0·005 m² at a rate of 60 m³/h. Find the rate of working in watts. (1 m³ of water weighs 1000 kg.)*

The work done by the pump is converted into potential energy due to the height through which the water is raised, and into kinetic energy due to the speed at which it passes through the pipe.

60 m³ of water weighs 60 000 kg, and so the mass of water raised in 1 s is

$$60\,000/3600 = 100/6 \text{ kg}.$$

Therefore potential energy is gained at a rate of

$$\frac{100}{6} g \times 42 = 700g \text{ W}.$$

Water is made to flow through the pipe at a rate of

$$60/3600 \text{ m}^3/\text{s} \equiv \frac{1}{60} \times \frac{1}{0\cdot005} \text{ m/s}$$

$$= 10/3 \text{ m/s}.$$

Therefore kinetic energy is gained at a rate of

$$\frac{1}{2} \times \frac{100}{6} \times \frac{100}{9} \text{ W} = \frac{2500}{27} \text{ W}.$$

Hence the pump works at a rate of

$$700g + \frac{2500}{27} \fallingdotseq 6860 + 92\cdot7$$

$$\fallingdotseq \underline{6950 \text{ W}}.$$

EXAMPLE 5   *A block of mass M kg is allowed to slide from rest down a rough plane of inclination $\sin^{-1} \tfrac{3}{5}$ to the horizontal and coefficient of friction $\tfrac{2}{5}$. Find its speed after sliding a distance of 75 cm.*

This is a problem which can be solved without direct reference to the Conservation of Energy—we could merely apply the principle: force =

mass × acceleration and the appropriate equations of motion. We demonstrate here though how the Conservation of Energy may be applied to advantage.

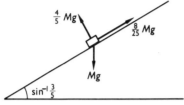

Fig. 102

Work is only done against the frictional force, and so the total energy at the beginning and end of the motion will differ by this amount. The work done against the frictional force is

$$\tfrac{2}{5}Mg \cos (\sin^{-1} \tfrac{3}{5}) \times 0\cdot 75 \text{ J} = \tfrac{2}{5} \times Mg \times \tfrac{4}{5} \times \tfrac{3}{4}$$

$$= \tfrac{6}{25}Mg \text{ J}.$$

Let the speed at the end of the motion be v m/s, and the level of zero potential energy to be that of the end of the slide—this is purely arbitrary since we are only concerned with the relative potential energies at the two positions. By the Conservation of Energy,

$$Mg \times 0\cdot 75 \sin (\sin^{-1} 3/5) = 6Mg/25 + \tfrac{1}{2}Mv^2,$$

$$\frac{9}{20}Mg = \frac{6}{25}Mg + \frac{1}{2}Mv^2,$$

$$\frac{21g}{100} = \frac{1}{2}v^2,$$

$$v = \frac{\sqrt{42g}}{10}.$$

The speed after sliding 75 cm is $\dfrac{\sqrt{42g}}{10}$ m/s.

EXAMPLE 6   *A light inelastic string passes over a smooth pulley and has particles of masses M and m (M > m) attached to the two ends. The system is held at rest with the string taut and vertical with both masses at a height d above an inelastic horizontal table. The system is released. Show that the height to which the larger mass will rise after it has hit the table once is*

$$\frac{m^2d}{(M+m)^2}.$$

Let v be the speed of the system when the heavier mass hits the table, and let the table be the level of zero potential energy. Applying the Conservation of Energy,

$$\tfrac{1}{2}(M+m)v^2 + 2mgd = (M+m)gd,$$

$$(M+m)v^2 = 2(M-m)gd,$$

$$v = \sqrt{\frac{2(M-m)gd}{(M+m)}}.$$

Let v' be the speed of the system immediately after the string again becomes taut. The velocity of the lighter particle just before this instant will be v (by the Conservation of Energy). The Conservation of Momentum now gives

$$(M+m)v' = mv,$$

$$v' = \frac{m}{M+m}\sqrt{\frac{2(M-m)gd}{(M+m)}}.$$

Let the heavier mass rise to a height h above the table, then by the Conservation of Energy

$$\tfrac{1}{2}(M+m)v'^2 + 2mgd = Mgh + mg(2d-h),$$

$$\tfrac{1}{2}(M+m)\cdot\frac{m^2}{(M+m)^2}\cdot\frac{2(M-m)gd}{(M+m)} = Mgh - mgh,$$

$$\frac{m^2(M-m)gd}{(M+m)^2} = (M-m)gh,$$

$$h = \frac{m^2 d}{(M+m)^2}.$$

The heavier mass rises to a height $m^2 d/(M+m)^2$ above the table.

Exercise 19

1 A particle of mass 0·1 kg is projected with a speed of 4 m/s up a rough plane of inclination 30° to the horizontal along the line of greatest slope, coefficient of friction $\tfrac{1}{10}$. Calculate the work done against friction up to the instant it returns through the point of projection.

2 A pump of power 4 kW is used to lift water through a height of $150/g$ m through a pipe of cross-section 20 cm². Find the rate of flow in kg/s, and calculate how long it will take to transfer 1000 m³ of water.
   (Hint: form and solve an equation for x, where x kg flow per second.)

3 A ball is dropped from a height of h m on to a horizontal floor. If it loses 16% of its kinetic energy at every bounce, show that the maximum height reached after

4 A conveyor belt moving at 0·4 m/s carries 20 kg of gravel per metre, lifting it through a height of 20 m in the process. Frictional resistances amount to 1000 N. Calculate the power of the engine required to drive the belt.
   the nth bounce is $0\cdot84^n h$.

5 When a mass of 50 g is suspended in equilibrium by an elastic string of natural length a from a fixed point O, it hangs at a point $5a/4$ below O. If it is now raised to the level of O and released, find the lowest point of its subsequent motion.

6 Two masses m_1 and m_2 are connected by a light inelastic string over a smooth pulley at the top of a fixed wedge. The mass m_1 rests on a rough face of the wedge inclined at $\sin^{-1}\frac{2}{5}$ to the horizontal, coefficient of friction $\frac{5}{16}$. The mass m_2 hangs freely from the pulley. The string is taut in the line of greatest slope and is of length 0·5 m, the m_2 mass being at the pulley. If the system is released, find the work done against friction up to the instant they are on the same horizontal level without evaluating the acceleration of the system, and hence find the total kinetic energy of the system at this instant.

7 A catapult is made from a light elastic string of natural length 10 cm attached by the ends to points A and B 8 cm apart. Find the speed of projection of a stone of 40 g if the string is released when the mid-point is 16 cm from the line AB, if the modulus of elasticity is 5 N.

8 Two masses of m and $2m$ are attached at either end of a light elastic string of modulus $\frac{1}{2}mg$. They are held at a distance $3a$ apart on a smooth horizontal table and released simultaneously. Find the velocities of the two masses the instant the string becomes slack if the natural length of the string is a. Where do they collide?

9 A bead of mass m is attached to one end of a light inelastic string of length a, the other end of which is attached to a fixed point O. The bead hangs at rest vertically below O when it is given a horizontal velocity of 8 m/s. Assuming that it moves in a complete vertical circle, find the velocity of the bead when it is vertically above O.

If when the bead is on the same level as O going up it becomes attached to another free particle of mass m which is stationary at the time of impact, calculate the loss in kinetic energy due to the impact, and find the subsequent velocity when vertically above O, assuming that it still moves in a full circle.

10 A light elastic string of modulus mg and natural length a has a mass m attached to its mid-point, and a mass of $2m$ to one end. The string and the masses lie on a smooth horizontal table. The free end is now slowly raised until both masses are just clear of the table. Find the total work done.

8.5 Stability of equilibrium

The Principle of Conservation of Energy enables us to formulate a test for the stability of a system in equilibrium. A system is said to be in stable equilibrium if, when slightly displaced, it will return to the original position of equilibrium. If on the other hand it goes into some contrary motion it is said to be unstable.

When a body is displaced from unstable equilibrium it must gain kinetic energy. This must be at the expense of the potential energy of the system. Thus the potential energy decreases; the potential energy has a maximum value in the equilibrium position. Conversely, when the body is displaced from stable equilibrium, work must be done on it to cause the displacement and the potential energy is increased. Thus in stable equilibrium the potential energy has a minimum value.

This principle is illustrated by Fig. 103. In each example a bead is in equilibrium at A, and B represents the displaced position. In example (a) the bead rests on a convex surface—a case of unstable equilibrium, where it will clearly roll off if displaced from A towards B. But since the position of A is higher than B, A is the point of maximum potential energy. In case (b) the bead rests on a concave surface at A, and if it is moved towards B it will then roll back to A. This represents stable equilibrium at A, and because A is lower than B, it is the point of least potential energy. Case (c) is that of neutral equilibrium. The bead will remain at either A or B, and the potential energy at each point is the same.

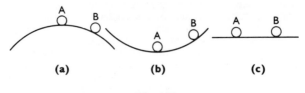

Fig. 103

This theory of stability gives us a further method of finding the positions of stability of a given system. By forming an expression for the potential energy in any position, in terms of a single variable, we can find by differentiation the stationary values of the function—i.e. those points at which equilibrium is possible. A minimum point will then indicate stability, whereas a maximum or point of inflection will indicate unstable equilibrium.

EXAMPLE 7   *A triangular framework* ABC *consists of three rods* AB, BC *and* CA *each made of the same material and such that* AB = 3 *units,* BC = 4 *units and* CA = 5 *units. If it is freely suspended from* A, *find the angle of* AB *to the vertical in the equilibrium positions, stating which is stable and which is unstable.*

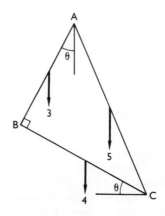

Fig. 104

By Pythagoras, angle ABC is $90°$ (3, 4, 5 triangle). Let AB make an angle θ with the vertical, and let A be the level of zero potential energy. The potential energy of the system then is

$$-3g \cdot \tfrac{3}{2} \cos \theta - 5g \cdot \tfrac{5}{2} \cos (\cos^{-1} \tfrac{3}{5} - \theta) - 4g(3 \cos \theta + \tfrac{4}{2} \sin \theta)$$

$$= -\tfrac{9}{2} g \cos \theta - \tfrac{25}{2} g(\tfrac{3}{5} \cos \theta + \tfrac{4}{5} \sin \theta) - 12g \cos \theta - 8g \sin \theta$$

$$= -24g \cos \theta - 18g \sin \theta$$

Hence if the potential energy is P, then

$$\frac{dP}{d\theta} = 24g \sin \theta - 18g \cos \theta.$$

The framework is in equilibrium when $\dfrac{dP}{d\theta} = 0$, i.e. when

$$24g \sin \theta - 18g \cos \theta = 0,$$

$$\tan \theta = \tfrac{3}{4}.$$

Hence $\theta = 36°\ 52'$ or $216°\ 52'$.

In this example it is evident that the former value gives stability and the latter does not, but we can show this formally by taking the second derivative.

$$\frac{d^2 P}{d\theta^2} = 24g \cos \theta + 18g \sin \theta.$$

When $\theta = 36°\ 52'$,

$$\frac{d^2 P}{d\theta^2} = 24g \cdot \tfrac{3}{5} + 18g \cdot \tfrac{4}{5}$$

which is positive, giving a minimum.
    When $\theta = 216°\ 52'$,

$$\frac{d^2 P}{d\theta^2} = 24g(-\tfrac{3}{5}) + 18g(-\tfrac{4}{5})$$

which is negative, indicating a maximum.
    Thus, in equilibrium AB makes an angle $36°\ 52'$ to the vertical (stable case), or $216°\ 52'$ to the vertical (unstable case).

8.6 Virtual work

If a system is in equilibrium under a set of forces, these forces can be of two kinds. Some of them may act at fixed points, such as at a hinge or a pivot, and because they restrict the system so as to allow it to move only in certain ways we refer to them as constraints. The significance of this is that in any displacement of the system they do not move and so can do no work. The remaining forces however will move in any displacement of the system subject to the constraints, and because they move they can do work. We refer to these as applied forces.

If a small displacement of a system is made, then each of the applied forces does a corresponding amount of work which we call **virtual work**— the term 'virtual' is used to stress its purely hypothetical nature, since we do not actually displace the system—we only imagine what would happen if we did. Its value lies in the following principle of virtual work:

> *If a system under constraints and applied forces is displaced through an arbitrary small displacement subject to the constraints then zero virtual work is done if and only if it is in equilibrium.*

If a system is in equilibrium and we select any point in that system, then the forces acting on that point must also be in equilibrium. Therefore in any displacement the forces at this point do not work. But this applies to every point within the system, and so no virtual work is done in any small displacement. On the other hand, if a system is not in equilibrium there must be some resultant force causing motion which must do work.

Consider first a simple case to illustrate the principle. A uniform rod AB of mass m and length $2a$ is pivoted in a vertical plane about a point D distant x from A, and maintained in a horizontal position by vertical forces R and S acting at A and B respectively (Fig. 105).

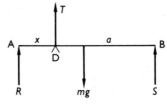

Fig. 105

The only displacement subject to the constraint at the pivot is a rotation about the point D.

Imagine an infinitesimal rotation through an angle $\delta\theta$ about D. The work done by R, S and the weight are respectively

$$- Rx\delta\theta, \quad (2a-x)S\delta\theta, \quad \text{and} \quad -(a-x)mg\delta\theta.$$

Since zero virtual work is done

$$(2a-x)S\delta\theta - Rx\delta\theta - (a-x)mg\delta\theta = 0,$$

$$(2a-x)S = Rx + (a-x)mg,$$

which is another way of arriving at the principle of moments.

We can bring the reaction at the pivot into our calculation by replacing the constraint at the pivot by an applied force T equal to the constraint.

We are then not limited to a rotation, and can consider a case where T is made to do virtual work.

It should be evident that the principle of virtual work is merely an alternative to the principles of moments and the resolution of forces. It is left to the individual to decide which method he prefers, or whether one will give a neater solution than the other in a particular problem.

EXAMPLE 8   AB, BC, CD, DA *and* BD *are five light rods smoothly jointed together to form a rhombus* ABCD, *such that the sides are 5 units long,* AC *is 8 units and* BD *is 6 units. A particle of mass M is attached at* C *and the frame is suspended freely under gravity from* A. *Find the stress in* BD.

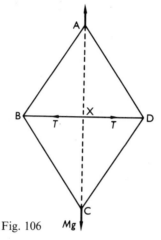

Fig. 106   Mg

The rod BD constitutes a constraint on the system, and to find the stress by the method of virtual work we 'remove' the rod BD and find the virtual work done when the frame is slightly distorted by drawing C downwards a small distance $2d$, say.

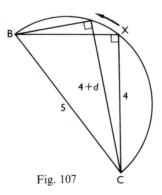

Fig. 107

If the mid-point of BD is X, angle BXC remains a right-angle even under the distortion. If BX becomes $3-e$ units long, then by Pythagoras,
$$(4+d)^2+(3-e)^2 = 25.$$

$$\therefore\ d^2+8d+e^2-6e = 0.$$

Ignoring terms of second order,

$$e = \tfrac{4}{3}d.$$

Let the stress in BD be a compression of magnitude T, then by the principle of virtual work,

$$2dMg+(-e)T+(-e)T = 0.$$

$$\therefore\ 2dMg = 2eT,$$

$$2dMg = 2\times\tfrac{4}{3}d\times T,$$

$$T = \tfrac{3}{4}Mg.$$

The stress in BD is a compression of $\tfrac{3}{4}Mg$.

8.7 Work done by a couple

We have so far confined our thinking about work to single forces, but a couple can also do work. Suppose a couple is represented by two forces of magnitude P acting at a distance d apart. If this system is turned through a small angle $\delta\theta$, the work done is $Pd\delta\theta$. Thus the work done in causing a rotation of θ is

$$\int_0^\theta Pd\,d\theta = Pd\theta.$$

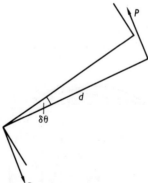

Fig. 108

Since Pd is the magnitude of the couple, M say, the work done by a couple of moment M in causing a rotation of θ is

$$M\theta.$$

The moment of a force or couple, sometimes referred to as the **torque**, has the same dimensions as work. To avoid confusion however we must not refer to the units of torque as joules. We refer to torque in newton metres (N m).

We conclude the chapter with two further examples, the first involving a couple, and the second a more difficult situation requiring calculus.

EXAMPLE 9   *A belt runs round a wheel of radius 25 cm as shown in Fig. 109, the upper and lower portions of the belt being parallel. The tensions in the upper and lower parts of the belt are T_1 and T_2 respectively, where*

$$T_1 + T_2 = 60 \text{ N},$$

and are such that when rotating at a speed of n rad/s

$$T_1 = 30 + n/2 \text{ N}.$$

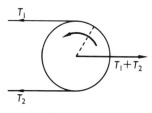

Fig. 109

A frictional couple of torque 4 N m acts at the axis. Find the effective rate of working when the wheel rotates at 60 rad/s, and also when the belt moves at 6 m/s.

The reaction to the two parts of the belt acts at the axis of the wheel, and the moments of the induced couples are $T_1 r$ and $- T_2 r$ where r is the radius.

At 60 rad/s,

$$T_1 = 30 + 60/2$$

$$= 60 \text{ N}.$$

$$\therefore \ T_2 = 0.$$

Thus couple at this speed is

$$(60 \times 0{\cdot}25 - 0 \times 0{\cdot}25 - 4) \text{ N m}.$$

The rate of working is

$$(15 - 4) \times 60 = 11 + 60$$

$$= 660 \text{ W}.$$

Rate of working at 60 rad/s is 660 W.

When the belt moves at 6 m/s, the wheel turns at a speed of $6/0.25$ rad/s = 24 rad/s. At this speed,

$$T_1 = 30 + 24/2$$
$$= 42 \text{ N}.$$
$$\therefore T_2 = 18 \text{ N}.$$

Thus the resultant couple at 24 rad/s is

$$(42 \times 0.25 - 18 \times 0.25 - 4) \text{ N m} = 2 \text{ N m}.$$

∴ the rate of working is

$$2 \times 24 = 48 \text{ W}.$$

Rate of working when belt moves at 6 m/s is 48 W.

It is evident that if the frictional force did not act the rate of working would be higher. In the former case the work would be done at a rate of

$$60 \times 0.25 \times 60 = 900 \text{ W},$$

and in the second case at a rate of

$$(42 - 18)0.25 \times 24 = 144 \text{ W}.$$

The ratio of work 'put in' to work 'put out' is sometimes called the **efficiency** of the machine, and is usually expressed as a percentage. $\frac{660}{900}$ is equivalent to $73\frac{1}{3}\%$, and $\frac{48}{144}$ is equivalent to $33\frac{1}{3}\%$, and so the machine is said to be $73\frac{1}{3}\%$ and $33\frac{1}{3}\%$ efficient in the respective cases.

EXAMPLE 10   *A uniform chain AB 1 m long weighing 20 kg lies on a rough portion of a horizontal floor, coefficient of friction $\frac{1}{4}$, so that A lies on the boundary of the rough portion and AB is straight. Find the work done in drawing the chain **slowly** in the direction BA horizontally onto the smooth part of the floor.*

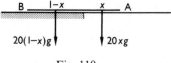

Fig. 110

Fig. 110 illustrates the position when a length x of the chain has been drawn onto the smooth part of the floor. The frictional force acting then is

$$20(1-x)g \times \tfrac{1}{4} \text{ N} = 5g(1-x) \text{ N}.$$

The work done in drawing the chain a further distance δx is $5g(1-x)\delta x$, and therefore the total work done against the frictional force is

$$\int_0^1 5g(1-x)dx = 5g\left[x - \frac{x^2}{2}\right]_0^1$$

$$= 5g/2 \text{ J}.$$

Work done in drawing the chain onto smooth part is $5g/2$ J.

Exercise 20

(Take g as 9·8 m/s² where necessary.)

1 A uniform rod BC is of length a and weight W, C being free to slide along a smooth vertical wire. An elastic string of natural length a is attached at one end to B and at the other to a fixed point A distant $2a$ from the wire. The system rests in equilibrium with BC at $30°$ to the horizontal. Find the modulus of elasticity of the string.

2 Three identical uniform rods AB, BC, CD each of weight $2W$ are smoothly jointed at B and C and are made to stand in a vertical plane with A and D on a smooth horizontal plane. They are kept in equilibrium by a light inextensible string joined to the mid-points of AB and CD such that both these rods are inclined at $60°$ to the horizontal. Use the principle of virtual work to find the tension in the string.

3 A uniform rod of mass m and length $2a$ has one end in contact with a smooth vertical wall and the other in contact with a smooth plane inclined at an angle α to the horizontal. The plane and the wall meet in a horizontal line, and the vertical plane containing the rod is perpendicular to this line. Show that there is only one position of equilibrium, and prove that it is unstable.

4 A uniform rod OA of mass m and length a is smoothly pivoted at O, the centre of a fixed smooth ring of radius a in a vertical plane. A is held on the circle by a light ring, and a second rod AB is smoothly hinged to OA at A, the end B being attached to the circle by another smooth ring. AB is of length $3a/2$ and mass $3m/2$. Find an expression for the potential energy of the system when OA makes an angle θ with the upward drawn vertical through O. Hence show that if it is in equilibrium $\theta = \tan^{-1} \frac{9\sqrt{7}}{37}$, and distinguish between the stable and unstable case.

5 Two light smooth pulleys are fixed on the same horizontal level distance $2d$ apart. A light inextensible string of length $2l$ has masses of $4m$ at both ends and a mass of $5m$ at the mid-point, and the string is made to pass over the two pulleys so that the $5m$ mass is suspended between them. If the inclined parts of the string make an angle θ with the vertical, form an expression for P, the potential energy of the system. Hence show that there is only one value of θ giving equilibrium and prove that it is stable.

6 Water is pumped up from a depth of 6 m through a pipe of 0·002 m² cross-section at a rate of 1 m³/min. If the engine is 70% efficient, find the power of the pump to the nearest 10 W. The water issues through a nozzle with the same cross-section as the pipe, held in position by a man. Find the force he must exert against the flow of water in order to hold it steady.

7 Two like electric charges repel each other with a force of kC_1C_2/r^2 N, where C_1 and C_2 are the magnitudes of the charges in micro-coulombs (μC), r is their distance apart in metres, and $k = \frac{1}{9} \times 10^{-9}$. Calculate the work done in bringing a charge of 10μC from infinity up to a point 2 cm away from a like charge of 50μC.

8 A chain AB of length 1·2 m and mass 32 kg lies straight on a rough table perpendicular to the edge of the table which is more than 1·2 m above the floor. A is at the edge of the table. If the coefficient of friction is $\frac{1}{4}$, find how much of the chain can be pulled over the edge so that the end A hangs freely before it begins to slide of its own accord.

Calculate the work done in slowly pulling the chain vertically down over the edge in this position. If it is then jogged from this position into motion, find the kinetic energy of the chain just as it clears the table.

9 Momentum, Impact and Impulse

9.1 Newton's Law of Restitution

We are concerned in this chapter with what happens when the motion of a body is suddenly altered, for example by a collision with another body, or by a sudden jerk in a string. We have already noted in passing that there are some surfaces which can be deemed **inelastic** in that when a body strikes such a surface all the momentum of that body normal to the surface is destroyed. When a surface is not inelastic a body will bounce back with a (generally) smaller velocity. If the body bounces back from a surface with speed equal to that at which it hit the surface then the surface is said to be **perfectly elastic**. Most surfaces will come well within these two extremes.

If a body strikes a fixed surface with speed u, and bounces back with speed v, both normal to the surface, then experiment establishes that

$$v = eu, \qquad\qquad 9.1$$

where e is a constant such that $0 \leqslant e \leqslant 1$. This constant is a measure of the elasticity of the body and the surface, and is called the **Coefficient of Restitution** (or Elasticity). The equation *9.1* is a special case of **Newton's Law of Restitution** (sometimes referred to as his Law of Impact):

> *When two bodies collide, the speed of separation along the line of impact is e times the speed of approach along the line of impact.*

In this section we consider impact on a fixed surface. Provided the surface is smooth no force will act tangentially and so its momentum tangentially to the surface will not be altered. We must therefore resolve the velocity into its components along and perpendicular to the line of impact.

EXAMPLE 1   *A ball is rolled down a corridor 1 m wide and 8 m long from the corner at one end so that initially its velocity is $8\sqrt{2}$ m/s at an angle of 45° to the wall. The floor is horizontal and the ball smooth. Determine*

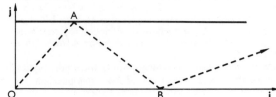

Fig. 111

how many times it hits the walls before reaching the other end, and its velocity as it does so, given that the Coefficient of Restitution between the ball and the walls is $\frac{1}{2}$.

It is often helpful in this context to use vector notation, as it is in this example. Let O be the point of projection and the origin of unit vectors **i** and **j**, **i** along the corridor and **j** across the corridor. The initial velocity is then

$$\mathbf{u}_1 = 8\mathbf{i} + 8\mathbf{j}.$$

The first point of impact, call it A, has position

$$\mathbf{a} = \mathbf{i} + \mathbf{j},$$

and the velocity at which the ball leaves A for the second point of impact B is

$$\mathbf{u}_2 = 8\mathbf{i} - 8e\mathbf{j}$$
$$= 8\mathbf{i} - 4\mathbf{j}.$$

The position of B relative to A is then

$$\mathbf{b} - \mathbf{a} = \tfrac{1}{4}(8\mathbf{i} - 4\mathbf{j})$$
$$= 2\mathbf{i} - \mathbf{j},$$

giving
$$\mathbf{b} = 3\mathbf{i}.$$

The velocity at which the ball leaves B for C, the third point of impact, is

$$\mathbf{u}_3 = 8\mathbf{i} + 4e\mathbf{j}$$
$$= 8\mathbf{i} + 2\mathbf{j}.$$

The position of C relative to B is then

$$\mathbf{c} - \mathbf{b} = \tfrac{1}{2}(8\mathbf{i} + 2\mathbf{j})$$
$$= 4\mathbf{i} + \mathbf{j},$$

giving
$$\mathbf{c} = 7\mathbf{i} + \mathbf{j}.$$

Between B and C it went 3 m down the corridor, and it goes further down between each impact. It will therefore not strike a wall again.
The ball strikes the walls 3 times.

The velocity at which it leaves C is

$$\mathbf{u}_4 = 8\mathbf{i} - 2e\mathbf{j}$$
$$= 8\mathbf{i} - \mathbf{j}.$$

Thus the velocity as it reaches the other end of the corridor is $\sqrt{65}$ m/s at an angle $\tan^{-1}\frac{1}{8}$ to the line of the corridor.

EXAMPLE 2   *A ball is thrown from a point* O *on horizontal ground to strike a smooth vertical wall a horizontal distance a from* O *and to return in the same vertical plane. If it is thrown with initial speed V at an angle of elevation* θ *to the horizontal, and the coefficient of restitution at the wall is e, show that it will not hit the ground between* O *and the wall provided that*

$$V^2 \sin 2\theta \geqslant \frac{ga}{e}(1+e).$$

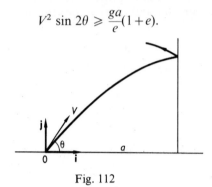

Fig. 112

Let O be the origin of unit vectors such that the initial velocity of the ball is

$$\mathbf{V} = V\cos\theta\mathbf{i} + V\sin\theta\mathbf{j}.$$

The position of the ball after time t is then

$$\mathbf{s} = Vt\cos\theta\mathbf{i} + (Vt\sin\theta - \tfrac{1}{2}gt^2)\mathbf{j}.$$

Thus when it strikes the wall

$$Vt\cos\theta = a,$$

$$t = \frac{a}{V}\sec\theta, \tag{1}$$

$$= t_1, \text{ say.}$$

Since the vertical velocity is not affected by the impact we can also deduce that it will strike the ground after a total time given by the **j** component of **s** being zero,

i.e. when

$$Vt\sin\theta = \tfrac{1}{2}gt^2,$$

$$t = \frac{2V}{g}\sin\theta. \tag{2}$$

The velocity of the ball when it strikes the wall is

$$\mathbf{v_w} = V\cos\theta\mathbf{i} + (V\sin\theta - gt_1)\mathbf{j}.$$

Therefore the velocity as it leaves the wall is

$$\mathbf{v_w'} = -eV\cos\theta\mathbf{i} + (V\sin\theta - gt_1)\mathbf{j}.$$

The position of the ball after a further time T is

$$\mathbf{s}' = (a - eVT \cos \theta)\mathbf{i} + S(T)\mathbf{j}.$$

We do not need to establish the exact form of the function $S(T)$ since we already know from (1) and (2) that it will strike the ground again when

$$T = \frac{2V}{g} \sin \theta - \frac{a}{V} \sec \theta.$$

It follows that it strikes the ground at the point

$$a - eV \cos \theta \left(\frac{2V}{g} \sin \theta - \frac{a}{V} \sec \theta \right) \mathbf{i}.$$

The condition that this is not between O and the wall is that

$$eV \cos \theta \left(\frac{2V}{g} \sin \theta - \frac{a}{V} \sec \theta \right) \geqslant a.$$

i.e.

$$\frac{2eV^2}{g} \cos \theta \sin \theta - ae \geqslant a,$$

$$\frac{eV^2}{g} \sin 2\theta \geqslant a(1 + e),$$

$$V^2 \sin 2\theta \geqslant \frac{ag}{e}(1 + e). \qquad \text{Q.E.D.}$$

Exercise 21

1 Show that a particle dropped from a height h onto a horizontal plane with co-efficient of restitution e will rise to a height $e^2 h$ after the first bounce.

2 A particle is fired along a smooth horizontal plane to strike a smooth vertical wall at an angle of $60°$ to the wall. It is deflected through an angle of $90°$ by the impact. Find the coefficient of restitution.

3 A bullet strikes a fixed metal sphere, coefficient of restitution $0·9$, and is deflected through an angle of $90°$. If O is the centre of the sphere and the initial path of the bullet is parallel to AO, where A is a point on the surface, find angle $\hat{A}OB$ if B is the point of impact to the nearest $\frac{1}{2}°$. (Ignore gravity.)

4 A billiard ball struck from the point $\mathbf{i} + 1·5\mathbf{j}$ hits the cushion at $1·5\mathbf{i} + 3\mathbf{j}$ and rolls into the corner pocket at $4\mathbf{i}$. The other corners of the table are given by the vectors $4\mathbf{i} + 3\mathbf{j}$, $3\mathbf{j}$, and the origin, $\mathbf{i}$ and $\mathbf{j}$ being mutually perpendicular unit vectors. Calculate the coefficient of restitution between the cushion and the ball.

5 A ball drops vertically from a height of 1 m onto horizontal ground, coefficient of restitution e. Show that the time that elapses between the rth and $(r+1)^{\text{th}}$ bounces is $2e^r \sqrt{\frac{2}{g}}$ s, and hence find the total time that elapses before it comes to rest.

6 A smooth stone falls vertically onto a roof inclined at an angle of $30°$ to the horizontal, its speed at the moment of impact being v m/s. The point of impact A is a m from the lowest point on the roof B. Find the minimum value of v if the stone is not to hit the roof again, given that the coefficient of restitution is $\frac{1}{6}$.

9.2 Direct impact of two bodies

Newton's Law of Restitution is also valid when two bodies collide, both being free to move. Provided that no external forces are acting, then the principle of Conservation of Momentum will give us a further equation. On the other hand there will still be a loss of energy due to the impact.

EXAMPLE 3   *Two beads A and B of mass m and 2m are moving along a smooth straight horizontal groove with speeds 6 m/s and 1 m/s respectively in the same direction, so that A is about to strike B. Determine the speeds of A and B after the impact, and calculate the loss of kinetic energy due to the collision, given that the coefficient of restitution is $\frac{4}{5}$.*

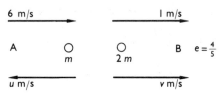

Fig. 113

It will generally be found helpful to adopt a standard diagrammatic summary of the situation, for example as in Fig. 113. The speeds before impact are marked above the beads, and the speeds after impact below. The direction in which bead A will move after impact is not necessarily obvious—there are many instances when the bead catching up will continue in the original direction after the impact. This will depend on both the coefficient of restitution and on their relative masses (see Exercise 22 No. 4). There is some advantage to be gained by always assuming that the two particles will move in opposite directions. Their relative speed after impact will then be the sum of the two speeds and is clearly positive. If the assumption was wrong, then one of the speeds would simply turn out to be negative.

Let the speeds of A and B be u and v m/s respectively in the directions indicated in the diagram.

By Newton's Law of Restitution:

$$v+u = e(6-1),$$

$$v+u = 5e. \tag{1}$$

By the Conservation of Linear Momentum:

$$m \times 6 + 2m \times 1 = -mu + 2mv,$$

$$8m = 2mv - mu,$$

$$2v - u = 8. \tag{2}$$

It is important in forming equation (2) to remember that momentum is a vector, and that we must therefore take direction fully into account.

Adding (1) and (2),

$$3v = 8 + 5e.$$

But $e = \frac{4}{5}$, giving

$$3v = 8 + 4,$$

$$v = 4.$$

Substituting back in (2)

$$u = 2v - 8$$

$$= 0.$$

$\therefore$ A is brought to rest, and B continues at 4 m/s after impact.

The kinetic energy before impact, K_1, was

$$\tfrac{1}{2}m \times 6^2 + \tfrac{1}{2} \times 2m \times 1^2 = 19m.$$

The kinetic energy after the impact is K_2 where

$$K_2 = \tfrac{1}{2}mu^2 + \tfrac{1}{2} \times 2mv^2$$

$$= 16m.$$

$$\therefore \; K_1 - K_2 = 3m.$$

The loss in kinetic energy was $3m$.

EXAMPLE 4   *Three beads A, B, C have masses m, 2m, 3m respectively, and lie in that order in a smooth straight horizontal groove. If initially B and C are stationary (a short distance apart) and A is made to strike B, find the condition on the coefficient of restitution e if A and B are not to collide again.*

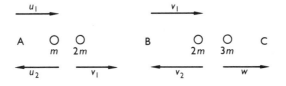

Fig. 114

Let the speeds of A before and after impact be u_1 and u_2, of B be v_1 and v_2 and of C be w, each in the directions indicated in Fig. 114.

1st Impact   By Newton's Law of Restitution

$$v_1 + u_2 = eu_1. \tag{1}$$

By the Conservation of Momentum,

$$2mv_1 - mu_2 = mu_1,$$

$$2v_1 - u_2 = u_1. \tag{2}$$

Adding (1) and (2)

$$3v_1 = (1+e)u_1,$$

$$v_1 = (1+e)u_1/3.$$

$\therefore$ from (2)

$$u_2 = \frac{2u_1}{3}(1+e) - u_1$$

$$= \frac{u_1}{3}(2e-1).$$

2nd Impact   By Newton's Law of Restitution

$$w + v_2 = ev_1. \tag{3}$$

By the Conservation of Momentum,

$$2mv_1 = 3mw - 2mv_2,$$

$$2v_1 = 3w - 2v_2. \tag{4}$$

Adding (4) to $2 \times (3)$

$$5w = 2v_1(1+e),$$

$$w = \tfrac{2}{5}v_1(1+e).$$

Substituting in (3),

$$v_2 = ev_1 - \tfrac{2}{5}v_1(1+e)$$

$$= \frac{v_1}{5}(3e-2).$$

Now A and B will not collide a second time if $v_2 \leqslant u_2$, i.e. if

$$\frac{v_1}{5}(3e-2) \leqslant \frac{u_1}{3}(2e-1).$$

Substituting for v_1 gives

$$\frac{u_1}{3 \cdot 5}(1+e)(3e-2) \leqslant \frac{u_1}{3}(2e-1),$$

$$3e^2 + e - 2 \leqslant 10e - 5,$$

$$3e^2 - 9e + 3 \leqslant 0.$$

$$e^2 - 3e + 1 \leqslant 0,$$

giving

$$\frac{3-\sqrt{9-4}}{2} \leqslant e \leqslant \frac{3+\sqrt{9-4}}{2}.$$

Since e must be less than or equal to 1,

$$e \geqslant \frac{3 - \sqrt{5}}{2} \text{ is a sufficient condition.}$$

A and B will not collide again if $e \geqslant (3 - \sqrt{5})/2$.

Exercise 22

1 A particle of mass m and speed v strikes a second stationary particle of mass $4m$ directly. The coefficient of restitution is $2/5$. Determine the velocities of both particles after impact.

2 Two particles of equal mass impinge directly, one having twice the speed of the other, moving in opposite directions. Half the total kinetic energy is lost due to the impact. Find the coefficient of restitution.

3 A bead of mass $7M$ moving with speed $3v$ is catching up with a second bead of mass $3M$ moving in the same direction with speed v. They impinge directly, the coefficient of restitution being $3/5$. Find their velocities after impact.

4 Two particles A and B of masses M and m respectively are moving directly towards each other, A with speed u_1 and B with speed u_2. If e is the coefficient of restitution and $\dfrac{M}{m} > e$, show that the condition for A to continue to move in the same direction after impact is
$$\frac{u_1}{u_2} > \frac{m(e+1)}{M - me}.$$

5 Three identical smooth beads A, B and C of equal masses lie in a straight groove in that order. A is projected so as to hit B. Show that there must be more than two impacts.

6 A bead of mass $2m$ having speed v catches up with a second bead of mass m moving in the same direction with speed u. After impact they continue to move in the same direction, the smaller bead with speed u' and the larger with speed v'. If $u' : v' = 2 : 1$, and the coefficient of restitution is e, show that
$$\frac{u}{v} = \frac{4e - 2}{4e + 1}.$$

7 Two beads X and Y lie in a smooth circular groove of radius d/π. They are projected from the same point A, X having twice the speed of Y, in opposite directions. The masses of X and Y are M and m respectively. If the second impact occurs at A, and Y returns along its own path to A, then show that either
$$M : m = 1 : 2 \quad \text{or} \quad M : m = (1 + 4e) : (2 - e)$$
provided that X does not pass through A without striking Y.

8 Two beads, one of mass $2m$ the second of mass $3m$, impinge directly, the former having a speed of $5v$ overtaking the second which has a speed of $2v$ in the same direction. If the coefficient of restitution is $\frac{1}{2}$, calculate the gain in kinetic energy of the heavier bead due to the impact.

9 When two particles A and B move directly towards each other with equal speeds they move in opposite directions after impact, A having three times the speed of B. Find the ratio of their speeds after impact if A overtakes B while moving twice as fast as B, and e is the coefficient of restitution.

9.3 Impulse

Newton's Law of Restitution is not applicable in all circumstances where a sudden change of motion occurs. There are many cases also where external forces come momentarily into play, thus invalidating the principle of Conservation of Momentum in its normal form. What happens for example when a nail is struck by a hammer, or a tow-rope given a sudden tug?

A jerk is really the action of a relatively large force $\mathbf{P}$ over a very brief time δt. It will not be possible to measure the time δt, nor can we assume that $\mathbf{P}$ will be constant. We can however measure its effect in terms of the integral

$$\mathbf{I} = \int_0^{\delta t} \mathbf{P} \, dt.$$

Taking force as mass × acceleration, $m \times \mathbf{a}$, then

$$\mathbf{I} = \int_0^{\delta t} m\mathbf{a} \, dt,$$

and if we assume that m is constant then

$$\mathbf{I} = \left[m\mathbf{v} \right]_{t=0}^{t=\delta t}$$

$$= m\mathbf{v} - m\mathbf{u},$$

where u and v are the velocities before and after the jerk. We refer to such a jerk as an **impulse**, the magnitude of which is equal to the change in momentum that it causes.

Since the impulse $\mathbf{I}$ is a vector, the change in momentum being in a specific direction, we can still apply the Conservation of Momentum perpendicularly to this direction. We can also use the fact that momentum in the direction of $\mathbf{I}$ will change by exactly the magnitude of the impulse. Where appropriate we can also consider components of the impulse when applying the Conservation of Momentum.

EXAMPLE 5   *A nail of mass 20 g is driven vertically into a block of wood by a hammer of mass 100 g. If the hammer strikes the nail with a speed of 5 m/s and does not rebound, and if the nail is driven 8 mm into the wood by the blow, calculate (a) the impulse given to the nail, and (b) the maximum force exerted by the wood (assuming it to be constant while the nail is moving).*

The impulse on the nail is the initial momentum given to it as a result of the blow. By the Conservation of Momentum, if v is the speed of the nail immediately after the blow,

$$0 \cdot 1 \times 5 = 0 \cdot 12 \times v,$$

$$v = 25/6.$$

Thus the initial momentum of the nail is $0 \cdot 02 \times (25/6)$ kg m/s

$$= 0 \cdot 5/6 \text{ kg m/s}.$$

∴ the impulse given to the nail is $\frac{1}{12}$ kg m/s.

Since the nail is driven in 8 mm against a constant force, the deceleration of the nail a m/s² is given by the equation of motion $v^2 = u^2 + 2as$:

$$\frac{25^2}{6^2} = 2a \times 0.008,$$

$$a = \frac{625}{36 \times 0.016}.$$

Thus the resistance due to motion is, by the principle force = mass × acceleration,

$$0.12 \times \frac{625}{36 \times 0.016} \text{ N}$$

$$= \frac{625}{3 \times 1.6}$$

$$= \frac{625}{4.8}$$

$$\doteqdot 130.2 \text{ N}.$$

But this is not the complete answer since this is only the retarding force. There is also the normal reaction which supports the weight of hammer and nail, moving or not, and this reaction is

$$0.12g = 1.175 \text{ N}.$$

∴ total resistance of wood is 131·4 N (to 4 significant figures).

The theory which has led us to the equation $\mathbf{I} = m\mathbf{v} - m\mathbf{u}$ is really a restatement of Newton's 2nd Law, that force is proportional to the rate of change of momentum. We can use it in reverse in order to find a constant force, as we illustrate in the next example.

EXAMPLE 6   *Calculate the approximate force required to hold a bucket of mass 200 g when containing $\frac{1}{2}$ l of water and being filled vertically beneath a tap at a rate of 200 000 mm³/s, the pipe having a cross-section of 50 mm².*

We cannot calculate the exact force required because we must assume that all the momentum of the water is destroyed. In fact because it is fluid it will swirl and eddy within the bucket.

The mass of water flowing in per second is

$$\frac{200\,000}{10^6} = 0.2 \text{ kg}.$$

The rate of flow is

$$200\,000 \text{ mm}^3/\text{s} \equiv 4000 \text{ mm/s}$$

$$\equiv 4 \text{ m/s}.$$

$\therefore$ momentum destroyed per second is

$$0{\cdot}2 \times 4 = 0{\cdot}8 \text{ kg m/s}.$$

This is the impulse due to the flow of water, and over t s it is $I = 0{\cdot}8t$. The force exerted is $\dfrac{dI}{dt}$, which is $0{\cdot}8$ N. Therefore the total force required is

$$(\tfrac{1}{2}g + 0{\cdot}2g + 0{\cdot}8) \text{ N} = 4{\cdot}9 + 1{\cdot}96 + 0{\cdot}8$$

$$= 7{\cdot}66 \text{ N}.$$

$\therefore$ Force required to hold bucket is $7{\cdot}7$ N (approximately).

EXAMPLE 7   A, B *and* C *are three smooth particles of masses* m, 2m *and* m *respectively, joined by two inelastic strings* AB *and* BC. *They lie on a smooth table with the strings just taut and such that angle* ABC *is* 150°. *If* B *is now subjected to an impulse of magnitude* mv *in a direction perpendicular to* BC *and away from* A, *determine the initial velocities of the three particles.*

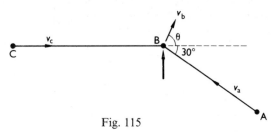

Fig. 115

Let the velocities of A, B and C be of magnitudes v_a, v_b and v_c respectively. Because the impulse can only be transmitted to A and C along the strings, the velocities of A and C must be directed along AB and AC respectively. Let the velocity of B be in a direction making an angle θ to CB produced. We can further deduce that because the strings remain taut the components of the velocity of B in the directions AB and CB must be of magnitude v_a and v_c. Thus we form two equations:

$$v_b \cos \theta = v_c, \tag{1}$$

and

$$v_b \cos (150° - \theta) = v_a,$$

$$v_b (\cos 150° \cos \theta + \sin 150° \sin \theta) = v_a,$$

$$v_b (\sin \theta - \sqrt{3} \cos \theta) = 2v_a. \tag{2}$$

By Conservation of Momentum perpendicular to the impulse,

$$mv_c + 2mv_b \cos\theta = mv_a \cos 30°,$$

$$2v_c + 4v_b \cos\theta = \sqrt{3}v_a. \tag{3}$$

The momentum of the system parallel to the impulse is equal to the impulse, i.e.

$$2mv_b \sin\theta + mv_a \sin 30° = mv,$$

$$4v_b \sin\theta + va = 2v. \tag{4}$$

Substituting for $v_b \cos\theta$ and $v_b \sin\theta$ from (1) and (4) into (2) and (3) gives

$$\tfrac{1}{4}(2v - v_a) - \sqrt{3}v_c = 2v_a,$$

giving

$$2v - 4\sqrt{3}v_c = 9v_a, \tag{5}$$

and

$$2v_c + 4v_c = \sqrt{3}v_a,$$

$$2\sqrt{3}v_c = v_a. \tag{6}$$

Substituting back in (5)

$$2v - 2v_a = 9v_a,$$

$$v_a = \frac{2v}{11}.$$

Hence from (6)

$$v_c = \frac{v}{11\sqrt{3}}.$$

From (1) and (4)

$$\tan\theta = \frac{2v - v_a}{4v_c}.$$

$$\therefore \ \tan\theta = \frac{2 - 2/11}{4/11\sqrt{3}}$$

$$= 5\sqrt{3}.$$

Hence

$$\cos\theta = \frac{1}{\sqrt{76}} = \frac{1}{2\sqrt{19}},$$

and

$$v_b = \frac{2\sqrt{19}v}{11\sqrt{3}}.$$

$\therefore$ velocities of A, B and C are $2v/11$ along AB, $\dfrac{2\sqrt{19}}{11\sqrt{3}}v$ at sec^{-1} $2\sqrt{19}$, and

$\dfrac{v}{11\sqrt{3}}$ along CB.

EXAMPLE 8   A, B *and* C *are three points equidistant from each other on a smooth horizontal plane. Particles of masses* M *and* m *lie at* A *and* B *respectively and are connected by a light inelastic string of length* AB. *If the mass at* A *is projected towards* C *with velocity* V, *the second being at rest, determine the impulsive tension in the string when it again becomes taut.*

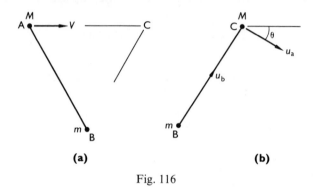

Fig. 116

The impulsive tension in the string is equal to the change in momentum of either mass in the direction of the string. Let the velocities of the masses after the string becomes taut be u_a at an angle θ to AC and u_b along BC (as in Fig. 116), then the impulsive tension will be mu_b.

By the Conservation of Momentum parallel to AC,

$$Mu_a \cos\theta + mu_b \cos 60° = MV,$$

$$2Mu_a \cos\theta + mu_b = 2MV. \tag{1}$$

By Conservation of Momentum perpendicular to AC,

$$Mu_a \sin\theta = mu_b \cos 30°$$

$$2MU_a \sin\theta = \sqrt{3}mu_b. \tag{2}$$

Equating velocity components along the string

$$u_b = u_a \cos(\theta + 60°)$$

$$= u_a (\cos\theta \cos 60° - \sin\theta \sin 60°),$$

$$2u_b = u_a (\cos\theta - \sqrt{3}\sin\theta). \tag{3}$$

Substituting for $u_a \cos\theta$ and $u_a \sin\theta$ from (1) and (2) into (3):

$$2u_b = \frac{2MV - mu_b}{2M} - \sqrt{3}\frac{\sqrt{3}mu_b}{2M},$$

$$4Mu_b = 2MV - mu_b - 3mu_b,$$

$$(4M + 4m)u_b = 2MV,$$

$$u_b = \frac{MV}{2(M+m)}.$$

$\therefore$ impulsive tension in the string is $\dfrac{mMV}{2(M+m)}$.

Note that the majority of connected particle situations can be analysed by two basic considerations: (1) momentum in two directions, and (2) equating velocity components along the strings. We can add to this that during any part of the motion in which no impulsive force acts, provided no work is done in any other way, then the kinetic energy is conserved. To illustrate this consider the following example.

EXAMPLE 9   *Two particles A and B each of mass m lie at rest on a smooth horizontal table connected by a light inelastic string which is just taut. An impulse of magnitude mv is applied to A in a direction perpendicular to AB. Form equations sufficient to find the velocities of A and B after the string has rotated through an angle θ, and hence deduce that A will come instantaneously to rest when $\theta = \pi$.*

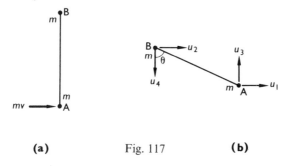

(a)   Fig. 117   (b)

Let the components of the velocities of A and B in the direction of the impulse be u_1 and u_2, and perpendicular to this direction be u_3 and u_4, each in the senses indicated in Fig. 117.

By the Conservation of Momentum parallel to the impulse,

$$mu_2 + mu_1 = mv, \tag{1}$$

since the initial velocity of A is v and of B is 0.

The Conservation of Momentum perpendicular to the impulse gives

$$mu_3 = mu_4. \tag{2}$$

Equating velocity components along the string,

$$u_1 \sin\theta - u_3 \cos\theta = u_2 \sin\theta + u_4 \cos\theta. \tag{3}$$

By the Conservation of Energy,

$$\tfrac{1}{2}mv^2 = \tfrac{1}{2}m(u_1^2 + u_2^2 + u_3^2 + u_4^2). \tag{4}$$

We have four equations to find the four unknown velocity components.

Taking $\theta = \pi$, and putting $u_4 = u_3$ from (2), equations (1), (3) and (4) become:

$$u_1 + u_2 = v, \tag{5}$$

$$u_3 = -u_3, \tag{6}$$

and
$$v^2 = u_1^2 + u_2^2 + 2u_3^2. \tag{7}$$

Equation (6) gives $u_3 = 0$, and eliminating v from (5) and (7),

$$(u_1 + u_2)^2 = u_1^2 + u_2^2,$$

$$2u_1 u_2 = 0.$$

But the force on B, conveyed through the string, has a positive component in the direction of the impulse for all θ, $0 < \theta < \pi$. Therefore $u_2 \neq 0$, giving

$$u_1 = 0.$$

A comes instantaneously to rest when $\theta = \pi$.

Exercise 23

1 A locomotive of mass 80 t backs up to a train of mass 50 t at a speed of 2 km/h. Determine the magnitude of the jolt felt by a passenger sitting in the train if he weighs 65 kg.

2 A pile of mass 400 kg is being driven into the ground by a pile-driver of mass 320 kg which is released under gravity from a point 1·2 m above the pile. Each blow drives the pile 0·05 m into the ground. If there is no rebound determine the resistance of the ground. (Take g as 9·8 m/s².)

3 If water is pumped through a nozzle at a rate of 0·1 m³/min, the cross-section being 150 mm², determine the force exerted on a plane wall if the jet is aimed directly at it.

4 A certain sheet of glass can stand a pressure of up to 10^5 N/m². If water is directed through a hose of cross-section 20 mm² at close quarters onto the glass determine the maximum rate of flow if the glass is not to be shattered.

5 A jet of water under high pressure is being used to clean the surface of a building. If it requires a pressure of 2 N/mm² and the nozzle has a cross-section of 16 mm², determine the rate of flow of water required in m/s. Find also the minimum power of the pump required.

6 Two beads A and B of masses m and $3m$ are attached by a light inextensible string and lie at rest on a smooth horizontal table with the string just taut. An impulse of magnitude mv is applied to A in a direction making an angle $\sin^{-1}(5/13)$ to BA produced. Determine the initial velocities of A and B.

7 Three particles A, B and C each of mass m lie at rest on a smooth horizontal plane. They are connected by two light inextensible strings AB and BC which are just taut and are such that angle ABC is 45°. An impulse of magnitude J is applied to B in the direction of AB. Find the impulsive tension in the string BC.

8 Two beads of masses M and m are connected by a light inextensible string. The beads are at rest on a smooth horizontal table with the string just taut when an impulse is applied to the bead of mass M. If this bead has an initial speed of $2v$,

the other having an initial speed v, find the angle of the impulse to the string and show that it has magnitude

$$v\sqrt{(4M^2 + 2Mm + m^2)}.$$

9 Two particles X and Y have masses $2m$ and $3m$ and are attached by a light inextensible string which is just taut, the two particles lying at rest on a smooth horizontal table. Determine the maximum impulse which can be applied to Y in a direction θ to XY produced if the string cannot take an impulsive tension of more than $6mv$.

10 Three particles A, B and C of masses m, m and $2m$ respectively lie on a smooth horizontal table in a straight line so that $AB = BC = a$. They are attached by light inelastic strings AB and BC both of length $2a$. If B is projected with speed v in a direction perpendicular to AC, determine the impulsive tensions in the strings as they become taut.

11 A light inextensible string of length a is attached by one end to a peg P, and a particle Q of mass m attached to the other end is held at a distance $a/2$ from the peg on the same horizontal level. If Q is released to fall under gravity find the impulsive tension in the string as it becomes taut, and show that the speed of Q as it reaches the lowest point of its subsequent path is

$$\left[\left(2 - \frac{3\sqrt{3}}{4} \right) ga \right]^{\frac{1}{4}}.$$

12 A particle A of mass $2m$ lies at rest on a smooth horizontal table. A second particle B of mass m also at rest on the table is attached to A by a light inextensible string which is just taut. If A is struck by an impulse of magnitude $2mv$ in a direction perpendicular to AB, find the velocities of A and B when the line of the string first becomes parallel to the direction of the impulse.

13 Four masses A, B, C and D of magnitudes m, M, m and M respectively lie at rest on a smooth horizontal table in the form of a square ABCD, and are connected by light inextensible strings AB, BC, CD and DA all of which are just taut. If an impulse of magnitude J is applied to A along the line CA, determine the initial velocities of B and D. Find also the velocities of B and D at the instant they are about to collide, and the velocities of A and C at the same instant.

14 A light inelastic string, just taut, connects two stationary particles of mass m_1 and m_2, $m_1 > m_2$, lying on a smooth horizontal table. The lighter mass is subjected to an impulse of magnitude J in a direction perpendicular to the string. Determine the velocity of the heavier mass when the string has turned through $180°$.

15 Project Example:
Consider more fully the system of No. 14, investigating for example the loci of the two particles, and their maximum and minimum speeds.

9.4 Oblique impact

In **9.2** we assumed that when two beads or particles collided that their velocities were in the same line and that they collided directly. In practice there are two possible extensions to this, namely that the particles need not have velocities in the same direction, nor need the size of the beads be negligible. The principles of solution however remain unaltered. If we resolve the velocities into components along and perpendicular to the line of impact, then the same methods apply to the former components. Provided the beads are smooth the velocities perpendicular to the line of impact will remain unchanged.

EXAMPLE 10   *Two particles A and B of masses 2m and m move with speeds 4v and 5v respectively so as to collide. The velocity of A is at 60° to the line of impact and of B is at an angle $\sin^{-1}\frac{3}{5}$ to the line of impact, the velocity components in the line of impact being directed towards each other, and perpendicular to this line in the same direction. If the coefficient of restitution is $\frac{1}{2}$, calculate the velocities of both particles after impact, and the total loss in kinetic energy due to the impact.*

We adopt a similar convention for the figure as for direct impact. Fig. 118 shows the velocities split into their components along the line of

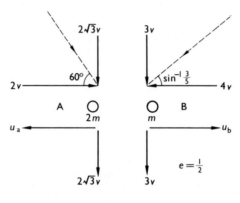

Fig. 118

centres, and perpendicular to this line. Let the velocity components along the line of impact be u_a and u_b in the senses shown.

By Newton's Law of Restitution,

$$u_a + u_b = \tfrac{1}{2}(2v + 4v),$$

$$u_a + u_b = 3v. \tag{1}$$

By the Conservation of Momentum,

$$2v \times 2m - 4v \times m = mu_b - 2mu_a,$$

$$u_b = 2u_a.$$

Substituting in (1),

$$3u_a = 3v,$$

$$u_a = v.$$

$$\therefore u_b = 2v.$$

The speed of A, by Pythagoras, is

$$\sqrt{(1+12)}v = \sqrt{13}v.$$

Similarly the speed of B is

$$\sqrt{(9+4)}v = \sqrt{13}v.$$

The velocity of A is $\sqrt{13}v$ at $\tan^{-1}(1/2\sqrt{3})$ to BA; the velocity of B is $\sqrt{13}v$ at $\tan^{-1}(3/2)$ to AB.

The kinetic energy before impact was

$$\tfrac{1}{2}.2m.16v^2 + \tfrac{1}{2}.m.25v^2 = 28\tfrac{1}{2}mv^2,$$

and after impact was

$$\tfrac{1}{2}.2m.13v^2 + \tfrac{1}{2}.m.13v^2 = 19\tfrac{1}{2}mv^2.$$

$\therefore$ the loss in kinetic energy was $9mv^2$.

EXAMPLE 11 *Two balls* A *and* B *have masses* 2m *and* 3m *respectively and are both of radius 1 cm. Their velocity vectors before impact are* 3i−4j *and* −4i−j, *and they impinge when* A *is at the origin and the line of centres* A *to* B *is along* +i. *Find the equation of the path of* B *after the impact, and calculate the angle through which* B *is deflected, ignoring gravity, and taking* i *and* j *as having magnitude 1 cm. The coefficient of restitution is 3/4.*

Since the balls are both of radius 1 cm, the centre of B is at $2\mathbf{i}$ at the instant of impact. Let the velocity vectors of A and B after impact be $\mathbf{v}_a$ and $\mathbf{v}_b$ where

$$\mathbf{v}_a = -x\mathbf{i} - 4\mathbf{j}$$

and

$$\mathbf{v}_b = y\mathbf{i} - \mathbf{j}.$$

By Newton's Law of Restitution,

$$x + y = \tfrac{3}{4}(3+4),$$

$$4x + 4y = 21. \tag{1}$$

By the Conservation of Momentum,

$$6m - 12m = -2xm + 3ym,$$

$$2x - 3y = 6. \tag{2}$$

Subtracting $2 \times$ (2) from (1),

$$10y = 9.$$

$$\therefore \mathbf{v}_b = \frac{9}{10}\mathbf{i} - \mathbf{j}.$$

The equation of the path of B is

$$\mathbf{r} = \left(2 + \frac{9t}{10}\right)\mathbf{i} - t\mathbf{j}.$$

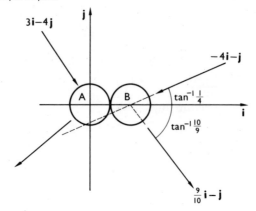

Fig. 119

The angle through which B is deflected is

$$180° - (\tan^{-1} \tfrac{1}{4} + \tan^{-1} \tfrac{10}{9}) = 180° - (14° \ 2' + 48° \ 1')$$
$$= 180° - 62° \ 3'$$
$$= 117° \ 57'.$$

B is deflected through an angle of 117° 57'.

EXAMPLE 12   *A particle of mass 2m is lying at rest on a smooth horizontal table and is attached by an inextensible string which is just taut to a fixed point on the table. A second particle of mass m has velocity v at 30° to the string in such a direction as to cause an impulsive tension in the string as it strikes the first particle, the line of centres on impact making an angle of 60° with the string. The coefficient of restitution between the particles is* $1/\sqrt{3}$. *Calculate the impulsive tension in the string caused by the impact.*

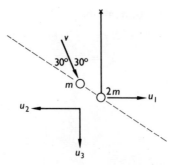

Fig. 120

Let the first mass have velocity u_1 after impact, and the second particle velocity components perpendicular and parallel to the string of u_2 and

u_3 as shown in Fig. 120. Let the impulsive tension in the string be J. By Newton's Law of Restitution,

$$(u_1+u_2) \cos 30° - u_3 \cos 60° = \frac{1}{\sqrt{3}} v \cos 30°,$$

$$(u_1+u_2)\sqrt{3} - u_3 = v. \tag{1}$$

By Conservation of Momentum perpendicular to the string,

$$mv \cos 60° = 2mu_1 - mu_2,$$

$$v = 4u_1 - 2u_2. \tag{2}$$

Since the impulsive tension in the string is equal to the momentum lost,

$$mv \cos 30° = mu_3 + J,$$

$$J = \frac{m}{2}(\sqrt{3}v - 2u_3). \tag{3}$$

As the particles are smooth the velocity of the second particle perpendicular to the line of impact is unaltered.

$$\therefore \ u_2 \cos 60° + u_3 \cos 30° = v \cos 60°,$$

$$u_2 + \sqrt{3}u_3 = v. \tag{4}$$

Substituting for u_1 from (2) into (1)

$$\left(\frac{v}{4} + \frac{3}{2}u_2\right)\sqrt{3} - u_3 = v.$$

Substituting from (4) for u_2,

$$\left(\frac{v}{4} + \frac{3}{2}v - \frac{3\sqrt{3}}{2}u_3\right)\sqrt{3} - u_3 = v,$$

$$\frac{7\sqrt{3}}{4}v - \frac{11}{2}u_3 = v.$$

$$\therefore \ 22u_3 = v(7\sqrt{3} - 4).$$

Hence substituting for u_3 in (3),

$$J = \frac{m}{2}\left(\sqrt{3}v - \frac{7\sqrt{3}}{11}v + \frac{4}{11}v\right)$$

$$= 2mv(\sqrt{3} + 1)/11.$$

The Impulsive Tension is $2mv(\sqrt{3} + 1)/11$.

Exercise 24

1 Two identical spheres impinge obliquely, the first moving with speed v at an angle of 30° to the line of impact, the second being at rest. If the coefficient of restitution

is e, show that the first sphere is deflected through an angle α where

$$\tan \alpha = \frac{\sqrt{3}(1+e)}{5-3e}.$$

2 Two particles have velocity vectors $8\mathbf{i}-10\mathbf{j}$ and $4\mathbf{i}-2\mathbf{j}$ (with usual notation), and they collide with the line of centres parallel to $\mathbf{i}$. The mass of the former is $3m$ and of the latter is m. Find the velocity vectors after impact if the coefficient of restitution is $3/4$, and calculate the loss of kinetic energy suffered by the first particle.

3 The coefficient of restitution between two particles of equal mass is e. If one is at rest and the other strikes it with velocity v at an angle θ to the line of centres, determine the impulse given to the one at rest, and show that if the other particle continues in a direction perpendicular to the line of impact then the particles are perfectly elastic.

4 Two perfectly elastic smooth spheres of masses m and M impinge obliquely so that both their velocities make angles of $30°$ to the line of centres. If the former has speed $2v$ and the latter speed v, determine their velocities after the impact.

5 Two particles A and B collide obliquely. A is of mass m and has a speed of $4v$ at $30°$ to the line of centres, and B has mass $2m$ and speed v in the direction $\overrightarrow{BA}$ at the moment of impact. If A is deflected through an angle of $60°$ find the coefficient of restitution e, and the speed of B after the impact.

6 Two beads of negligible size have velocities $\mathbf{v}_1 = 3\mathbf{i}-8\mathbf{j}$ and $\mathbf{v}_2 = 6\mathbf{i}+4\mathbf{j}$, and they impinge at the point given by $2\mathbf{i}+3\mathbf{j}$ with their line of centres in the direction of $\mathbf{j}$. Find the equations of their paths after impact and the loss in kinetic energy given that they are both of mass m and that the coefficient of restitution is $\frac{2}{3}$.

7 Two particles of masses m and $2m$ are moving with equal speeds at right-angles to each other, and they impinge so that the line of centres is at an angle $\tan^{-1}\frac{3}{4}$ to the velocity of the former and so that their velocity components along the line of centres are directed towards each other. By a suitable choice of unit vectors for a frame of reference and use of the scalar product, or otherwise, show that the angle between their paths after the impact is $\cos^{-1}\frac{7}{\sqrt{130}}$, given that the coefficient of restitution is $\frac{1}{2}$.

8 Two spheres A and B of masses m and M impinge obliquely. A is travelling with speed u at an angle α to the line of impact AB, and B is travelling with speed v along the line of impact in the direction BA. If the coefficient of restitution is $\frac{3}{4}$ and if A is deflected through an angle of $90°$, show that α is given by the equation

$$4(M+m)u \sec^2 \alpha = 7M(u+v \sec \alpha).$$

9 A ball A of mass M and radius $\sqrt{2}$ units has position $\mathbf{a} = (6t-9)\mathbf{i}+3\mathbf{j}$ after time t. Ball B of mass $2M$ and radius $\sqrt{2}$ units has position $\mathbf{b} = (13-4t)\mathbf{i}+(8t-15)\mathbf{j}$ after time t. Show that they will collide with their line of centres in the direction of $\mathbf{i}-\mathbf{j}$.

If the coefficient of restitution is $\frac{1}{3}$, find their positions at time T after the impact.

10 A bead of mass m lies at rest on a smooth horizontal table and is attached by a light string just taut to a fixed point on the table. A second bead also of mass m strikes the first directly with speed v at an angle of $45°$ to the string in such a way that an impulsive tension is induced in the string. Determine the magnitude of this impulse if the coefficient of restitution is $\frac{1}{2\sqrt{2}}$.

Support Exercise C

Miscellaneous examples which may be worked concurrently with Chapters 8 and 9

1 The resistance to motion in two cars, models A and B, is the same in each case and is $25(1+v)$ N where v is the speed in km/h. Model A has a total mass of $20M$ kg, and is able to work at a maximum rate of 42 kW. Model B has a total mass of $23M$ kg, and is able to work at a maximum rate of 56 kW. Find the ratio of the accelerations of the two cars at 60 km/h at full power in the form $1:n$.

2 State the principle known as the Triangle of Vectors.

A uniform rod AB lies in equilibrium between two smooth planes inclined at angles α and β to the horizontal, A resting on the former and $\beta > \alpha$, such that the vertical plane containing AB is perpendicular to the intersection of the two planes. Find the ratio of the reactions at A and B.

Show that AB will make an angle θ to the horizontal where

$$\tan \theta = \frac{\sin (\beta - \alpha)}{2 \sin \alpha \sin \beta}.$$

3 A light inextensible string AB passes over a smooth fixed light pulley. The end A is free, but the end B is attached to a second smooth small pulley of mass $3M$. A second light inextensible string CD passes over this pulley. A mass of $11M$ is attached at D, and C is fixed to the floor. Assuming that all strings are vertical and that the pulleys are far enough apart, calculate the steady force required to be applied vertically at A in order to lift the $11M$ mass from rest on the floor through a vertical distance of 2 m in 5 s.

4 Show that the four forces

$$\begin{aligned}
\mathbf{F}_1 &= 3\mathbf{i}+4\mathbf{j} & \text{acting at } 2\mathbf{i}+\mathbf{j}, \\
\mathbf{F}_2 &= 2\mathbf{i}-\mathbf{j} & \text{acting at } 2\mathbf{i}-\mathbf{j}, \\
\mathbf{F}_3 &= 5\mathbf{j} & \text{acting at } \mathbf{i}+2\mathbf{j}, \\
\mathbf{F}_4 &= -5\mathbf{i}-8\mathbf{j} & \text{acting at } \mathbf{i}-2\mathbf{j},
\end{aligned}$$

reduce to a couple. If this couple is represented by two equal and opposite forces $\mathbf{R}_1$ and $\mathbf{R}_2$ where $|\mathbf{R}_1| = \sqrt{2}$ and acts along the line $\mathbf{r}_1 = t\mathbf{i}+(1+t)\mathbf{j}$, find the line of action of $\mathbf{R}_2$ and the magnitude of the couple.

5 Three uniform rods AB, BC, CD each of weight W and length $4a$, are smoothly hinged at B and C, and also to fixed points at A and D such that A is $6a$ units horizontally from D and $2\sqrt{3}a$ units below D. The system is supported with CD at 60° to the horizontal, CA being $4a$ units and B above AC, by a smooth peg P on CD such that OP $= a$. Find the reaction at the peg and the reactions at A and D.

6 A ship has position vector $\mathbf{s}$ relative to the end of a quay at 0900 hours where

$$\mathbf{s} = -8\mathbf{i}+6\mathbf{j}$$

(distances in nautical miles). It is travelling with velocity $9\mathbf{i}+6\mathbf{j}$ (knots). A launch

capable of $3\sqrt{26}$ knots sets out from the quay to intercept the ship as soon as possible. Find
- (1) the velocity vector of the launch,
- (2) the point of interception,
- (3) the time of interception.

7 A particle, subject only to the force of gravity, is projected from a point A with given speed and direction. A light, fixed at a point B on the path of the particle, casts a shadow of the particle on a fixed vertical wall. Prove that this shadow moves with constant velocity as the particle goes from A to B.   (O)

8 Water is pumped through a fireman's hose at a rate of 720 l/min. The nozzle has a cross-sectional area of 1200 mm^2. Find the power of the pump, and the force that the fireman must exert to hold the hose steady, assuming no significant difference in water levels. (1 l of water weighs 1 kg.)

9 ABCD is a rectangle such that AB = 2BC. Forces represented in magnitude, position and direction by $3\overrightarrow{DC}$, $\overrightarrow{BC}$ and $3\overrightarrow{BD}$ act on the system together with a force Q which acts along AB. Show that the resultant acts through a point Z on AB such that AZ:ZB = 1:3, and find the value of Q in the form $k\overrightarrow{AB}$ if the resultant is to pass through C.

10 A ship S is travelling due north with velocity $\mathbf{v} = 24\mathbf{j}$. At 0600 hours S is at the origin of perpendicular unit vectors $\mathbf{i}$ and $\mathbf{j}$, and a ship A lying due east of S has position $5\mathbf{i}$, while a ship B has position $-4\mathbf{i}$. The velocities of A and B are $\mathbf{v}_a$ and v_b respectively. If A appears to move in a direction 300° (N 60° W) and B appears to move in a direction 045° (north-east) both relative to S, find $\mathbf{v}_a$ and $\mathbf{v}_b$ if at 0645 hours both A and B lie due north of S. Find the distances of A and B from S at this time.

   (Distances and speeds are in km and km/h.)

11 By Stokes' Law the resistive force acting on a sphere of radius a falling with constant speed v under gravity through a viscous liquid having coefficient of viscosity η is proportional to $\eta a v$. Determine the dimensions of η.

   Hence, using the method of dimensions, show that the volume of a viscous liquid which flows per unit time through a circular capillary tube of uniform radius R under the action of a constant pressure difference P per unit length is proportional to

$$\frac{R^4 p}{\eta}.$$ (NI)

12 A uniform pyramid ABCDE has a square base ABCD with centre O and sides of length $2a$. OE is perpendicular to the base and is of length h. Show from first principles that the centre of mass of the pyramid is $\frac{1}{4}h$ from O.

   The pyramid is cut into two sections by a plane parallel to ABCD at a distance $\frac{1}{2}h$ from O. The larger section is freely suspended from A and it is found that in equilibrium AC makes an angle $\frac{1}{6}\pi$ with the vertical. Find the ratio of $h:a$.   (W)

13 A light spring of natural length 4 cm is held in a smooth cylindrical pipe of the same width in such a way that it is under a minimum compression of 0·5 cm. Find the work done in compressing the spring a further distance x cm from minimum compression if the modulus of the spring is $g/4$ N.

   A bead of mass 0·01 kg is inserted into the pipe so as to rest against the spring. If the spring is compressed to a length of 2 cm, calculate the speed of projection of the bead when the spring is released.

14 A is a point on a smooth plane inclined at an angle α to the horizontal. $\mathbf{i}$ and $\mathbf{j}$ are unit vectors passing through A, $\mathbf{i}$ horizontal in the plane and $\mathbf{j}$ in the line of greatest slope. A point C has position $x\mathbf{i} + y\mathbf{j}$ relative to A. A particle is projected from A in the face of the plane with speed V at a variable angle β to $\mathbf{i}$. If it can only just reach C show that

$$\frac{x}{2}(\tan \beta - \cot \beta) = y.$$

15 If three coplanar forces are in equilibrium, show that they must be either concurrent or parallel.

A cylinder, of weight W and radius a, is to be raised over a step of height $\frac{1}{2}a$.
(Fig. 121.) A cord has one end attached to the surface of the cylinder and a pull is
exerted on the other end of the cord. The cord is in a vertical plane perpendicular
to the axis of the cylinder.

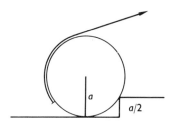

Fig. 121

(i) If the pull is horizontal, find the required pull and the least possible value of
μ, the coefficient of friction between the cylinder and the step.
(ii) If $\mu = \frac{3}{4}$, find the maximum angle the pull can make with the horizontal.

(AEB)

16 Three points A, B and C have position vectors **a**, **b** and **c** respectively relative to
O, the origin of perpendicular unit vectors **i** and **j**. Show by vector theory that the
line joining the mid-points X and Y of AB and AC is parallel to BC and half BC
in length.

The whole system is subjected to a transformation ϕ such that every position
vector $x\mathbf{i}+y\mathbf{j}$ is changed to the position vector $(x-y)\mathbf{i}+(x+y)\mathbf{j}$. (You may write
this as $\phi(x\mathbf{i}+y\mathbf{j}) = (x-y)\mathbf{i}+(x+y)\mathbf{j}$.) Show that the transformation of XY
(written as $\phi(XY)$) is parallel to and half of $\phi(BC)$.

17 The figure shows a light framework ABCD of five rods. The system is smoothly
pivoted at A in a vertical plane, and a weight of mass 200 kg is hung from D.
The frame is supported at C by a force F perpendicular to DC so that AB is

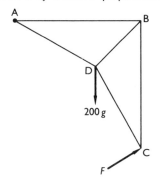

Fig. 122

horizontal. Angles BAD, BCD both equal 30°, and angles ADB, BDC are both
105°. Find graphically or otherwise the force F, the reaction at A, and the stresses
in the rods, stating clearly in each case the nature of the stress.

18 A chair-lift of length 350 m can carry a maximum of 50 people at any given time through a vertical distance of 140 m. Under this maximum load the lift conveys 480 people per hour of average weight 65 kg. Resistance to motion is $(500+4n)$ N where n is the number of people being carried at a given time. Find the power of the engine, and the time taken for the journey up when carrying only 25 people if it continues to work at the same rate.

19 Forces of magnitudes $2F$, $3F$, $4F$ and F act along the sides AB, CB, DC and AD of a rectangle in the directions indicated by the order of the letters. AB is $3a$ units and AD is $2a$ units. Find the resultant stating where it cuts AB (produced if necessary).

Forces P and Q are added to the system along AC and BD so as to reduce the system to a couple. Show that their magnitudes are in the ratio $1:3$, and find the moment of this couple.

20 A particle moving in a straight line OD with uniform retardation leaves point O at time $t = 0$, and comes to instantaneous rest at D. On its way to D the particle passes points A, B, C at times $t = T, 2T, 4T$, respectively, after leaving O, where $AB = BC = l$. Find, in terms of l, (i) the length of CD and (ii) the length of OA.
(JMB)

21 Two particles P_1, P_2 having masses m, $2m$ respectively are moving in a plane with coordinates (x_1,y_1), (x_2,y_2) referred to a rectangular frame of reference having origin O and perpendicular axes Ox, Oy. If

$$x_1 = 4+2t-2t^2, \qquad y_1 = 2+3t+t^2,$$
$$x_2 = 1+2t+t^2, \qquad y_2 = 3-3t+t^2,$$

where t is the time, find:
(i) the total kinetic energy T_O of the pair of particles referred to O(x,y);
(ii) the total kinetic energy T_G of the pair of particles in their motion relative to the rectangular frame of reference G(x,y) with origin at the centre of mass G of the two particles and axes Gx, Gy parallel to Ox, Oy respectively.
    Hence show that

$$T_O - T_G = \frac{3mV^2}{2}$$

where V is the velocity of G referred to O(x,y).
(NI)

22 A particle is projected from the origin of unit vectors, $\mathbf{i}$ horizontal and $\mathbf{j}$ vertical, with an initial velocity of $u\mathbf{i}+v\mathbf{j}$ so as to strike a vertical wall at the point given by $h\mathbf{i}+\frac{h}{3}\mathbf{j}$. The speed on impact is $3/\sqrt{13}$ times the speed of projection. Find the ratio $u:v$.

23 Two uniform straight rods, AB of length $2a$ and weight W_1 and BC of length $2b(b > 4a)$ and weight W_2, are smoothly hinged at B. The end A is smoothly hinged to a fixed point and BC passes through a small smooth ring freely pivoted at a fixed point D at a height $2a$ vertically above A. Find an expression for the potential energy of this system when the angle BDA is θ and prove that, if $b < 4a(2+W_1/W_2)$, there is an unsymmetrical position of equilibrium which is unstable.
(O)

24 A uniform circular table top is supported on a rough floor by three equal vertical legs AA′, BB′, CC′, each of height h, placed symmetrically so that their feet form an equilateral triangle of side $2a$, and their tops form another equilateral triangle A′B′C′. The weight of the whole table is W, and a force F, not sufficient to move the table, is applied along the line A′B′. The forces exerted by the ground on the legs can be resolved into vertical forces X, Y, Z up the legs and horizontal forces together equivalent to forces P, Q, R along BA, AC, CB respectively. Show that $Q = R = 0$, and find X, Y, Z in terms of F, W, a, h. To what value must F be increased to make the table tilt?
(S)

25 A naval frigate A is attempting to cut off a vessel B. The velocity of A is $\mathbf{v_a} = 42\mathbf{j}$

(km/h) and at a certain instant its position is $s_a = 0$. The velocity of B is $v_b = 15\sqrt{3}i + 15j$ (km/h) and at the same instant it is at $s_b = -500i + 500\sqrt{3}j$ (m). A fires a shell across B's bows—the shell has an initial speed of 120 m/s, and is fired at an angle of 26° to the ship at an elevation of 20° to the horizontal. Show that the velocity vector of the shell is approximately

$$-49{\cdot}4i + 113{\cdot}1j + (41{\cdot}0 - gt)k$$

t s after firing. Use this value to find where the shell strikes the sea relative to B (giving components to the nearest metre).
(Take g as 9·8 m/s².)

26 A block of mass m is to be drawn up a rough slope of inclination 45° to the horizontal, coefficient of friction $\frac{1}{2}$. A light inelastic string attached to the block passes up over a small smooth pulley at the top of the plane and under a second smooth pulley of mass $4m$ vertically below the first, and up to a fixed point above the pulleys. The system is such that the block is then drawn from rest up the full length of the plane in time T_1. A weight of mass $4m$ is now added to the pulley, and the corresponding time for the same motion is T_2. Show that the ratio $T_1^2 : T_2^2$ is

$$1 : \frac{3(4\sqrt{2} - 3)}{2(8\sqrt{2} - 3)}.$$

27 At $\frac{3}{4}$ full power a lorry of mass 1·75 t maintains a steady speed of 78 km/h on the level, resistance being proportional to speed. At full power the lorry can ascend a hill of gradient $\sin^{-1}\frac{1}{8}$ at a steady speed of 60 km/h. Calculate (a) the full power of the lorry, and (b) the acceleration in km/h/s of the lorry at 30 km/h on the level at half full power.

28 Define the centre of mass of n particles of masses $m_1, m_2, \ldots, m_n$, placed at points whose position vectors with respect to an origin O are $r_1, r_2, \ldots, r_n$ respectively, and show that it is independent of the choice of origin.
    Find the position vector of the centre of mass of particles of masses 4, 3, 2, 3 units at rest at the points

$$i + j, \quad 2i - j, \quad 2i + j, \quad 2i + 3j$$

respectively. If each mass is acted upon by a force directed towards the origin and proportional to its distance from the origin, find the direction of the initial acceleration of the centre of mass. (L)

29 Two smooth planes inclined at acute angles α and β to the upward vertical, and situated on opposite sides of it, meet in a horizontal line. A uniform rod of mass M and length $2l$ is placed with its ends on the smooth planes, in a vertical plane normal to both of them, and inclined at an angle θ to the vertical. Find the potential energy of the rod as a function of the angle θ. Hence, or otherwise, derive a formula for θ when the rod is in a position of equilibrium and determine whether the equilibrium position is stable or unstable. (Assume that $\alpha > \beta$.)   (NI)

30 A uniform lever AB has weight $2W$ and is pivoted at B so as to turn freely in a vertical plane. B is a point on a horizontal floor, coefficient of friction μ, and a rod CD of weight W and half the length of AB is pivoted at D to the mid-point of AB, the end C resting on the floor in the same vertical plane as AB. The system is positioned so that triangle BCD is equilateral, and a force F is applied at A perpendicularly to AB downwards in the plane ABC. If C is in limiting equilibrium about to move away from B, show that

$$\mu = \frac{8F + 5W}{\sqrt{3}(8F + 7W)}.$$

Find the reaction at D if $F = 2W$, stating at what angle it acts to the vertical.

31 ABCD is a smooth fixed horizontal tray with vertical sides AB, BC, CD, DA each of length 4 units in the shape of a square. A particle is projected along the

tray from A towards the mid-point of BC. The coefficient of restitution is e, and the successive points of impact are P_1, P_2, P_3, ... Prove that the first four lines traced out by the particle form a parallelogram of area $8(1-e^2)$. Find the range of values of e if $AP_4 \leqslant 1$ unit, and show that in the limiting case the parallelogram traced out is a rectangle.

32 Two particles are projected with the same speed from the same point. The angles of projection are 2α and α and a time T elapses between the instants of projection. If the particles collide in flight, find the speed of projection in terms of T and α.

If the collision occurs when one of the particles is at its greatest height, show that α is given by

$$4 \cos^4 \alpha - \cos^2 \alpha - 1 = 0. \qquad \text{(AEB)}$$

33 Show that if the position vectors of points A and B relative to the point O are $\mathbf{a}$ and $\mathbf{b}$ then the equation of the line AB is given by

$$\mathbf{r} = \lambda\mathbf{a} + (1-\lambda)\mathbf{b}.$$

The vertices of a triangle ABC have position vectors $\mathbf{a}$, $\mathbf{b}$, $\mathbf{c}$ relative to a point O. The mid-points of the sides BC, CA, AB are D, E, F, and of the lines AO, BO, CO are L, M, N. Find the equations of LD, ME and NF in terms of $\mathbf{a}$, $\mathbf{b}$ and $\mathbf{c}$, and prove that they bisect each other. Find the position of their common point in terms of $\mathbf{a}$, $\mathbf{b}$ and $\mathbf{c}$.

34 A and B are two points on a smooth horizontal floor each 1 m distant from a smooth vertical wall. A bead is projected along the floor from A so as to strike the wall at an angle of $30°$ to the normal and to then pass through B. If the coefficient of restitution is 3/4, find the distance between A and B.

If the bead is now projected along the floor from a point C 0·5 m from the wall and such that AC is perpendicular to the wall, so as to still pass through B, find at what angle to AC it must be projected.

35 (a) An organ pipe having length l contains air of density ρ at pressure p. Using the method of dimensions show that the periodic time of sound vibrations along the length of the pipe is proportional to

$$l\left(\frac{\rho}{p}\right)^{\frac{1}{2}}.$$

(b) The energy of a light wave is given by $h\nu$ where ν is its frequency and h is Planck's constant, while the energy of the electron in a hydrogen atom is given by e^2/a where e is the electron charge and a is the distance of the electron from the nucleus of the atom.

Find the dimensions of the quantities h and e and hence, by using the method of dimensions, show that the distance a is proportional to

$$\frac{h^2}{me^2}$$

where m is the mass of the electron. (NI)

36 The mass per unit length of a ladder increases uniformly from the top to the bottom of the ladder, and is twice as great at the bottom as at the top. Find the position of its centre of mass.

The ladder stands on a horizontal plane and rests against a vertical wall, and makes an angle θ with the horizontal. The coefficient of friction at both ends of the ladder is μ. If the ladder is just about to slip, prove that

$$\tan \theta = \frac{1}{9}\left(\frac{4}{\mu} - 5\mu\right). \qquad \text{(O \& C)}$$

37 Three smooth beads, A, B and C have masses of magnitudes 1, 2 and 3 respectively. If they lie in order in a straight line, all stationary and having the same

coefficient of restitution e, and A is projected towards B, show that more than two impacts will occur only if $e < \frac{1}{2}(3 - \sqrt{5})$.

38 A uniform rod AB of mass m and length $2a$ is smoothly pivoted to a fixed point at A, and an inelastic string of length $5a$ attached to B passes through a smooth ring C fixed on the same level as A such that $AC = 3a$. A weight of mass M is attached to the other end of the string and allowed to hang freely under gravity below the ring. If the system is in equilibrium when AB is at an angle θ below the horizontal show that

$$13 - 12 \cos \theta = 36 \tan^2 \theta \frac{M^2}{m^2}.$$

Hence find M in terms of m if $\theta = \tan^{-1} \sqrt{7}/3$, and show that the equilibrium is stable.

39 A particle of mass $3m$ is projected vertically upwards with speed $3V$. T seconds later a second particle of mass m is projected upwards in the same line with speed $2V$. Show that if they are to collide above the point of projection then

$$2V/g < T < 6V/g.$$

If $T = 4V/g$, show that they collide at a point $\dfrac{16V^2}{9g}$ above the point of projection. If they coalesce at this point, find with what speed they return through the point of projection.

40 Two equal particles are projected at the same instant from points A and B at the same level, the first from A towards B with velocity u at $45°$ above AB, and the second from B towards A with velocity v at $60°$ above BA. If the particles collide directly when each reaches its greatest height, find the ration $v^2 : u^2$ and prove that $u^2 = ga(3 - \sqrt{3})$, where a is the distance AB.

After the collision the first particle falls vertically. Show that the coefficient of restitution between the particles is $(\sqrt{3} - 1)(\sqrt{3} + 1)$.   (JMB)

41 Define the scalar product $\mathbf{a} . \mathbf{b}$ of two vectors $\mathbf{a}$ and $\mathbf{b}$, and show by considering the parallelogram of vectors or otherwise that

$$\mathbf{a} . (\mathbf{b} + \mathbf{c}) = \mathbf{a} . \mathbf{b} + \mathbf{a} . \mathbf{c}.$$

A particle P has position vector after time t given by $\mathbf{p} = \mathbf{b} + 2t\mathbf{v}$. Similarly Q is a particle with position vector $\mathbf{q} = \mathbf{a} + t\mathbf{v}$. A third particle R has position $\mathbf{r} = \mathbf{a}$ when $t = 0$, and $\mathbf{r} = \mathbf{b}$ when $t = 1$. If R is moving in a straight line with constant speed, and if $|\mathbf{b} - \mathbf{a}| = |\mathbf{v}| = v$, and $(\mathbf{b} - \mathbf{a}) . \mathbf{v} = 0$, show that after time t

$$\cos PRQ = (3t - 1)/\sqrt{2(1 - 2t + 5t^2)}.$$

42 (a) A particle of mass m, moving with velocity u in a direction making an angle θ with a smooth wall rebounds from the wall with velocity v at an angle ϕ to the wall. Sketch a vector diagram showing the relation between the impulse exerted by the wall and the momenta before and after impact. Show how the coefficient of restitution e can be represented on this diagram. Hence or otherwise prove that $v > eu$.

(b) A ball is dropped onto an irregular surface, hitting the surface with vertical velocity u and bouncing away with velocity v at $30°$ to the vertical. Show that the impulse exerted by the surface is in a direction at less than $15°$ to the vertical. Find the magnitude of this impulse (stating the units) if the mass is $\frac{1}{4}$ kg and the velocities 3 m/s and 2 m/s.   (Adapted, S)

43 Three particles P, Q and R of equal mass m lie on a smooth horizontal table at the vertices of an equilateral triangle. Light inelastic strings connecting P to Q and Q to R are just taut. If Q is given an impulse in a direction perpendicular to PR and towards PR of magnitude $3mv$, determine the impulsive tensions in PQ and QR when the strings become taut. Find also the velocities of P and R at the instant they collide.

44 ABCD is a quadrilateral. Forces acting along the sides are represented in magnitude and direction by $\overrightarrow{BA}$, $2\overrightarrow{BC}$, $\overrightarrow{DC}$ and $4\overrightarrow{DA}$. Prove that if the system reduces to a couple then ABCD is a trapezium with AD parallel to CB. If AB is perpendicular to BC, angle BCD $= \theta$ and AD $= 3$ units then show that the moment of the couple is $-14\tan\theta$.

45 Show that the centre of gravity of a uniform semi-circular lamina of radius r is at a distance $4r/3\pi$ from the centre.

A uniform solid right circular cone, of height h, has vertex O and ACB is a diameter of the base whose radius is r and whose centre is C. The cone is cut into two equal parts by a plane perpendicular to ACB and containing the axis of the cone. Find the distance of the centre of gravity of the half, AOC, of the cone from (i) OC, (ii) AC.

If this portion is freely suspended from C the line OA is horizontal. Find the ratio $r:h$. (AEB)

46 Two particles P and Q both of unit mass are connected by a light inelastic string. Initially they are at rest on a smooth table, P lying in a smooth groove and the string just taut perpendicular to the groove. If P is struck by an impulse of magnitude $2\sqrt{2}$, form a sufficient set of equations to find the velocities of P and Q when the string makes an angle θ with the groove. Find the velocities of P and Q just as θ becomes zero, and show that when $\theta = 45°$ the velocity of Q is $\frac{2}{\sqrt{3}}(4-\sqrt{3})^{\frac{1}{2}}$ at an angle $\tan^{-1}(2\sqrt{3}-3)$ to the string.

47 An elastic string of natural length a is attached by one end to a fixed peg P. A mass of magnitude m is attached to the other end, and when suspended freely under gravity from P the mass remains in equilibrium at a depth $3a$ below P. The mass is now pulled downwards and released, and in the ensuing motion it just misses the peg to reach a point X height a above P. Determine the length of the string at the instant it was released.

If instead the mass strikes the peg, the line of impact being vertical and the coefficient of restitution being $\frac{1}{2}$, determine the depth to which the mass will fall.

48 A horizontal rectangular tray ABCD, in which AB $= 72$ cm, is surrounded by a small vertical edge. A small smooth sphere is projected horizontally from E in AD, where AE $= 24$ cm, across the tray with components of velocity 8 cm/s along DA and 6 cm/s parallel to AB. The coefficient of restitution between the sphere and the edge of the tray is $\frac{1}{2}$. As the sphere leaves E a second identical sphere is projected with speed 6 cm/s from the mid-point of CD towards the mid-point of AB. If the spheres collide, calculate the length BC.

Immediately before the spheres collide their line of centres is parallel to AD. The coefficient of restitution between the spheres is $2/5$. Find the velocities of the spheres immediately after impact and find also where the first sphere next strikes the edge of the tray.

If the mass of each sphere is m grammes, calculate the loss of kinetic energy caused by the collision of the spheres. (AEB)

49 In a system of mutually perpendicular unit vectors $\mathbf{i}$, $\mathbf{j}$, $\mathbf{k}$, O is the origin, A the point $3\mathbf{i}$, and B the point $3\mathbf{i}+4\mathbf{j}$. Particles P, Q and R are initially at O, A and B respectively and move with steady speeds each in the direction of $\mathbf{k}$ in such a way that angle OAP $=$ angle ABQ $=$ angle BOR. If P moves with velocity $\mathbf{k}$, find the velocities of Q and R. Find also the equation of the fixed line of rotation of the plane PQR.

50 A vertical cross-section through a wedge is in the form of a triangle ABC, with AC horizontal and B above AC. If AC $= b$, angle BAC $= \theta$ and angle BCA $= \phi$, show that the initial speed of a projectile fired from A so as to just clear B and strike C is

$$\left[\frac{gb}{2}\left(\frac{\sin(\theta+\phi)}{\cos\theta\cos\phi}+\frac{\cos\theta\cos\phi}{\sin(\theta+\phi)}\right)\right]^{\frac{1}{2}}.$$

10 Circular Motion (1)

10.1 Angular velocity

Although it is possible to consider the speed of a particle moving in a circle in linear form, such as in metres per second, it is generally more appropriate to use an angular measure. Consider a particle P moving in a plane in which OX is a fixed line of reference. If the angle POX is θ at time t, then the **angular velocity** of P about the point O is the rate of change of θ with respect to t, viz. $\frac{d\theta}{dt}$. It is common practice to use the Greek letter ω for angular velocity.

In the case of a rigid body we should note that the angular velocity of P about any other point Q in the body is the same irrespective of the points P and Q chosen. This is made evident by considering any two lines drawn in the body; they will both turn at the same rate. However, the angular velocity of P about an external fixed point O, ω_1, is not the same as its angular velocity about any other external point X, nor is it the same as the angular velocity of Q about O, ω_2 (Fig. 123).

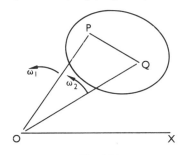

Fig. 123

Angular velocity is a vector—a change in θ must take place about a particular axis in a particular plane in a particular sense. The direction of the vector is perpendicular to the plane of rotation along the axis of rotation through O, and the sense is determined according to the right-hand screw rule, i.e. if the rotation is in the plane of this page in an anti-clockwise sense, then the vector is directed perpendicularly upwards out of the page, and vice versa. The examples in this chapter can all be solved without a particular consideration of the vector form, but when using it in its scalar form we should refer to it as angular speed.

Although angular speed is usually referred to in terms of revolutions per unit time in lay usage, it is mathematically more relevant to measure it in terms of radians per unit time. The S.I. unit is radians per second (rad/s). Measuring angles in radians, i.e. as the ratio of arc length to radius, leads us to deduce that an angle has no dimension, and that angular velocity must have the dimension of inverse time—$[T^{-1}]$. It will be evident that 2π rad/s is equivalent to 1 rev/s.

By the definition of a radian, an angle θ subtended at the centre of a circle radius r by an arc of length s is given by

$$\theta = \frac{s}{r}.$$

Differentiating with respect to time,*

$$\dot{\theta} = \dot{s}/r,$$

i.e. $$\omega = v/r.$$

This relationship between angular and linear speed is of frequent application.

10.2 Circular motion at constant speed

Let O be the origin of perpendicular unit vectors $\mathbf{i}$ and $\mathbf{j}$ and the position of a particle at time t be $\mathbf{p}(t)$. If the particle P moves in a circle of radius r, centre O, and is at the point $r\mathbf{i}$ when $t = 0$, then

$$\mathbf{p}(t) = r \cos \theta \mathbf{i} + r \sin \theta \mathbf{j}, \qquad 10.1$$

where θ is the angle OP makes with $\mathbf{i}$ and is a function of t. Differentiating with respect to t, the velocity is

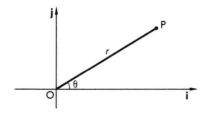

Fig. 124

---

* We adopt Newton's dot notation at this point for the derivatives with respect to time. Thus $\dot{x}$ and $\ddot{x}$ are equivalent to dx/dt and d^2x/dt^2 respectively. We use it here for its convenient simplicity, but it should never be used for a derivative with respect to any other variable.

$$\dot{\mathbf{p}}(t) = -r \sin \theta . \frac{d\theta}{dt}\mathbf{i} + r \cos \theta . \frac{d\theta}{dt}\mathbf{j}$$

$$= -r\omega \sin \theta\mathbf{i} + r\omega \cos \theta\mathbf{j}. \qquad 10.2$$

Similarly the acceleration vector is

$$\ddot{\mathbf{p}}(t) = (-r\omega^2 \cos \theta - r\dot{\omega} \sin \theta)\mathbf{i} + (-r\omega^2 \sin \theta + r\dot{\omega} \cos \theta)\mathbf{j}. \qquad 10.3$$

Let the angular speed ω be constant, then $\theta = \omega t$. Equations 10.1–10.3 then become

$$\mathbf{p}(t) = r \cos \omega t\mathbf{i} + r \sin \omega t\mathbf{j},$$

$$\dot{\mathbf{p}}(t) = -\omega r \sin \omega t\mathbf{i} + \omega r \cos \omega t\mathbf{j},$$

and

$$\ddot{\mathbf{p}}(t) = -\omega^2 r \cos \omega t\mathbf{i} - \omega^2 r \sin \omega t\mathbf{j}.$$

By the principle: force = mass × acceleration it follows that if P has mass m then the force acting on P to cause the circular motion is $m\ddot{\mathbf{p}}(t)$. Comparing equations 10.1 and 10.3,

$$m\ddot{\mathbf{p}}(t) = -m\omega^2\mathbf{p}(t).$$

Also,

$$m|\ddot{\mathbf{p}}(t)| = m\omega^2 r,$$

$$= mv^2/r,$$

where v is the linear speed of P. It follows therefore that the force required to cause circular motion with constant speed is of magnitude $m\omega^2 r$ (or mv^2/r) and is directed towards the axis of rotation.*

EXAMPLE 1   *A particle of mass m is attached to a light elastic string of natural length a, the other end of which is attached to a fixed point on a smooth horizontal table. When rotating on the table with constant angular speed of 10 rad/s about the fixed point the length of the string is 3a/2. Find the modulus of elasticity of the string.*

If the string will snap if extended beyond a total length of 7a/4, calculate the maximum permissible angular speed if it is not to break.

The tension in the string at an angular speed of ω rad/s is $m\omega^2 r$, where r

---

* This force must not be confused with the centrifugal force. The centrifugal force is a purely imaginary one introduced into problems by mathematicians when their frame of reference is also rotating. By so doing they are able to treat their problem as if their frame of reference was stationary. For example, in the above case if we take P as our point of reference then we must introduce a fictitious force equal to $m\omega^2 r$ acting away from the centre so that the forces on P are then in equilibrium. However it is not necessary to use it here and it can cause some confusion if it is introduced. It is therefore not mentioned in the text. The student should refer to more advanced texts should he wish to understand it further.

is the radius. Therefore at 10 rad/s the tension in the string is

$$10^2 \times \frac{3am}{2} \text{ N} = 150ma \text{ N}.$$

Let the modulus of elasticity be λ, then applying Hooke's Law,

$$150ma = \tfrac{1}{2}\lambda.$$

∴ the modulus of elasticity is 300ma N.

By Hooke's Law, the tension in the string when at breaking point is

$$300ma . \frac{3a/4}{a} \text{ N} = 225ma \text{ N}.$$

If it rotates with speed ω rad/s in the limiting case, then

$$225ma = m\omega^2 . \frac{7a}{4},$$

$$\omega^2 = \frac{900}{7}.$$

∴ the maximum speed of rotation is $30/\sqrt{7}$ rad/s.

EXAMPLE 2   *A particle of mass M is suspended from a fixed point* X *by a light inextensible string of length l, and is rotating with constant angular speed ω rad/s in a horizontal circle. Find the angle the string makes with the vertical.*

We refer to this kind of system as a conical pendulum. We obtain the solution by resolving the forces acting on the particle. In the vertical direction their resultant must be zero; horizontally the force must be that which is required to maintain the circular motion.

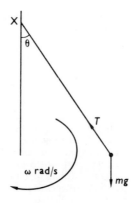

Fig. 125

Let the tension in the string be T, and the angle it makes with the vertical θ. Resolving the forces on the particle vertically,

$$T \cos \theta = mg. \tag{1}$$

The horizontal force required to maintain circular motion is $m\omega^2 l \sin \theta$. Thus resolving horizontally,

$$T \sin \theta = m\omega^2 l \sin \theta,$$
$$T = m\omega^2 l. \tag{2}$$

Substituting for T in (1),

$$m\omega l^2 \cos \theta = mg,$$

$$\cos \theta = \frac{g}{\omega^2 l}.$$

$\therefore$ the string makes an angle $\cos^{-1}(g/\omega^2 l)$ with the vertical.

EXAMPLE 3   *A light inelastic string of length 27 cm is attached to two points A and B distance 21 cm apart, A being vertically above B. C is a smooth ring of mass 100 g threaded on the string. The system is such that C moves with constant speed in a horizontal circle. Find the angular speed of C about AB and the tension in the string if C is 6 cm vertically above the level of B.*

Let the radius of the circle in which C moves be r cm, and let BC be x cm, then by Pythagoras

$$r^2 = x^2 - 36, \tag{1}$$

and $$r^2 = (27-x)^2 - 225. \tag{2}$$

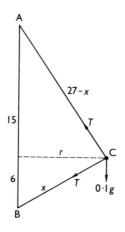

Fig. 126

Subtracting (2) from (1),

$$0 = 54x - 27^2 + 189,$$
$$0 = 2x - 27 + 7,$$
$$x = 10.$$

By Pythagoras, $r = 8$ (6, 8, 10 triangle).

Let the tension in the string be T N, and the angular speed ω rad/s. Resolving the forces acting on the ring vertically,

$$T \cos CAB = 0.1g + T \cos CBA,$$
$$\frac{15}{17}T = \frac{g}{10} + \frac{3}{5}T,$$
$$\frac{24}{85}T = \frac{g}{10},$$
$$T = \frac{17}{48}g.$$

The horizontal component must maintain circular motion:

$$\frac{8}{17}T + \frac{4}{5}T = 0.1\omega^2 \times 0.08,$$
$$\frac{108}{85}T = 0.008\omega^2,$$
$$\omega^2 = \frac{108T}{0.008 \times 85}.$$

Substituting for T,

$$\omega^2 = \frac{108 \times 17 \times g}{0.008 \times 85 \times 48}$$
$$= \frac{9g}{0.16}.$$
$$\therefore \omega = 3\sqrt{g/0.4}$$
$$= 15\sqrt{g/2}.$$

The ring rotates at $15\sqrt{g/2}$ rad/s.

Exercise 25

1 Use the theory of dimensions to prove that the force acting on a particle of mass m rotating with angular speed ω about a point distance d away is proportional to $m\omega^2 d$. Deduce similarly an expression for its kinetic energy in terms of m, ω and d.

2 The inelastic light string of a conical pendulum is of length 30 cm, and the bob is of mass 0·36 kg. Find the tension in the string when the bob moves in a horizontal circle with speed 6 rad/s. If the string breaks when it makes an angle of 45° to the vertical, the bob moving in a horizontal circle, show that the breaking strain of the string is approximately 5·0 N, and find the angular speed when it breaks.

3 A particle of mass m is attached to one end of a light elastic string of natural length a. When held by the free end under gravity the particle will rest in equilibrium with the string stretched to a length of $5a/4$. If the free end is now attached to a fixed point on a smooth horizontal table and the particle made to rotate in a circle at constant speed round the fixed point on the table, find the angular speed about the fixed point when the radius of the circle is $7a/4$.

4 A particle of mass $\frac{1}{4}$ kg is rotating in a horizontal circle at 5 rad/s. The string to which it is attached is fixed to a point above the centre of the circle and is elastic. The natural length of the string is 0·2 m, and it makes an angle of 30° with the vertical. Find the modulus of elasticity λ of the string.

5 A light inextensible string OA of length $2a$ is attached at O to a fixed point on a smooth horizontal table, and a particle of mass m is attached to A. A is rotating in a circle of radius $2a$ about O with speed ω rad/s when the string is caught by a peg P distant a from O. Calculate the new angular speed about P, and the change in the tension of the string.

6 Two light inelastic strings AB, BC of lengths 0·45 m and 0·60 m are attached to a bob of mass m at B and to fixed points A and C such that A is 0·75 m vertically below C. The bob is made to move in a horizontal circle with AB being just taut but under no tension. If the angular speed is then doubled, calculate the new tensions in both strings.

7 A particle of mass m is attached to two strings AB and BC at B. AB is inelastic of length $2a$; BC is elastic of natural length a and modulus of elasticity mg. A and C are two fixed points distant $3a/2$ apart, A being vertically above C. Find the angular speed at which B must rotate in a horizontal circle about AC if BC is to equal AB.

8 A light inelastic string of length $5a$ has masses of magnitudes $4M$ and M attached at the ends. The string passes through a small smooth ring which is fixed, and the larger mass is allowed to hang vertically below the ring. It is supported at a depth less than $5a$ below the ring by the lighter mass being made to rotate in a horizontal circle under gravity. Obtain an expression for the depth d of the larger mass below the ring in terms of the angular speed of the smaller mass, and find the angle of inclination of the string to the vertical.

10.3 Applications

In Chapter 5 it was pointed out that there was a distinction to be drawn between the Centre of Mass of a body, and the Centre of Gravity. The Centre of Gravity is the point through which a force of attraction can be taken to act. In a situation not complicated by external forces, a force causing a body to rotate in a circle will act through the centre of gravity. Provided the circle is sufficiently large then the Centre of Gravity through which this force acts will coincide with the Centre of Mass.

If we consider a vehicle rounding a corner of a road then it will not be possible for forces to be directly applied through the Centre of Gravity— the necessary force must be applied at the point of contact with the road. Consider the case of a cyclist. Most of us know from our own experience that when we round a corner on a bicycle we have to lean into the curve which we are rounding. If the necessary force F could be applied through the Centre of Gravity G, then we could round the corner in the upright position, our weight W and the normal reaction R of the road at A being the only forces acting (Fig. 127a). But in practice the rotating force acts at A. Thus, to be equivalent to the first case, a couple must also be introduced, and we obtain this by leaning inwards. Thus the rotational force at G is replaced by an equal force acting at A plus the couple which is represented by the weight and the normal reaction at A (Fig. 127b).

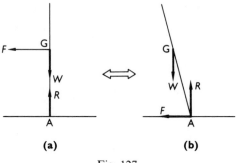

Fig. 127

The same type of situation will arise in the case of any vehicle rounding a corner, but in the case of a four-wheeled vehicle the couple is obtained by a combination of reactions on the ground together with the weight. A full consideration in such instances is made difficult because friction is not generally limiting at all four wheels, nor even at any wheel, and so too many variables come into the equations. However we can analyse some special cases, e.g. when no friction acts at all, when a car begins to slide, or when the reactions on the inside wheels are zero and the vehicle begins to pivot about the outside wheels. We can also consider the motion round a curve of a railway truck. In this case the rotating force can only be applied on the outside wheels on the flange that keeps it on the track. We illustrate the principles involved in the following examples.

EXAMPLE 4   *A man and his bicycle together weigh 100 kg, and when in the upright position the Centre of Gravity of the man and bicycle together is 1 m above the ground. Find at what angle he must lean over in order to round a corner of radius 20 m at a speed of 18 km/h.*

The example is illustrated by Fig. 127. Since 18 km/h is equivalent to 5 m/s, the force F required to maintain the circular motion is

$$100 \times 25/20 \text{ N} = 125 \text{ N}.$$

Let the man lean over at an angle θ to the vertical. Since (a) and (b) are equivalent in Fig. 127, it follows that moments about the Centre of Gravity G must be zero.

$$\therefore \quad 125 \cos \theta = 100g \sin \theta,$$

$$\tan \theta = 1\cdot25/g$$

$$\doteqdot 0\cdot1275.$$

$$\theta = 7° \ 16'.$$

∴ man must lean at 7° 16′ to the vertical.

EXAMPLE 5   *A car of mass 950 kg can round a horizontal curve of radius 40 m at a maximum speed of 72 km/h, friction being sufficiently great to prevent sliding at greater speed. If the width of the car is 1·8 m, find the height of the Centre of Gravity above the road.*

Find at what angle the road should be banked so that the car can round the curve at 36 km/h without any frictional force being required at the contact with the road. Find the new maximum speed for the car to round the corner assuming that it will still pivot before it slides.

Because friction is large enough to prevent sliding at a greater speed, the car is about to pivot on the outer wheels at 72 km/h round this curve. Let the Centre of Gravity be a m above the level of the road. Fig. 128(a) illustrates the ideal case where the necessary force acts through the Centre of Gravity and Fig. 128(b) the actual case where it is applied at the road. The two situations must be equivalent.

The force required to give the turning motion is

$$950 \times 20^2/40 \ \text{N} = 9500 \ \text{N},$$

(since 72 km/h ≡ 20 m/s).

Taking moments about the Centre of Gravity,

$$9500a = 950g \times 0\cdot9,$$

$$a = 0\cdot09g$$

$$\doteqdot 0\cdot882.$$

The Centre of Gravity is 0·88 m above the road (to 2 significant figures).

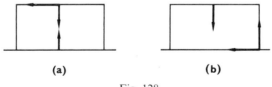

(a)   (b)

Fig. 128

We do not need to know anything about this car to find the optimum banking required for a speed of 36 km/h. In this situation no frictional force acts; the horizontal component of the normal reaction to the road must be sufficient to cause the circular motion. The normal reaction and the weight are the only forces acting, and so the situation can be summarized as in Fig. 129.

Let the normal reaction be T, and the curve be banked at an angle θ to the horizontal. Resolving vertically,

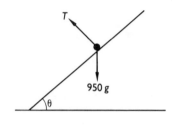

Fig. 129

$$T \cos \theta = 950g.$$

Since $36 \text{ km/h} \equiv 10 \text{ m/s},$

the horizontal force required is

$$950 \times 10^2/40 = T \sin \theta.$$

Hence $$\tan \theta = \frac{9\cancel{5}0 \times 10\cancel{0}}{9\cancel{5}0g \times 4\cancel{0}}$$

$$= \frac{5}{2g}.$$

$$\theta = 14° \; 18'.$$

The road must be banked at 14° 18' to the horizontal.

Let the new maximum speed be v km/h, the reaction at the outside wheel be R N normally and F N the frictional component (Fig. 130). Taking moments about the Centre of Gravity,

$$0.882 \, F = 0.9 \, R,$$

$$R = 0.98F.$$

Resolving vertically,

$$R \cos 14° \; 18' = 950g + F \sin 14° \; 18',$$

$$0.951F = 9310 + 0.247F,$$

$$F = \frac{9310}{0.704}$$

$$= 13\,230.$$

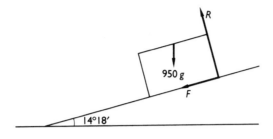

Fig. 130

Resolving horizontally

$$R \sin 14° \ 18' + F \cos 14° \ 18' = 950v^2 \times \frac{10^2}{36^2}/40,$$

$$(0·242 + 0·969)F = 9500v^2/(4 \times 36^2),$$

$$v^2 = \frac{1·211 \times 4 \times 36^2 \times 13\,230}{9500}$$

$$\fallingdotseq 8750.$$

$$v \fallingdotseq 92·7.$$

∴ the new maximum speed is 92·7 km/h (to 3 significant figures).

EXAMPLE 6   *A railway carriage of mass 4 t rounds a curve of radius 80 m at a speed of 48 km/h. The track is of width 1·44 m and is horizontal. If the Centre of Gravity of the carriage is 1·5 m above the rails, find the vertical forces exerted by the rails, and the horizontal force exerted by the outer rail on the wheel flanges.*

Let the vertical reactions on the inner and outer rails be R N and S N respectively, and the horizontal force exerted on the flanges be T N. Resolving vertically,

$$R + S = 4000g. \tag{1}$$

Resolving horizontally (noting that 48 km/h ≡ 40/3 m/s),

$$T = 4000 \times \frac{1600}{9}/80$$

$$= 80\,000/9. \tag{2}$$

Taking moments about the centre of gravity,

$$0·72R + 1·5T = 0·72S,$$

$$12R + 25T = 12S. \tag{3}$$

Substituting in (3) from (2),

$$12R + 2\,000\,000/9 = 12S.$$

Substituting for R from (1),

$$48\,000g + 2\,000\,000/9 = 24S.$$

$$\therefore\ S = 2000g + \frac{2\,000\,000}{216}$$

$$\doteqdot 19\,620 + 9260$$

$$= 28\,880.$$

From (1)
$$R \doteqdot 39\,240 - 28\,880$$

$$= 10\,360.$$

$\therefore$ force on inner rail is 10 400 N; vertical force on outer rail is 28 900 N; horizontal force on flanges is 8890 N (all to 3 significant figures).

10.4 Instantaneous centre

If a lamina is moving in its own plane, then there exists a point I fixed relative to the lamina which is stationary at a given instant relative to the frame of reference. This point is called the **Instantaneous Centre of Rotation**; it is the point about which the lamina can be said to be rotating at that particular instant. If the lamina is moving in a straight line then the instantaneous centre is at infinity. The corresponding situation in three dimensions gives an instantaneous axis—the line about which a body can be said to be rotating at a particular instant.

Suppose a lamina is moving in its own plane, and at a given instant the point I is the instantaneous centre. If X is any point in the lamina then, because it is rigid, the velocity of X must be perpendicular to the line IX. Thus if we know the velocities of two points X and Y in the lamina not in line with I, we can find I by considering the perpendiculars to the velocities at X and Y, I being at their intersection (Fig. 131a).

By way of further illustration, let X and Y be the ends of a rigid rod of length a, and suppose X and Y are constrained so that X can move along Ox, and Y along Oy, Ox and Oy being rectangular axes with origin O. Since X moves on Ox, the instantaneous centre I lies on a line through X parallel to Oy. Similarly I lies on a line through Y parallel to Ox (Fig. 131b).

After a certain interval, let X be at X' and Y at Y', then the instantaneous centre I' is the fourth vertex of the rectangle OX'I'Y'. Since OXIY is always a rectangle it is evident that OI must always equal XY. Thus the locus of the instantaneous centre is a circle of radius a and centre O. Notice that it follows that the rod momentarily rotates about X just as Y passes through O, the rod lying along Ox.

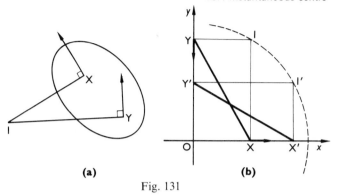

(a)   (b)

Fig. 131

If a lamina is rolling without slipping on a fixed surface, then the point of contact will be the instantaneous centre. The case of a wheel rolling along on a straight road is an obvious example.

EXAMPLE 7   *Find the velocity of a point* P *on the rim of a wheel of radius r m at a height h m above the road if it is rolling at 30 rev/min.*

Let the instantaneous centre, the point in contact with the ground, be C and let O be the centre of the wheel. Let angle OCP be θ. The velocity of P must then be perpendicular to CP. We note that there are two possible cases in that P can be moving either up or down.

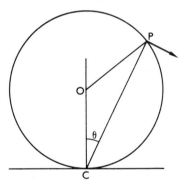

Fig. 132

The angular speed of the wheel about C is the same as it is about any other point on the wheel. This is true for any lamina provided that we are considering the angular speed about a particular point in the lamina or the instantaneous centre. We must however distinguish this from the angular speed about a fixed point of reference (other than the instantaneous centre) external to the lamina.

$$30 \text{ rev/min} \equiv 2\pi \times \tfrac{1}{2} \text{ rad/s} = \pi \text{ rad/s}.$$

The speed of P is v m/s where

$$v = \pi \times CP$$
$$= \pi \times h \sec \theta.$$

But
$$h = r(1 + \cos 2\theta)$$
$$= 2r \cos^2 \theta.$$
$$\therefore \quad \cos \theta = \sqrt{\frac{h}{2r}},$$

and
$$v = \pi h . \sqrt{\frac{2r}{h}}$$
$$= \pi \sqrt{2rh}.$$

The velocity of P is $\pi \sqrt{2rh}$ m/s at an angle $\cos^{-1} \sqrt{h/2r}$ above or below the horizontal.

It is useful to note an alternative approach to this example which emphasizes the dual nature of the motion. The motion is composed of two parts: a translation of the whole wheel in the direction of the road at a speed of v m/s $= \pi r$ m/s, and a rotation of π rad/s about O. Therefore the velocity of P has a horizontal component of $v = \pi r$, and a component $v = \pi r$ perpendicular to OP. Adding these two components together gives us the same result as before. In general, any motion can be considered in two separate parts, one of translation and the other of rotation.

EXAMPLE 8   *At a given moment, two points* A *and* B *moving in the* **i,j***-plane have positions given by the vectors*

$$\mathbf{a} = 3\mathbf{i} + 2\mathbf{j} \quad \text{and} \quad \mathbf{b} = \mathbf{i} - 4\mathbf{j}.$$

Their velocity vectors at this instant are

$$\dot{\mathbf{a}} = -2\mathbf{i} + 10\mathbf{j} \quad \text{and} \quad \dot{\mathbf{b}} = 10\mathbf{i} + 6\mathbf{j}.$$

Show that this is consistent with the hypothesis that they are both points on a rigid lamina, and find the instantaneous centre.

The line through A perpendicular to $\dot{\mathbf{a}}$ is

$$\mathbf{r}_1 = (3 + 5s)\mathbf{i} + (2 + s)\mathbf{j},$$

and through B perpendicular to $\dot{\mathbf{b}}$ is

$$\mathbf{r}_2 = (1 + 3t)\mathbf{i} - (4 + 5t)\mathbf{j}.$$

Putting $\mathbf{r}_1 = \mathbf{r}_2$,

$$2 + 5s = 3t, \tag{1}$$

and $$6+s = -5t.$$ (2)

Subtracting $5 \times (2)$ from (1),

$$-28 = 28t,$$

$$t = -1.$$

$\therefore$ the point of intersection is $\mathbf{c} = -2\mathbf{i}+\mathbf{j}$.

If A and B are part of a rigid lamina, then this will be the instantaneous centre, and their angular velocities about this point must be equal. The angular velocity of A about $\mathbf{c}$ is

$$|\dot{\mathbf{a}}|/|\mathbf{a}-\mathbf{c}| = \frac{2\sqrt{26}}{\sqrt{26}} = 2.$$

Similarly

$$|\dot{\mathbf{b}}|/|\mathbf{b}-\mathbf{c}| = \frac{2\sqrt{34}}{\sqrt{34}} = 2.$$

$\therefore$ it is consistent that A and B be points on a rigid lamina, and the instantaneous centre is the point $-2\mathbf{i}+\mathbf{j}$.

Exercise 26

1 A curve of radius 60 m in a railway track is banked at an angle of 5° to the horizontal. Determine at what speed (in km/h) a train will round the curve without exerting any sideways thrust on the rails.

2 A man and his bicycle together weigh 90 kg. He rounds a bend of radius 36 m leaning over at an angle of 6° from the vertical, the road being flat. Determine his speed as he rounds the corner.

3 A car of width 1·6 m has its centre of gravity 0·6 m above the ground. If the coefficient of friction between the road and the tyres is $\frac{4}{5}$, determine whether it will tend to pivot on the outer wheels or slide round a bend of radius 35 m which is banked at an angle of 8° to the horizontal, assuming that it is being driven at the maximum safe speed. Find this maximum speed in km/h.

4 A car can just round a certain bend at 60 km/h without sliding, the coefficient of friction between road and tyres being $\frac{3}{4}$. The road is banked at an angle of 9° to the horizontal. Find the radius of the curve.

If the coefficient of friction is reduced to $\frac{1}{2}$ in wet weather, find the maximum safe speed in wet conditions.

5 A parcel of weight 0·25 kg rests on the back shelf of a car, coefficient of friction μ. The parcel just begins to slide forward when the car brakes at a rate of $2g/3$ m/s². Find μ, and determine the speed in km/h at which the parcel will begin to slide when rounding a horizontal bend of radius 25 m.

6 A hoop, radius R, rolls in a vertical plane along a straight horizontal road. A wheel of radius r rolls inside the hoop so that they are always in rough contact at the lowest point. If the hoop rolls at 10 rad/s, find the angular speed of the wheel. Find also the greatest linear speed of a point on the rim of the wheel.

7 At a given moment two points A and B of a plane lamina have position vectors

$$\mathbf{a} = \mathbf{i}+3\mathbf{j} \quad \text{and} \quad \mathbf{b} = 2\mathbf{i}+\mathbf{j}.$$

The velocity of A is $\dot{\mathbf{a}} = -6\mathbf{i}-9\mathbf{j}$, and of B is $\dot{\mathbf{b}} = k(\mathbf{i}+\mathbf{j})$. Find the position vector of the instantaneous centre, and the value of k. Find also the velocity vector of C, a third point on the lamina with position vector $\mathbf{c} = 3\mathbf{i} + 4\mathbf{j}$.

8 A square lamina ABCD is moving in its own plane. The motion is composed of a translation of 2 m/s such that X, the intersection of the diagonals, moves along the line $\mathbf{r} = p\mathbf{i}$ and is at the origin when $t = 0$, and also a rotation of 1 rad/s. Show that the velocity of A after time t is

$$\dot{\mathbf{a}} = (2 + \cos t)\mathbf{i} + \sin t\mathbf{j},$$

given that A is at $-\mathbf{j}$ when $t = 0$. Write down the position and velocity vectors of C, and hence find the path of the instantaneous centre.

9 A railway track is being built in which there is a curve of radius 115 m. If the width is 1·44 m, find how much the outside rail must be above the inner if a train travelling at 54 km/h is to round the curve without putting sideways pressure on the rails.

Determine the magnitude of the force exerted on the inside rail by a wagon of mass 1·8 t rounding the curve at 24 km/h if its Centre of Mass is 1·2 m above the rails.

10 Project Example:

By taking realistic proportions, investigate the cornering characteristics of a car before it reaches any limiting state. Justify any assumptions that you have to make. In particular, compare the limiting cases due to friction and pivoting with different degrees of banking.

10.5 Motion in a vertical circle

If a particle is moving in a vertical circle without any work being put into the motion, then the Conservation of Energy enables us to determine the speed of the particle at any instant. But if the particle is attached to a string then it is possible that it will not reach the top, but will break away into a parabolic motion.

Suppose the particle P is attached by a light inextensible string OP to a fixed point O, and that P is moving in a vertical circle, centre O. P will

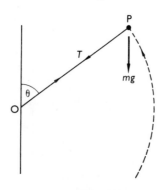

Fig. 133

move in this circle so long as there is some tension in the string. Let the tension in the string be T when OP makes an angle θ with the upward vertical through O, and the mass of the particle be m. The force along PO must be that which is required to maintain circular motion. Thus if $OP = r$,

$$T + mg \cos \theta = \frac{mv^2}{r}$$

where v is the speed of P. At the point when the string becomes slack $T = 0$, and

$$mg \cos \theta = \frac{mv^2}{r}. \qquad \qquad 10.4$$

Now if P is moving upwards θ is decreasing, and so $mg \cos \theta$ is increasing. But since the particle is gaining potential energy, mv^2/r must get less. In other words the force acting along PO becomes greater than that which is required for circular motion, and the particle is 'pulled' out of the circular path.

Equation 10.4 demonstrates the further point that if P just reaches the highest point of the circle then the particle will continue in the circle. If it just reaches the top then $mg = mv^2/r$. As it continues, $mg \cos \theta$ begins to decrease, and mv^2/r will increase, so that

$$mg \cos \theta < mv^2/r.$$

Thus the circular motion is maintained.

EXAMPLE 9   *A particle P of mass m is attached by a light inextensible string of length r to a fixed point O. If it is projected from a point distant r vertically below O with speed v horizontally, find the minimum value of v if it is to move in a complete vertical circle. For this value of v find the tension in the string when OP makes an angle of 60° with the upward vertical through O.*

If instead the string goes slack when OP makes an angle of 60° with the upward drawn vertical through O, find the new value of v.

In general, if OP makes an angle θ with the upward drawn vertical through O, then the speed of P at this instant is given by the Conservation of Energy:

$$\tfrac{1}{2}mv^2 = \tfrac{1}{2}mu^2 + mg(r + r \cos \theta).$$

If it just reaches the highest point of the circle then this equation becomes

$$\tfrac{1}{2}mv^2 = \tfrac{1}{2}mu^2 + 2mgr,$$

and the weight is just equal to the force required for circular motion (equation 10.4).

$$\therefore \ mg = mu^2/r.$$

Eliminating u^2,

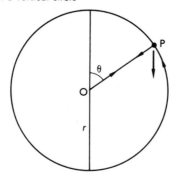

Fig. 134

$$\tfrac{1}{2}mv^2 = \tfrac{1}{2}mgr + 2mgr,$$
$$v^2 = 5gr.$$

∴.Minimum value of v is $\sqrt{5gr}$ for complete circular motion.

When $\theta = 60°$, the energy equation becomes

$$\tfrac{1}{2}mv^2 = \tfrac{1}{2}mu^2 + \tfrac{3}{2}mgr.$$
$$\therefore\ 5gr = u^2 + 3gr,$$
$$u^2 = 2gr.$$

Therefore the force required to maintain circular motion is $2mgr/r = 2mg$. But the weight of the particle only has a component of $mg \cos 60° = \tfrac{1}{2}mg$ along PO. The tension in the string is the difference.

∴ Tension in the string is $\tfrac{3}{2}mg$ when at $60°$ to the vertical.

If in fact the string goes slack in this position, then the force causing circular motion is equal to the component of the weight along PO—$\tfrac{1}{2}mg$. Let the speed of P at this moment be u', then

$$\tfrac{1}{2}mg = mu'^2/r,$$
$$u'^2 = gr/2.$$

The Conservation of Energy now gives

$$\tfrac{1}{2}mv^2 = \tfrac{1}{2}mu'^2 + \tfrac{3}{2}mgr,$$
$$v^2 = gr/2 + 3gr,$$
$$= \frac{7gr}{2}.$$

∴ new initial speed is $\sqrt{7gr/2}$.

EXAMPLE 10   *A smooth wire is bent in the form of a circle of radius r,*
and is fixed in a vertical plane. A bead B of mass m threaded on the wire is
projected from the lowest point P with speed $\sqrt{3gr}$. Show that the reaction
between the bead and the wire is zero when BP makes an angle $\cos^{-1} \sqrt{\frac{2}{3}}$
with the vertical.

Find the angle BP makes with the vertical when the bead first comes to
rest.

Let BP make an angle θ with the vertical, then if O is the centre of the
circle BO makes an angle 2θ with the vertical. Let the speed of the bead be
v when the reaction is zero, then

$$mg \cos 2\theta = mv^2/r. \qquad (1)$$

By the Conservation of Energy

$$\tfrac{1}{2}m.3gr = \tfrac{1}{2}mv^2 + mgr(1 + \cos 2\theta)$$

$$\Rightarrow \frac{mv^2}{r} = 3mg - 2mg(1 + \cos 2\theta)$$

$$= mg - 2mg \cos 2\theta.$$

Substituting in equation (1)

$$mg \cos 2\theta = mg - 2mg \cos 2\theta,$$

$$\cos 2\theta = \tfrac{1}{3}.$$

But $\cos^2\theta = \tfrac{1}{2}(\cos 2\theta + 1)$.

$$\therefore \cos^2 \theta = \tfrac{1}{2}(\tfrac{1}{3} + 1)$$

$$= \tfrac{2}{3}.$$

$$\therefore \theta = \cos^{-1} \sqrt{\tfrac{2}{3}}. \qquad \text{Q.E.D.}$$

By the Conservation of Energy the bead comes to rest when

$$\tfrac{3}{2}mgr = mgr(1 + \cos 2\theta)$$

$$\Rightarrow \cos 2\theta = \tfrac{1}{2}$$

$$\Rightarrow \cos^2 \theta = \tfrac{3}{4}.$$

$\therefore$ BP makes an angle of $\cos^{-1} \frac{\sqrt{3}}{2}$ with the vertical when the bead first
comes to rest.

EXAMPLE 11   *A particle P of mass m lies at rest on the highest point A*
of a smooth fixed sphere of radius r, centre O. B is the other end of the dia-
meter AOB, and is in contact with a horizontal plane. If the mass is just
slightly dislodged from equilibrium, find the angle OP makes with AB at
the instant it leaves the surface of the sphere.

Find also the distance from B of the point X at which the particle strikes the plane.

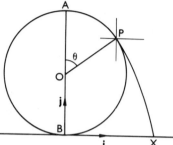

Fig. 135

At the instant the particle leaves the sphere, let angle POA $= \theta$, and the speed be u. The Conservation of Energy then gives

$$mgr = mgr \cos \theta + \tfrac{1}{2}mu^2,$$

$$u^2 = 2gr(1 - \cos \theta).$$

The force required for circular motion is $mg \cos \theta$, and so in this limiting position

$$mg \cos \theta = 2mgr(1 - \cos \theta)/r,$$

$$\cos \theta = 2 - 2 \cos \theta,$$

$$\cos \theta = \tfrac{2}{3}.$$

OP makes an angle $\cos^{-1} \tfrac{2}{3}$ with AB when P leaves the sphere.

If $\mathbf{i}$ and $\mathbf{j}$ are unit vectors through B, $\mathbf{i}$ horizontal and $\mathbf{j}$ vertical, the position of P relative to B at this instant is

$$\mathbf{p}(0) = r \sin \theta \mathbf{i} + r(1 + \cos \theta)\mathbf{j}$$

$$= \frac{\sqrt{5}}{3}r\mathbf{i} + \frac{5}{3}r\mathbf{j}.$$

The velocity of P at this instant is

$$\dot{\mathbf{p}}(0) = u \cos \theta \mathbf{i} - u \sin \theta \mathbf{j}$$

$$= \frac{2}{3}u\mathbf{i} - \frac{\sqrt{5}}{3}u\mathbf{j},$$

where, from the energy equation above, $u^2 = 2gr/3$.
After a further time t the position of P will be

$$\mathbf{p}(t) = \tfrac{1}{3}(\sqrt{5}r + 2ut)\mathbf{i} + \tfrac{1}{3}(5r - \sqrt{5}ut - \tfrac{3}{2}gt^2)\mathbf{j}.$$

Thus it will strike the ground when

$$3gt^2 + 2\sqrt{5}ut - 10r = 0.$$

Since t must be positive

$$t = \frac{-2\sqrt{5}u + \sqrt{20u^2 + 120gr}}{6g}.$$

Putting $u^2 = 2gr/3$

$$t = \frac{-\sqrt{5}u + 10\sqrt{gr/3}}{3g}.$$

Thus the position of X is given by

$$\mathbf{p}(t) = \frac{1}{3}\left(\sqrt{5}r + 2u \cdot \frac{-\sqrt{5}u + 10\sqrt{gr/3}}{3g}\right)\mathbf{i}$$

$$= \frac{1}{3}\left(\sqrt{5}r - \frac{2\sqrt{5}}{3g}\cdot\frac{2gr}{3} + \frac{20}{3g}\cdot\frac{\sqrt{2gr}}{3}\right)\mathbf{i}$$

$$= \frac{r}{27}(9\sqrt{5} - 4\sqrt{5} + 20\sqrt{2})\mathbf{i}$$

$$= \frac{5r}{27}(\sqrt{5} + 4\sqrt{2})\mathbf{i}.$$

The particle strikes the plane $\frac{5r}{27}(\sqrt{5} + 4\sqrt{2})$ from B.

EXAMPLE 12   *A particle P of mass m is attached to a fixed point O by a light inextensible string of length 3a. P is projected from the point 3a vertically below O with a horizontal velocity of magnitude v. When the string makes an angle of 60° with the downward vertical through O it comes into contact with a smooth peg Q which is a distance 2a from O. If after coming into contact with Q the string breaks when the particle is vertically below Q, find the breaking tension, assuming that v is sufficiently large for P to move in a complete vertical circle about Q.*

The additional complication of this example is that P rotates first about O and subsequently about Q. Since however the string is perpendicular to the velocity of P when it comes in contact with the peg, the momentum of P must remain unaltered at that instant. All that happens is that the radius of the rotation is suddenly shortened, so that the tension in the string is suddenly increased.

Let the velocity of P be u as the string touches the peg, then the Conservation of Energy gives

$$\tfrac{1}{2}mu^2 + 3mga(1 - \cos 60°) = \tfrac{1}{2}mv^2,$$

$$u^2 + 3ga = v^2,$$

$$u^2 = v^2 - 3ga.$$

Notice that at this point the impulsive tension in the string will be

$$\frac{mu^2}{a} - \frac{mu^2}{3a} = \frac{2mu^2}{3a}.$$

The particle now continues its motion about Q, and by the Conservation of Energy the speed u' when vertically below Q is given by

$$\tfrac{1}{2}mu'^2 = \tfrac{1}{2}mu^2 + \tfrac{1}{2}mga$$

$$= \tfrac{1}{2}mv^2 - \tfrac{3}{2}mga + \tfrac{1}{2}mga$$

$$= \tfrac{1}{2}m(v^2 - 2ga).$$

The tension in the string at this moment is

$$\frac{mu'^2}{a} + mg = \frac{m}{a}(v^2 - 2ga) + mg$$

$$= \frac{m}{a}(v^2 - ga).$$

The breaking tension of the string is $\dfrac{m}{a}(v^2 - ga)$.

Exercise 27

1 A particle of mass m attached by a light inelastic string of length r to a fixed point X is projected horizontally with speed $\sqrt{3gr}$ from a point depth r below X. Find the angle of the string to the vertical when it goes slack.

2 A particle of mass m is projected horizontally from the highest point of a fixed smooth sphere with speed $\sqrt{\dfrac{ga}{3}}$ where a is the radius. Find at what depth below the point of projection the particle leaves the surface of the sphere.

3 A particle of mass 10 g is attached to a light inextensible string of length 0·5 m, the other end of which is attached to a fixed point O. The particle is projected vertically downwards from a point 0·5 m from O on the same horizontal level as O with speed 2 m/s. Calculate the tension in the string when it reaches its lowest point. Show that it will not complete a full circle, and find at what point the string becomes slack.

4 A bead P of mass m is threaded on a smooth circular wire which is fixed in a vertical plane. The bead is projected from the lowest point L of the wire and just reaches the highest point H. Find angle PHL when the reaction between the bead and the wire is zero.

5 A bead of mass m is threaded on a smooth circular hoop of radius a fixed in a vertical plane. The bead is projected from the highest point on the hoop with speed $\dfrac{\sqrt{ga}}{2}$. Find at what depth below the point of projection the reaction between the bead and the hoop is zero. Find also the maximum reaction.

6 A bead B threaded on a smooth circular wire, centre O, fixed in a vertical plane, is projected from the highest point with speed u. Find the reaction between the bead and the wire when OB makes an angle ϕ with the vertical in terms of m, u, ϕ, g and the radius r.

7 A particle P of mass m is connected by a light inextensible string of length r to a fixed point O. It is projected horizontally with speed $2\sqrt{2gr}$ from a point distant r

vertically above O and the string snaps just when OP makes an angle of 30° with the downward vertical through O. Find the breaking tension of the string.

8 A particle P of mass m is attached to a fixed point O by a light inextensible string of length $3a$. The particle hangs at rest below O when it is given a horizontal velocity of magnitude v. When OP subsequently makes an angle of 60° with the upward vertical through O it comes into contact with a peg Q which is a distance a from O. P continues in a complete circle about Q. Find the maximum tension in the string as P rotates about Q.

9 A light inextensible string of length $2a$ is attached to a fixed point O at one end and has a particle X of mass m attached to the other. The string passes from O round a smooth peg P on the same horizontal level as and at a distance a from O, and back to X which is held at O. X is now given a velocity vertically upwards from O so as to just be able to move in a full circle round P. As X falls below the line OP the string loses contact with P. Find the angle of OX to the upward vertical when the string first becomes slack.

10 Two beads A and B of masses m_1 and m_2 are threaded on a smooth circular wire of radius a fixed in a vertical plane. B is stationary at the lowest point when A is gently dislodged from rest at the highest point. The impulse given to B is just great enough to carry it to the level of the centre of the circle, while A is brought immediately to rest by the impact. Show that

$$m_1 : m_2 = 1 : \sqrt{2}.$$

11 A particle of mass m is attached to the end of a light inextensible string of length $2a$ the other end of which is attached to a fixed point P. The particle is projected horizontally from the point $2a$ below P with speed v. As it comes level with P, a peg Q distant a from P catches the string. In the subsequent motion the particle can just describe a full circle about Q. Find v.

12 A bead of mass m is attached by a light inextensible string to a fixed point P, and is moving about P in a vertical circle. At the lowest point of its path the velocity of the bead is $4\sqrt{ga}$ where a is the length of the string. Show that when it has turned through an angle θ about P from this point the acceleration of the bead is

$$(3\cos^2\theta + 56\cos\theta + 197)^{\frac{1}{2}}g$$

at an angle to the horizontal of

$$\tan^{-1}\left(\frac{\operatorname{cosec}\theta}{14 + 3\cos\theta} - \cot\theta\right).$$

13 A particle on the end of a light inelastic string which is of length a and is attached to a fixed point X is projected with speed v horizontally from the point Y at a depth a below X. At a certain point the string becomes slack, and the particle then follows a parabolic path so as to pass directly through Y. Find v.

11 Simple Harmonic Motion

11.1 Definition and equations of motion

Apart from a few examples in which acceleration has been a simple function of time, we have confined our study to motion under a constant force. When the acceleration of a particle is dependent on velocity or position then more advanced methods of integration are required. It is now assumed that the student will be familiar with the necessary techniques.

We note first a most important and useful relation, i.e. with the usual notation

$$\frac{d^2x}{dt^2} = v\frac{dv}{dx}. \qquad\qquad 11.1$$

That this is true is evident when we write the left-hand side of *11.1* as

$$\frac{dv}{dt} = \frac{dv}{dx}\cdot\frac{dx}{dt} = v\cdot\frac{dv}{dx}.$$

Simple Harmonic Motion is defined by the equation of motion

$$\frac{d^2x}{dt^2} = -\omega^2x, \qquad\qquad 11.2$$

where ω is a constant. From the principle that force is mass × acceleration, it is seen to be equivalent to the motion of a particle acted upon by a force which is always directed towards a fixed point and is of magnitude proportional to its distance from that fixed point.

As with motion under a constant force we can deduce further relevant equations of motion by integration. Applying *11.1* to the equation *11.2* gives

$$v\frac{dv}{dx} = -\omega^2x.$$

Separating the variables* and integrating,

$$\int v\,dv = -\int\omega^2x\,dx,$$
$$\Rightarrow \tfrac{1}{2}v^2 = -\tfrac{1}{2}\omega^2x^2 + c.$$

* For further examples of this technique refer to Chapter 14.

By putting the constant $c = \frac{1}{2}\omega^2 a^2$, we have

$$v^2 = \omega^2(a^2 - x^2). \qquad 11.3$$

Since $v = 0$ when $x = \pm a$ it follows that the maximum distance from the fixed point is a. The distance a is referred to as the **amplitude** of the motion.

To integrate again we write *11.3* as

$$\frac{dx}{dt} = \omega\sqrt{(a^2 - x^2)}.$$

$$\therefore \; \omega\int dt = \int \frac{dx}{\sqrt{a^2 - x^2}}$$

$$\Rightarrow \omega t + \varepsilon = \sin^{-1}\frac{x}{a}, \text{ where } \varepsilon \text{ is a constant.}$$

$$\therefore \; x = a \sin(\omega t + \varepsilon). \qquad 11.4$$

The value of ε depends on the instant in time at which we begin measuring x. It is referred to as the **epoch**. It will be evident that *11.4* can equally well be written as

$$x = a \cos(\omega t + \varepsilon').$$

Alternatively, by using our knowledge of trigonometry,

$$x = a \sin(\omega t + \varepsilon)$$

$$= a(\sin \omega t \cos \varepsilon + \cos \omega t \sin \varepsilon)$$

$$= A \sin \omega t + B \cos \omega t,$$

where $A = a \cos \varepsilon$ and $B = a \sin \varepsilon$. Each form has its use, but where possible we take ε or ε' as zero.

It is evident by substitution or by differentiation that alternative forms of the definitive equation *11.2* are

$$\ddot{x} = -\omega^2 a \sin \omega t,$$

and

$$\ddot{x} = -\omega^2 a \cos \omega t.$$

Further, $\dot{x} = a \cos \omega t$ or $-a \sin \omega t$ are alternative forms to equation *11.3*.

Suppose the particle P is performing simple harmonic motion about the point O in the straight line AOB, where $AO = OB = a$. If we take the equation

$$x = a \sin \omega t$$

then we have the condition that P is at O when $t = 0$. Alternatively, if we take the form

$$x = a \cos \omega t,$$

we have the condition that P is at A or B when $t = 0$; taking the direction AOB to be positive gives P at B.

At this point, let us assume that P is at O when $t = 0$. Then $x = a \sin \omega t$. When P is subsequently at O,

$$a \sin \omega t = 0$$

$$\Rightarrow \omega t = n\pi.$$

where n is an integer. However it is only passing through O in the positive direction AOB when

$$\omega t = 2n\pi$$

$$\Rightarrow t = 2n\pi/\omega.$$

The time that elapses between two such consecutive occurrences is

$$2(n+1)\pi/\omega - 2n\pi/\omega = 2\pi/\omega.$$

In this time it is said to have completed one **cycle** since after this time it begins to repeat an identical motion over again. The time for one such cycle, $2\pi/\omega$, is called the **periodic time** (or more loosely just the period) and is often referred to by the Greek letter τ.

If one cycle is completed in time $2\pi/\omega$ then $\omega/2\pi$ cycles are performed in unit time. The number of cycles performed per unit time, $\omega/2\pi$, is called the **frequency** of the motion and has dimension $[T^{-1}]$. The S.I. unit of frequency is the **hertz** (Hz), and is a frequency of one cycle per second.

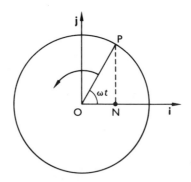

Fig. 136

Consider the equation of a circle of radius a, centre O the origin of perpendicular unit vectors **i** and **j**. It is

$$\mathbf{r} = a \cos \theta \mathbf{i} + a \sin \theta \mathbf{j},$$

(Fig. 136). Suppose P is a point moving round the circle with constant angular speed ω rad/s, then $\theta = \omega t$ and the position of P is given by

$$\mathbf{p} = a \cos \omega t \mathbf{i} + a \sin \omega t \mathbf{j}.$$

Thus

$$\dot{\mathbf{p}} = -a\omega \sin \omega t \mathbf{i} + a\omega \cos \omega t \mathbf{j},$$

and

$$\ddot{\mathbf{p}} = -a\omega^2 \cos \omega t \mathbf{i} - a\omega^2 \sin \omega t \mathbf{j}.$$

If p_i and $\ddot{p}_i$ are the $\mathbf{i}$-components of $\mathbf{p}$ and $\ddot{\mathbf{p}}$, then it is evident that

$$\ddot{p}_i = -\omega^2 p_i.$$

In other words, the projection N of P onto the $\mathbf{i}$-axis moves with simple harmonic motion about O with period $2\pi/\omega$. A similar result applies to the projection of P onto the $\mathbf{j}$-axis. This example of simple harmonic motion associated so directly with uniform circular motion is the main reason why ω is the Greek letter generally chosen for the constant in the definitive equation *11.2*.

Examples of simple harmonic motion range widely from the rise and fall of tides to the motion of springs and elastic strings, of clock pendulums to alternating current and oscillator circuits in electricity.

EXAMPLE 1   *A particle P performing simple harmonic motion in a straight line about a point O has speeds of 5 m/s and 3 m/s at two points A and B which are 0·2 m and 0·6 m respectively from O. Find the amplitude and frequency of the motion. Find also the length PO at the instant the velocity of the particle is 2/3 the maximum velocity of the motion.*

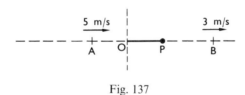

Fig. 137

Let the distance of P from O after t s be x m where

$$x = a \sin \omega t.$$

By the equation of motion *11.3*

$$\dot{x}^2 = \omega^2(a^2 - x^2).$$

$\therefore$ at A,

$$25 = \omega^2(a^2 - 0.04), \tag{1}$$

and at B,

$$9 = \omega^2(a^2 - 0.36). \tag{2}$$

Hence

$$\frac{25}{9} = \frac{a^2 - 0.04}{a^2 - 0.36},$$

$$(25 - 9)a^2 = 25 \times 0.36 - 9 \times 0.04,$$

$$16a^2 = 9 - 9 \times 0.04$$

$$= 9 \times 0.96.$$
$$\therefore \ a^2 = 9 \times 0.06$$
$$= 0.54,$$
$$\Rightarrow a \doteq 0.735.$$

The amplitude of the motion is 0·735 m (to 3 significant figures).

Substituting back into (2),

$$9 = \omega^2(0.54 - 0.36)$$
$$= \omega^2 \times 0.18.$$
$$\therefore \ \omega^2 = 50,$$
$$\omega \doteq 7.07.$$

Thus the frequency of the motion is
$$\omega/2\pi \ \text{Hz} \doteq 7.07/2\pi$$
$$\doteq 1.125 \ \text{Hz}.$$

The frequency is 1·125 Hz (to 3 decimal places).

The maximum velocity of P occurs when $x = 0$, and is ωa m/s, which is
$$\sqrt{50 \times 0.54} = \sqrt{27}$$
$$= 3\sqrt{3} \ \text{m/s}.$$

Thus when the velocity is 2/3 maximum, it is $2\sqrt{3}$ m/s, and by the equation of motion *11.3*

$$12 = 50(0.54 - x^2).$$

Thus
$$x^2 = 0.54 - 0.24$$
$$= 0.3,$$

and
$$x = \sqrt{0.3},$$
$$\doteq 0.548.$$

When the velocity is 2/3 maximum, PO is 0·548 m (to 3 significant figures).

11.2 Elastic strings and springs

In this section we consider simple harmonic motion induced by elastic strings and springs. We take first the relatively simple case in which a particle of mass m is suspended from a fixed point X by a light elastic string of natural length l and modulus of elasticity λ. The equilibrium position of the particle is then at a depth $l+e$ below X where by Hooke's Law

$$mg = \lambda\frac{e}{l}. \qquad\qquad 11.5$$

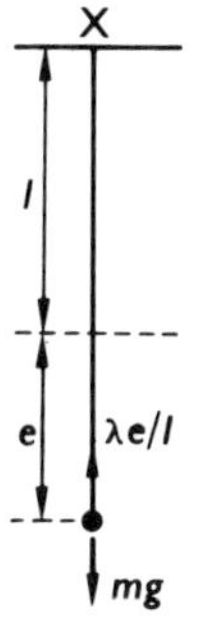

Fig. 138

If the particle is held at a point A, a distance a above the equilibrium position O, and released, then provided $a \leqslant e$ the particle will perform simple harmonic motion about O. Consider the force acting on the particle when at a height x above O. The force is the resultant of the tension in the string and the weight, and is

$$\lambda\frac{e-x}{l} - mg = \lambda\frac{e-x}{l} - \lambda\frac{e}{l} \text{ by } 11.5,$$

$$= -\lambda\frac{x}{l},$$

where the direction OA is taken as positive. By the principle, force = mass × acceleration, it follows that

$$\ddot{x} = -\frac{\lambda}{ml}x, \qquad\qquad 11.6$$

which is the definitive equation for simple harmonic motion. Hence we deduce that the amplitude of the motion is a, the periodic time is $2\pi\sqrt{\dfrac{ml}{\lambda}}$, and the frequency is $\dfrac{1}{2\pi}\sqrt{\dfrac{\lambda}{ml}}$ c/unit time. It is perhaps odd at first sight to discover that the periodic time of the motion is independent of the amplitude—it is dependent solely on permanent properties of the material concerned.

EXAMPLE 2   *A particle of mass 40 g is suspended from a fixed point by an elastic light string of natural length 0·8 m and modulus of elasticity 1·4 N.*

Find the period of small oscillations of the particle in a vertical line through the point of equilibrium.

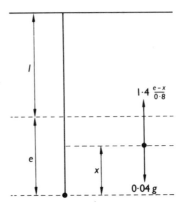

Fig. 139

Let the point of equilibrium of the particle be at a depth of $(0.8 + e)$ m below the fixed point. When the particle is at a height x above O the restoring force is by Hooke's Law

$$\left\{ 0.04g - 1.4\left(\frac{e-x}{0.8}\right) \right\} \text{ N.}$$

But in the equilibrium position, Hooke's Law also gives

$$0.04g = \frac{1.4e}{0.8}.$$

Thus the restoring force is

$$\frac{1.4}{0.8}x \text{ N} = 1.75 \text{ N.}$$

Applying the principle, force = mass × acceleration, the equation of motion is

$$\ddot{x} = -\frac{1.75}{0.04}x,$$

i.e. $\ddot{x} = -43.75x.$

The periodic time is therefore $2\pi\sqrt{43.75} \text{ s} = 0.951 \text{ s}.$

Periodic time = 0.95 s (to 2 significant figures).

The motion of the particle on an elastic string is only pure simple harmonic if $a \leqslant e$. If $a > e$ then there is a part of the motion which is solely under gravity. In such cases the motion must be analysed in two separate parts. In one stage the equations of motion *2.1–2.3* would apply, and in the other the equations of motion *11.2–11.4* must be used. This may give rise to much more calculation, but the application of the principle of conservation of energy can often reduce this considerably. Fig. 140 illustrates the velocity-time graphs for the two cases $a \leqslant e$ and $a > e$, emphasizing the essential difference between them. The motion of a spring differs from that of elastic strings only in so far as it is simple harmonic motion for all values of a.

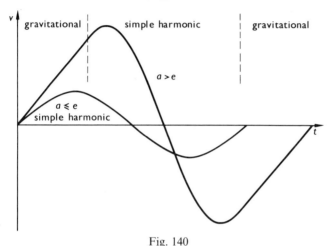

Fig. 140

EXAMPLE 3   *A particle of mass m is attached to the end of a light elastic string of natural length a and modulus of elasticity mg. The other end of the string is attached to a fixed point X. If the particle is released from rest at X, find the maximum speed of the particle and the time that elapses before it returns to X.*

The point of equilibrium O is at a depth of $2a$ below X (by Hooke's Law). Suppose that the particle falls to a depth d below X, then by the Conservation of Energy

$$\tfrac{1}{2}mg\frac{(d-a)^2}{a} - mgd = 0$$

where X is taken as the level of zero potential. Hence

$$d^2 - 2ad + a^2 - 2ad = 0,$$
$$d^2 - 4ad + a^2 = 0.$$

$$\therefore\ d = \frac{4 \pm \sqrt{16-4}}{2}a$$

$$= (2 \pm \sqrt{3})a.$$

Since $d > 2a$,

$$d = (2+\sqrt{3})a.$$

Thus the amplitude of the simple harmonic part of the motion is

$$d-2a = \sqrt{3}a.$$

The force acting on the particle when it is at a point distance x above O $(x \leqslant a)$ in the direction OX is, by Hooke's Law

$$mg\frac{a-x}{a} - mg = -mgx/a.$$

$$\therefore \ddot{x} = -\frac{g}{a}x.$$

From equation *11.3* it follows that the maximum speed of the particle is

$$\sqrt{\frac{g}{a}} \cdot \sqrt{3a} = \sqrt{3ga}.$$

Let $x = a$ when $t = 0$, then equation *11.4* (in the cosine form as x initially decreases) gives

$$a = \sqrt{3}a \cos \varepsilon.$$

$$\therefore \varepsilon = \cos^{-1}\frac{1}{\sqrt{3}}.$$

If T s elapse before it again reaches this point then

$$\cos \varepsilon = \cos\left(\sqrt{\frac{g}{a}}T+\varepsilon\right),$$

i.e.

$$\sqrt{\frac{g}{a}}T+\varepsilon = 2\pi-\varepsilon,$$

$$\Rightarrow T = 2\sqrt{\frac{a}{g}}\left(\pi-\cos^{-1}\frac{1}{\sqrt{3}}\right).$$

To this we must add the time taken to fall the distance a from X, say T' s, and back again. Using the equation of motion: $s = ut+\frac{1}{2}at^2$,

$$a = \frac{1}{2}gT'^2,$$

$$\Rightarrow T' = \sqrt{\frac{2a}{g}}.$$

$\therefore$ Maximum speed is $\sqrt{3ga}$, and total time for one complete oscillation is

$$2\sqrt{\frac{a}{g}}\left(\pi-\cos^{-1}\frac{1}{\sqrt{3}}+\sqrt{2}\right) \text{ s.}$$

EXAMPLE 4   *A spring balance is composed of a vertical spring of natural length a and modulus of elasticity 10mg, together with a flat hori-*

zontal pan of mass m fixed to the top of the spring. A weight of mass 4m is held just touching the pan which is in equilibrium and is released. Show that the subsequent motion of the pan is simple harmonic of period $\sqrt{\dfrac{2a}{g}}\pi$.

By Hooke's Law, the equilibrium position of the empty pan is such that the spring is compressed a distance $a/10$. If the weight and pan were in equilibrium then the total compression would be $a/2$ by the same Law. It follows that if the motion is simple harmonic that it must have amplitude $(a/2 - a/10) = 2a/5$, and that the centre of the oscillation is at a height $a/2$ above the base of the spring. Let this point be P.

The force acting on the pan towards P when it is at a distance x above P is

$$5mg - 10g\frac{a/2 - x}{a} = 5mg - 5mg + 10gx/a$$

$$= 10gx/a.$$

By the principle, force = mass × acceleration, it follows that the acceleration of the pan upwards is

$$\ddot{x} = -10gx/5a$$

$$= -\frac{2a}{a}x.$$

This is simple harmonic motion of period $2\pi\sqrt{\dfrac{a}{2g}} = \sqrt{\dfrac{2a}{g}}\pi$.   Q.E.D.

EXAMPLE 5   *Suppose that in Example 4 the weight had been released from a point distance d above the pan. Find the maximum value of d if the weight is not to leave the face of the pan in the subsequent motion, assuming that the pan is inelastic.*

We approach the question by considering first the motion of the pan. In Example 4 it was shown that the pan will oscillate according to the equation

$$\ddot{x} = -\frac{2g}{a}x,$$

which is independent of the amplitude of the motion. Now the weight will only leave the pan if the maximum acceleration exceeds g. Thus the amplitude in the limiting case is A where

$$2\frac{g}{a}A = g,$$

$$A = \frac{a}{2}.$$

Just as the weight strikes the pan, $x = 2a/5$. Let the speed immediately after the weight strikes the pan be v, then by *11.3*

$$v^2 = \frac{2g}{a}\left(\frac{a^2}{4} - \frac{4a^2}{25}\right)$$

$$= \frac{9ag}{50}.$$

If the speed of the weight was u just before the impact then by the Conservation of Momentum,

$$4u = 5v.$$

Hence

$$u^2 = \frac{25}{16}\cdot\frac{9ag}{50}$$

$$= \frac{9ag}{32}.$$

But by the equation of motion $v^2 = u^2 + 2as$,

$$u^2 = 2gd.$$

$$\therefore d = \frac{9a}{64}.$$

The maximum value of d if the weight does not rebound is $9a/64$.

Exercise 28

1 A particle of unit mass is moving along a straight line OX under the action of a force of magnitude v towards O where v is the speed. When time $t = 0$, $x = 10$ and $v = 10$. Use the substitution

$$\frac{d^2x}{dt^2} = v\frac{dv}{dx}$$

to show that

$$(20-x)e^t = 10.$$

2 The acceleration of a particle of unit mass is $\frac{1}{v}$ m/s^2 where v is its speed. Form an expression for the distance x of the particle from O after time t s if it passes through O when $t = 0$ with velocity 2 m/s.

In questions 3–6, P is a point oscillating with simple harmonic motion between two points A and B a distance $2a$ apart.

3 Find the velocity of P when a distance $\frac{a}{2}$ from A if the frequency of the motion is 2 Hz and $a = 30$ mm.

4 Find the position of P when time $t = \frac{\pi}{12}$ given that P is at A when $t = 0$, the periodic time is $\frac{\pi}{4}$, and the amplitude of the motion is 40 mm.

5 Find the amplitude of the motion if P is moving with speed 42 mm/s when 3 mm from A, and with speed 120 mm/s when 30 mm from A, given that both points are nearer A than B. Find also the period of the motion.

6 C and D are points on AB such that $AC = CD = \frac{a}{3}$. Find the ratio of the velocities at C and D, and the time which elapses between successive arrivals at C and D if the periodic time is T.

7 A particle P is moving with simple harmonic motion between two points A and B on a straight line. The amplitude of the motion is 25 mm and the frequency is $6/\pi$ Hz. Find the maximum acceleration and the maximum speed of P.

8 A point of light is moving across a screen along a straight line AB with simple harmonic motion. AB is 250 mm long, and the frequency of the oscillation is 4 Hz. Find the maximum acceleration and maximum velocity of the point. Find also the speed and acceleration at the point C on AB if $AC = \frac{1}{4}CB$.

9 A particle passes through 3 successive points A, B and C on a straight line with speeds 336 mm/s, 600 mm/s and 720 mm/s respectively. If it is performing simple harmonic motion of amplitude 240 mm and period 0.4π s, determine the lengths of AB and BC to the nearest 0.1 mm.

10 An elastic string of modulus $mg/2$ and natural length a is suspended from a fixed point X. A particle of mass m is attached to the other end. If the system is in equilibrium and then the particle is slightly displaced in a vertical line find the period of the subsequent motion.

If the amplitude of the motion is $a/4$, find the maximum speed and maximum acceleration of the particle.

11 A particle of mass 0.2 kg is attached to one end A of a light elastic string AB of natural length a and modulus g N. The end B is attached to a fixed point on a smooth horizontal table, and A is held on the same table at a distance $4a$ from B. If A is released find the speed of the particle at B and the time it takes to reach B from A.

12 A particle of mass m is attached to the mid-point of an elastic string of natural length $2a$ and modulus of elasticity λ. The ends of the string are attached to points A and B distant $4a$ apart on a smooth horizontal table. Show that if the particle is displaced from the equilibrium position a distance $d(<a)$ towards one of the fixed points and then released, that it will perform simple harmonic motion. Find the periodic time.

13 A particle of mass m is attached to the mid-point of a light elastic string of natural length 1 m. The ends are attached to two points A and B, A being 1.4 m vertically above B. Determine the elasticity of the string if the particle will remain at rest at a depth of 0.8 m below A.

If the particle is now pulled downwards through a distance 0.1 m and then released, show that it will perform simple harmonic motion, and deduce the frequency.

14 A light spring is hung from a fixed point X and is of unstretched length 15 cm. The modulus of elasticity of the spring is 4.9 N. A small pan of mass 0.08 kg is attached to the end and rests in equilibrium. If a particle of mass 0.2 kg is now held just touching the pan and is released, show that the pan performs simple harmonic motion, stating the amplitude and frequency. (Take g as 9.8 m/s².)

15 A pan of weight $g/3$ N is attached to the top of a light vertical spring with modulus of elasticity $4g$ N. A weight of mass $\frac{1}{2}$ kg is placed on the pan, and the pan oscillates with an amplitude of 5 mm, the natural length of the spring being 80 mm and the bottom end being fixed. Find the maximum and minimum reactions between the pan and the weight.

16 An elastic string of natural length a and modulus mg is attached by one end to a fixed point X on a smooth horizontal table. It passes through a small smooth ring Y fixed to the table so that $XY = a$, and the other end is attached to a bead of mass $m/2$ which slides on a smooth rail on the table, the rail being perpendicular to XY at a distance $2a$ from X. If the bead is displaced along the rail, show that it will move with simple harmonic motion of period $\pi\sqrt{\dfrac{2a}{g}}$.

11.3 The simple pendulum and other approximations

There are a number of instances in which an oscillatory motion will very closely resemble simple harmonic motion, generally when subject to the condition that the amplitude of oscillations is small. An important case is that of the simple pendulum, being a bob connected to a fixed point by a light inelastic string.

Let the bob of a simple pendulum be of mass m, and let the length of the string be l. When the string makes a small angle $\delta\theta$ with the vertical the resultant force acting on the bob is perpendicular to the string and is

$$mg \sin \delta\theta$$

Let the length of the arc from the bob to the equilibrium position be x, then

$$\delta\theta = x/l.$$

But since $\delta\theta$ is small, $\sin \delta\theta \doteqdot \delta\theta$, and so the force on the bob is

$$mg\delta\theta = mgx/l.$$

Also for small oscillations the distance of the bob from the point of equilibrium is approximately the arc length, and applying the principle: force = mass × acceleration,

$$m\ddot{x} = -mgx/l,$$

i.e. $$\ddot{x} = -\frac{g}{l}x.$$ 11.7

Fig. 141

This is simple harmonic motion of period $2\pi\sqrt{\dfrac{l}{g}}$. We must emphasize however that this is only true for small oscillations.

A pendulum which performs one swing in one second (i.e. half a cycle, having a periodic time of 2 s) is called a **seconds pendulum**. In this case the above expression for the periodic time gives us

$$2\pi\sqrt{\frac{l}{g}} = 2, \quad \cdot$$

so that
$$l = g/\pi^2.$$

This is a length of approximately 0·994 m.

Whilst this illustrates the principle behind a clock pendulum, it does not allow for the more complex mass distribution of such mechanisms. We consider these later in Chapter 12.

EXAMPLE 6   *Find the length of a simple pendulum to 3 significant figures, which will oscillate with a frequency of $\frac{4}{\pi}$ Hz.*

We have shown that the equation of motion of the simple pendulum of length l is *11.7*, and hence the frequency is $\frac{1}{2\pi}\sqrt{\frac{g}{l}}$. Thus in this example

$$\frac{1}{2\pi}\sqrt{\frac{g}{l}} = \frac{4}{\pi},$$

$$\frac{g}{l} = 64,$$

$$l = \frac{9\cdot81}{64}$$

$$\doteqdot 0\cdot1532.$$

Length of pendulum is 153 mm (to 3 significant figures).

EXAMPLE 7   *A weight of mass m is suspended from a fixed point by a light elastic string of modulus 2mg and natural length 0·5 m, and it performs simple harmonic motion about the equilibrium position in a vertical line. Find the length of the equivalent simple pendulum.*

We know from *11.6* that the equation of motion of the weight is given by

$$\ddot{x} = -\frac{\lambda}{ml}x,$$

where λ is the modulus of elasticity and l is the natural length. So in this example the equation of motion is

$$\ddot{x} = -\frac{2mg}{0\cdot5m}x$$

$$= -4gx.$$

This is simple harmonic motion of period $2\pi/\sqrt{4g} = \pi/\sqrt{g}$ s.

An equivalent simple pendulum is one which will oscillate with the same frequency. But the periodic time of a simple pendulum of length l is

$$2\pi\sqrt{\frac{l}{g}}.$$

$$\therefore\ 2\pi\sqrt{\frac{l}{g}} = \pi\sqrt{\frac{1}{g}},$$

$$l = \frac{1}{4}.$$

The length of the equivalent simple pendulum is 0·25 m.

The next example is rather more complex, but it does illustrate another situation in which the motion can be taken to be simple harmonic if the oscillations are small.

EXAMPLE 8   *A particle of mass m lies on a smooth horizontal table and is attached to a fixed point A by an inextensible light string of length a. An elastic string is also attached to the particle, and to a fixed point B a distance 3a from A on the table. Show that if the particle is displaced from the equilibrium position with the first string remaining taut for a small enough distance then it will perform approximate simple harmonic motion.*

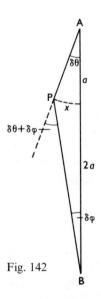

Fig. 142

Let the particle be displaced to a point P such that angle PAB $= \delta\theta$ and angle PBA $= \delta\phi$. Let PB $= l$, then by the cosine rule in triangle PAB,

$$l^2 = 10a^2 - 6a^2 \cos \delta\theta$$
$$= 10a^2(1 - \tfrac{3}{5} \cos \delta\theta).$$

But for $\delta\theta$ sufficiently small, $\cos \delta\theta \doteqdot 1$, so that

$$l^2 \doteqdot 4a^2,$$
$$l \doteqdot 2a.$$

Thus the length of the elastic string does not appreciably change, and we can say that for $\delta\theta$ sufficiently small the tension in the string can be taken as constant. Let this tension be T.

The restoring force must act perpendicularly to the inextensible string, and it is

$$T \sin (\delta\theta + \delta\phi) \doteqdot T(\delta\theta + \delta\phi)$$

taking $\cos \delta\theta \doteqdot \cos \delta\phi \doteqdot 1$. But if the particle is displaced a distance x, then $\delta\theta \doteqdot \dfrac{x}{a}$, and $\delta\phi \doteqdot \dfrac{x}{2a}$. Thus the restoring force is

$$T\left(\frac{x}{a} + \frac{x}{2a}\right) = \frac{3Tx}{2a}.$$

Applying the principle, force $=$ mass $\times$ acceleration, we have

$$\frac{d^2x}{dt^2} = -\frac{3Tx}{2ma}.$$

This is simple harmonic motion of period $2\pi\sqrt{\dfrac{2ma}{3T}}$.   Q.E.D.

Exercise 29

(Take g as 9.81 m/s^2 where required.)

1 Find the period of a simple pendulum of length 0.6 m to 3 significant figures.

2 Find the length of a simple pendulum if it oscillates with a frequency of 100 cycles/min, to the nearest millimetre.

3 A simple pendulum used on earth is of length 0.8 m. Find the length of an equivalent simple pendulum set up on the moon's surface if acceleration due to gravity on the moon is g_m m/s$^2 = 1.8$ m/s^2.

4 Find the frequency of a simple pendulum of length 500 mm to the nearest 0.05 Hz.

5 Find the length of the simple pendulum equivalent to a system composed of a vertical spring of natural length 200 mm fixed at the lower end and with a mass of 0.25 kg attached to the upper end oscillating in a vertical line. The spring is compressed 45 mm by the weight in the equilibrium position.

6 If the length of a seconds pendulum is miscalculated so that it is made 0.5 mm too long, determine how 'slow' it would be after 24 hours, to the nearest second.

7 A simple pendulum of length l has frequency f Hz. When the length is reduced by 200 mm the frequency becomes $3f$ Hz. Find f and l.

8 Assuming the inverse square law of gravitational attraction determine the frequency of a simple pendulum at altitudes of 100 km and 200 km if it has a frequency of 10 Hz at sea level.

(Take the radius of the earth as 6360 km.)

9 A small bead is oscillating under gravity in a smooth fixed hemispherical bowl. Show that, provided the amplitude is small, the motion is simple harmonic of period $2\pi\sqrt{\dfrac{a}{g}}$.

10 A string of natural length $2a$ and modulus of elasticity λ is stretched between two fixed points A and B on a smooth horizontal table such that $AB = 3a$. A mass of magnitude m is attached to the mid-point of the string and makes small oscillations in a horizontal line perpendicular to AB. Show that it performs simple harmonic motion of frequency $\dfrac{1}{\pi}\sqrt{\dfrac{\lambda}{6ma}}$.

11 A light elastic string of natural length 0·4 m is stretched between two fixed points A and B on a smooth horizontal table where AB is 1 m. A particle of mass 200 g is attached to the mid-point of the string and performs small oscillations in a horizontal line perpendicular to AB. Find the modulus of the string if the period is 0·5 s.

12 Project Example:
A particle P is moving in the **i,j**-plane so that when it has position vector $x\mathbf{i}+y\mathbf{j}$ the force acting on P is $-a^2x\mathbf{i}-b^2y\mathbf{j}$. Investigate the locus of P.

Support Exercise D

Miscellaneous examples which may be worked concurrently with Chapters 10 and 11

1 A body starts from rest at a point O when time $t = 2$ (measured in seconds) with a constant acceleration of 10 units/s^2. Prove from first principles that the distance from O at time $t(\geqslant 2)$ is s where

$$s = 5(t-2)^2.$$

A second particle B is moving towards A along the same line of motion, but is being retarded at a rate of $2t$ units/s^2 until it comes to rest, and then accelerated away from O at a rate of 12 units/s^2. If A and B just touch when $t = 4$ but do not interfere with the motion of either, find expressions for x, the distance OB, for $t \geqslant 0$. Sketch the distance-time and velocity-time curves.

2 A uniform solid hemisphere of radius r and mass m is suspended by a light inextensible string of length a by a point on the rim to a point on a smooth vertical wall. If the rim makes an angle ϕ to the horizontal and the string an angle θ to the wall in equilibrium show that

$$\cos \phi - \tan \theta = \frac{3}{8}.$$

Find the length of and tension in the string if $\phi = \tan^{-1} \frac{3}{2}$.

3 Particles A and B, each of mass m, are attached one to each end of a light inextensible string, and a third particle C of mass $2m$ is attached to the mid-point of the string, which lies just taut on a smooth horizontal table with A, C and B collinear. The particle C is suddenly given a horizontal velocity v at right-angles to AB. Use the principles of conservation of energy and of momentum to find the velocities of the three particles when A and B first collide.

If the particles A and B are perfectly elastic, find the velocities of the three particles when they are next collinear. (L)

4 A light wire ABC is straight along AB and BC and angle ABC is $90°$. A light inelastic string of length $3a/2$ is attached to C and has a particle of mass m attached to the other end. If BC = a, and the system is rotated about AB with angular speed ω rad/s, B vertically above A, show that the string makes an angle θ with the vertical where

$$2g \tan \theta = \omega^2 a(2 + 3 \sin \theta).$$

A second light inelastic string of length $2a$ is now attached to the particle at one end and to a small smooth ring of mass m' threaded on AB at the other. Find m' if the particle is required to move in a circle of radius $3a/2$ about AB at $\sqrt{\frac{g}{a}}$ rad/s.

5 Three points A, B and C have position vectors $-\mathbf{i}+\mathbf{j}+\mathbf{k}$, $\mathbf{i}-\mathbf{j}+\mathbf{k}$ and $\mathbf{i}+\mathbf{j}-\mathbf{k}$ respectively. A particle P is at A when $t = 0$ and moves with constant speed v units/s towards the mid-point of BC. If it takes 0.2 s to reach this point find v.

A second particle Q is at B when $t = 0$ and moves with constant speed u units/s along BA so that it reaches A after 0·2 s. Find u, and an expression for cos PQA after time t s.

6 A particle is projected under gravity at an angle of elevation α to the horizontal. Find an expression for the horizontal range R in terms of α and d, the maximum height attained.

For a certain value of α, $R = 2d$. Assuming the same initial speed of projection, prove that the alternative angle of projection which gives the same horizontal range is $\sin^{-1}(1/\sqrt{5})$. If the maximum height in this case is d', find the ratio $d:d'$.

7 A small bead of mass m is threaded onto a rough circular wire of radius a, coefficient of friction $\frac{1}{2}$. The wire, initially at rest with the bead near to the lowest point, is spun about a diameter AB which is vertical. Find the least angular speed required if the bead is to be made to move in a horizontal circle of radius $\sqrt{3}a/2$. Find also the least speed required to maintain it in this path.

8 Fig. 143 illustrates a circular cylinder of weight W_1 held in limiting equilibrium by the frictional forces exerted by a uniform beam of length $4a$ and a plane of inclination θ to the horizontal. The beam is of weight W_2 and is horizontal; it is hinged to the plane at A and the distance from A to the point of contact with

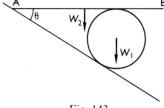

Fig. 143

the cylinder is $3a$. If the coefficients of friction between the beam and the cylinder and the plane and the cylinder are μ_1 and μ_2 respectively, show that $\mu_2 = \sin\theta/(1+\cos\theta)$ and find the value of μ_1.

9 A block of mass $3m$ lies on a rough plane, coefficient of friction $\frac{1}{4}$, inclined at an angle $\sin^{-1}(1/3)$ to the horizontal. A light inelastic string attached to the block passes up over a small smooth pulley at the top of the plane, down under a smooth pulley of mass $2m$, and up to a fixed point vertically above the pulleys. Show that if the block is stationary with the string taut then it will remain so unless further forces are applied.

The free pulley is now given an initial downward velocity of u. Determine the distance the block will move in coming to rest and the time taken to do so, assuming that the block does not reach the pulley.

10 Given that the Moon circles the Earth once every 27·4 days and that it is 384 000 km from the Earth, calculate the mass of the Earth to two significant figures. (Take G as $6·67 \times 10^{-11}$; ignore the effect of the Sun, etc.)

A satellite of mass 500 kg is to be put into a circular orbit of altitude 400 km above the Moon's surface. Calculate the time it will take for one orbit and find the linear speed at which it must enter the orbit. (Take the radius of the Moon as 1740 km and its mass as $8·2 \times 10^{22}$ kg.)

11 A smooth circular horizontal table has a smooth vertical rim around its edge. A particle is projected horizontally with velocity u across the table from a point A on the edge. The direction of projection makes an angle θ with the diameter AB and the coefficient of restitution between the particle and the rim is e. After n impacts with the rim the particle then strikes the rim at B.

(i) If $n = 1$, show that $\tan^2 \theta = e$, and find, in terms of e and u, the speed with which the particle reaches B.

(ii) If $n = 2$, show that $\tan^2 \theta = e + e^2 + e^3$.   (AEB)

12 A smooth billiard ball of mass m, resting on a horizontal table is struck by a cue with an impulse I parallel to the table surface. The ball subsequently collides with another billiard ball having equal mass which is initially at rest. If the direction of motion of the first ball is inclined at an angle α to the line of centres just before the moment of impact, find the magnitudes and directions of the velocities of the two spheres after the collision in terms of m, I, α and the coefficient of restitution e. Further find the loss in the kinetic energy as a result of the collision.   (NI)

13 Fig. 144 illustrates a steam governor. It consists of four light rods AB, AC, LN and NM smoothly hinged at A, L and M, where L and M are the mid-points of AB and AC, and AB = AC = 2LN = 2MN. Small weights each of mass m are attached to B and C. A collar of mass m is attached to N and can slide freely on the vertical shaft to which A is fixed. If the system closes the steam valve when angle LNM = 120°, show that the speed of rotation of the shaft when the valve just closes is $\sqrt{\dfrac{3g}{2a}}$ rad/s.

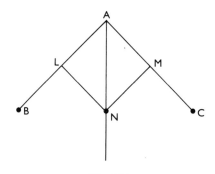

Fig. 144

14 A triangular lamina ABC made of uniform sheet metal has sides AB = 2 units, BC = CA = 4 units. If D and F are the mid-points of the sides BC and AB, and the lamina is folded along DF so that triangle BDF is perpendicular to the plane AFDC, find the distance of the centre of mass from the two planes AFDC and BDF. If the lamina is suspended freely from D, show that the angle of DF to the vertical when in equilibrium is approximately 29°.

15 A triangle consists of two uniform rods AB and AC both of weight W and a non-uniform rod BC of weight $2W$. The centre of mass of BC divides BC in the ratio $1:2$. All three rods are equal in length and are smoothly hinged at A, B and C, the system being suspended freely under gravity by a string attached to A. Find the angle of AB to the vertical and the vertical components of the reactions at B and C when the system is in equilibrium.

16 One end P of a rod PQ of length b describes with uniform angular velocity ω a circle with centre O and radius a $(a < b)$. If N is the foot of the perpendicular from P to OA, prove that

(i) the angular velocity of the rod (measured in the same sense as ω) is $\omega \cdot ON/QN$, where the senses of ON and QN are taken into account.

(ii) the velocity of Q is $\omega \cdot OQ \cdot NP/QN$.   (O & C)

17 Four forces $\mathbf{F}_1$, $\mathbf{F}_2$, $\mathbf{F}_3$ and $\mathbf{F}_4$ all act through the point $\mathbf{i}+\mathbf{j}+\mathbf{k}$, and are such that

$$\mathbf{F}_1 = \mathbf{i}+2\mathbf{j}+3\mathbf{k}, \qquad \mathbf{F}_2 = \mathbf{i}+\mathbf{j}-2\mathbf{k},$$
$$\mathbf{F}_3 = -\mathbf{i}+3\mathbf{j}-2\mathbf{k}, \qquad \mathbf{F}_4 = 2\mathbf{i}-2\mathbf{j}+2\mathbf{k}.$$

Find their resultant and the equation of the line of action of the resultant.

What force acting at $\mathbf{i}-\mathbf{j}+2\mathbf{k}$ should be added to reduce the system to a couple? Find the magnitude of this couple, and the direction of the line of rotation it induces.

18 Two smooth spheres A and B each of radius 10 mm are in positions $-100\mathbf{i}+170\mathbf{j}$ and $100\mathbf{i}+30\mathbf{j}$ (mm) respectively and have constant velocities of $60\mathbf{i}-60\mathbf{j}$ and $-30\mathbf{i}+10\mathbf{j}$ (mm/s^2) respectively. Show that they will collide after 2 s and find where the collision occurs, and the line of centres at this instant.

If after impact the sphere A passes through the origin find the coefficient of restitution e. If on the other hand A continues in a positive $\mathbf{i}$-direction, find the maximum value of e.

19 A particle is alternately accelerated and decelerated at a rate of 50 m/s^2 in such a way that it oscillates symmetrically through a point P and is alternately instantaneously at rest at points A and B on either side of P. If 1 s elapses between successive arrivals at A, calculate the distance AB, and draw the distance-time and velocity-time graphs.

Find the force which must act on a second particle of mass 10 g to cause it to oscillate in a similar manner through P between two points A′ and B′ such that A′B′ = AB but A′B′ is not parallel to AB, if it takes 2 s between successive arrivals at A′. Show that if they start at the same instant from A and A′ respectively that they will not collide at P.

20 Three smooth spheres, each of radius a and weight W, are suspended from a fixed point O by three light inextensible strings, each of length a. One end of each string is attached to the point O and the other end is attached to a point on the surface of one of the spheres. Find the tensions in the strings and the reaction between any two of the spheres in the equilibrium position.   (O)

21 If two points A and B have position vectors $\mathbf{a}$ and $\mathbf{b}$ respectively, what is the position vector of the point X, lying on AB, such that $AX:XB = \alpha:\beta$?

A triangle ABC has vertices with position vectors $\mathbf{a}$, $\mathbf{b}$, $\mathbf{c}$, and D, E, F are the mid-points of BC, CA, AB respectively. Show by a **vector method** that AD, BE, CF (the medians of ABC) are concurrent in a point G with position vector $\frac{1}{3}(\mathbf{a}+\mathbf{b}+\mathbf{c})$.

If P, Q, R are points on BC, CA, AB respectively such that

$$BP:PC = CQ:QA = AR:RB = \alpha:\beta$$

$(\alpha+\beta \neq 0)$., show by a **vector method** that the medians of the triangle PQR all pass through G.   (W)

22 A particle is projected from a point X with speed V on a plane of inclination α to the horizontal at an angle of elevation θ relative to the plane. The projection of the path onto the plane makes an angle ϕ with the line of greatest slope. Prove that for V and θ constant, the locus of points at which the particle may strike the plane is a circle of radius

$$V^2 \sin 2\theta/g \cos \alpha.$$

23 A particle of mass m is attached to a fixed point O by a light inextensible string of length a. The particle is released from rest from a point height $a/2$ above O with the string taut. Find the impulsive tension in the string as it comes taut below O.

Show also that in the subsequent motion the particle will break away from a circular path when the string makes an angle $\cos^{-1}\frac{1}{6}$ with the vertical.

24 A pile-driver, whose hammer weighs 1000 kg is used to drive a pile weighing 100 kg into the ground. The pile is driven 0·005 m into the ground as the result of a single blow of the hammer, which falls from rest through a height of 1 m onto the pile without any rebound. Find the average resistance of the ground in newtons.   (NI)

25 Six uniform rods, equal in length and each of weight W, are freely jointed to form a hexagon ABCDEF. The framework hangs in the form of a regular hexagon, with AB fixed in a horizontal position, and is maintained in this shape by two light inelastic strings, one connecting A and E, and the other connecting B and D. Use the principle of virtual work to determine the tension in these strings.   (O)

26 Forces of magnitudes $2F$, $3F$ and $4F$ act along the sides AB, AC, CB of an equilateral triangle ABC of side $2a$ in the directions indicated by the order of the letters. Find their resultant and the point at which it cuts BC (produced if necessary).

If each force is now translated so as to act through the corresponding opposite vertex, find the couple which must be added if it is still to be equivalent to the original system.

27 A particle of mass m is attached by a light inextensible string of length a to a fixed point O, and is projected from the point A, depth a vertically below O, with a horizontal velocity of magnitude $2\sqrt{2ga}$. Show that P will complete a vertical circle such that the minimum tension in the string is $3mg$.

Find angle AOP at those points when the acceleration vector of P is horizontal.

28 A particle moves in a straight line against a resistance which varies as the cube of the speed. Prove that the distance travelled in any time is the same as if the particle was to move uniformly during this time with its speed at the mid-point of the distance.   (O)

29 A wedge of mass M has a vertical cross-section ABC such that AC is the line of greatest slope of the corresponding face, AB is in contact with a smooth horizontal table, and angle $\text{CAB} = \sin^{-1} \frac{3}{5}$. When held stationary and gently released a block of mass m on the face AC rests in limiting equilibrium. Show that if the wedge is now given a constant horizontal acceleration $a (\leqslant 4g/3)$ away from the block that the block will move down the wedge with acceleration of magnitude $5a/4$ relative to the wedge. (Assume that the coefficients of static and dynamic friction are equal.) Find also the magnitude of the normal reaction between the block and the wedge during the motion.

30 The unit vectors $\mathbf{i}$, $\mathbf{j}$, $\mathbf{k}$ are drawn from the origin O along the axes Ox, Oy, Oz respectively. Write down the position vector of the centre of mass of a system of three particles of masses m_1, m_2, m_3 placed at the points $\mathbf{i}$, $\mathbf{j}$, $\mathbf{k}$ respectively.

A uniform solid sphere with centre O has radius a. Find the position vectors with respect to O of the centres of mass of
(a) the hemisphere for which x is positive,
(b) the octant for which x, y, z are positive.   (L)

31 Six uniform straight rods AB, BC, CD, DE, EF, FA, each of length $2a$ and mass m, are freely jointed together at their ends to form a hexagon ABCDEF. A seventh rod XY of length $7a/2$ and mass m', has small, light, smooth rings fixed at its ends. One of these rings can slide on BC and the other on DE. The rod FA is **fixed** in a horizontal position and the framework hangs symmetrically from A and F in a vertical plane with both CD and XY horizontal, and CD vertically below AF. Show that if θ is the angle made by AB, BC, DE, EF with the vertical, then the potential energy of the framework may be written as

$$V = -4ga(3m+m') \cos \theta + \tfrac{3}{4}m'ga \cot \theta + \text{constant}.$$

Using this, or otherwise, show that if in equilibrium

$$\theta = \frac{\pi}{6}, \quad \text{then} \quad m' = 6m.$$

Find the reaction at X between BC and XY.   (W)

32 Two relatively smooth spheres A and B are each of radius 1 unit. A of mass $2m$ is at $-\mathbf{i}+4\mathbf{j}$ when it collides with B of mass m at $\mathbf{i}+4\mathbf{j}$. The velocity vector of A before impact was $2\mathbf{i}-\mathbf{j}$ whilst B was stationary. The coefficient of restitution between the spheres is $\frac{1}{2}$.

After impact A strikes a smooth wall, coefficient of restitution e, which has position $s\mathbf{i}$. On the rebound it hits B again in such a way that the line of centres is parallel to the $\mathbf{j}$-vector. B has been retarded during this time by a constant force kmg. Find k in terms of e.

33 The Sun attracts a planet of mass m with a force $\gamma mM/r^2$ where M is the mass of the Sun, r is the distance between the two bodies and γ is a constant.

A planet travels with constant speed in a circular orbit of radius R round the Sun as centre. If the time taken by the planet to make one complete revolution round the Sun is T show that

$$\frac{T^2}{R^3} = \frac{4\pi^2}{\gamma M}.$$

Calculate the distance of the planet Mars from the Sun given that Mars takes 687 days to trace a single circular orbit round the Sun and that the Earth moves in a circular orbit of radius 150×10^6 kilometres round the Sun in 365 days.

Hence find the speed of Mars in kilometres/s.   (NI)

34 A cylindrical drum of radius 150 mm has four slits cut parallel to the axis, each a quarter of the way round the circumference from the previous one. The drum revolves about the axis of symmetry at a constant speed of 100 rev/s. A light source inside the drum is detected outside by a photo-electric cell a relatively large distance from the drum. If the cell can only detect the light if the slit appears to move at a speed less than 50 m/s, determine the period pattern for which it is sensitized, giving times to the nearest 0·01 ms.

35 Two particles of equal mass are connected by an elastic string of natural length a, the modulus of elasticity of the string being equal to the weight of one particle. The particles are held at rest at a distance $3a$ apart with the string horizontal. If the particles are released simultaneously, find the distance fallen before they collide.   (L)

36 Define the scalar product $\mathbf{a} \cdot \mathbf{b}$ of two vectors $\mathbf{a}$ and $\mathbf{b}$, and show that if $\mathbf{c}$ is another vector, then

$$\mathbf{a} \cdot (\mathbf{b}+\mathbf{c}) = \mathbf{a} \cdot \mathbf{b}+\mathbf{a} \cdot \mathbf{c}.$$

If k is a number, state what other theorems concerning the scalar product are required to justify

$$(k\mathbf{a}+\mathbf{b})^2 = \mathbf{a}^2 k^2 + 2(\mathbf{a} \cdot \mathbf{b})k + \mathbf{b}^2.$$

A is a point with position vector $\mathbf{a}$ at unit distance from the origin O, and B is a point with position vector $\mathbf{b}$ at a distance of two units from O. The angle between the directions of $\mathbf{a}$ and $\mathbf{b}$ is $\cos^{-1}\frac{1}{4}$. If l is the straight line through O and A,

(i) show that the position vector of the point P on l, such that PB is perpendicular to OB, is $8\mathbf{a}$;

(ii) find the position vectors of both the points on l at a distance 4 units from B.   (W)

37 A bead of weight W is threaded on a smooth circular wire of radius a which is fixed in a vertical plane. A light elastic string of natural length a and modulus W joins the bead to the topmost point of the wire.

(i) Show that, when the bead performs small oscillations about the lowest point of the wire, the length of the equivalent simple pendulum is $2a$.

(ii) Given that, when the bead moves over a finite arc of the circle, the greatest angle which the string makes with the vertical is α, where $\cos \alpha \geqslant \frac{1}{2}$, prove that the pressure on the wire vanishes when the string makes an angle θ with the vertical, where $\cos \theta = \frac{1}{5}(1+4 \cos \alpha)$. What is the significance of the restriction on α?   (O)

38 A ball thrown with initial speed $\sqrt{2gh}$ strikes a vertical wall which stands at a distance d from the point of projection. Show that the point on the wall that is hit by the ball cannot be at a height greater than $(4h^2 - d^2)/4h$ above the point of projection.

Show also that the area of the wall that is within range of the ball is bounded by a parabola. (L)

39 Fig. 145 illustrates a light framework consisting of seven rods AB, BC, CD, DE, EA, AD and DB all smoothly jointed at their ends. A weight of 5 kN is suspended from B, and AB and EC are maintained in the horizontal position by a wire

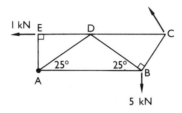

Fig. 145

attached at C making an angle of 50° with CE, together with a horizontal force of 1 kN at E, the system being smoothly pivoted to a fixed point at A. Angles DAB, DBA = 25°; angles AED, DBC = 90°. Find graphically or otherwise the stresses in the rods (clearly stating their nature) and the reaction at A.

40 A small mass of magnitude 0·12 kg is attached to the mid-point of a light elastic string of natural length 0·48 m. The string is stretched between two points A and B in a vertical line 1·08 m apart, and in equilibrium the mass is at rest 0·36 m above B. Find the modulus of elasticity of the string.

The mass is now displaced a small distance horizontally and released. Show that it will oscillate in simple harmonic motion of period $1·2\pi/\sqrt{g}$ s.

41 A particle of mass m is describing the ellipse $x = a \cos \theta$, $y = b \sin \theta$ under the action of a force towards the centre of the ellipse. Prove that $\dot{\theta}$ is constant and find, in terms of this constant and of the other given constants, the average value of the kinetic energy of the particle, the average being taken with regard to time and over a complete period. (O)

42 Water is being pumped from a depth of 5 m through a pipe of cross-section 250 mm² by a pump at a rate of 10 m³/h. Determine the rate of working of the pump.

If the water is directed horizontally from the nozzle determine the force required to hold the nozzle in position ignoring its weight.
(1 m³ of water weighs 1000 kg; take g as 9·81 m/s².)

12 Circular Motion (2)

12.1 Moments of inertia

In this chapter we consider the motion of rotating bodies. In general we are able to apply two basic principles, i.e. the Conservation of Energy and the Conservation of Angular Momentum. The latter in effect replaces the Principle of Conservation of Linear Momentum which we have used extensively so far. We state the principle of angular momentum later in this chapter. At this point we consider the kinetic energy of a rotating body.

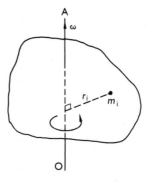

Fig. 146

Consider a body of mass M to be composed of a set of elementary particles of mass m_i each at a respective distance r_i from the axis of rotation OA, $i = 1, 2, \ldots$. Suppose that the body is rotating about OA with angular velocity ω, then each particle is moving with speed ωr_i. Thus the total kinetic energy of the body is

$$\sum \tfrac{1}{2} m_i \omega^2 r_i^2 = \tfrac{1}{2} \omega^2 \sum m_i r_i^2.$$

For a given axis of rotation, $\sum m_i r_i^2$ is a constant peculiar to the particular rigid body. We use the letter I for this value, and it is called the **moment of inertia** of the body about the axis OA. Thus the kinetic energy of the body rotating about the axis OA with angular velocity ω is

$$\tfrac{1}{2} I \omega^2.$$

To find the value of *I* about a particular axis for a given body generally calls for a summation by integration similar to that which was required to find the centre of mass. We illustrate by means of the examples that follow.

EXAMPLE 1   *Find the moment of inertia of a thin uniform rod of mass M and length 2a about an axis perpendicular to the rod through the midpoint.*

Fig. 147

Let the mass per unit length be *m*, then the mass of an elementary portion of length δx distant *x* from the mid-point is $m\delta x$, and the moment of inertia *I* about the given axis is

$$I = \operatorname*{Lim}_{\delta x \to 0} \sum m x^2 \delta x$$

$$= \int_{-a}^{a} m x^2 dx$$

$$= 2ma^3/3.$$

But $M = 2am$. $\therefore I = \dfrac{Ma^2}{3}.$

The moment of inertia of a thin uniform rod of mass *M* and length 2*a* about the mid-point is $\dfrac{Ma^2}{3}$.

EXAMPLE 2   *Find the moment of inertia of a solid sphere of mass M and radius a about an axis passing through the centre. Hence calculate the*

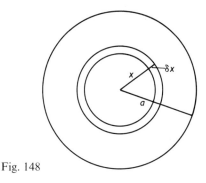

Fig. 148

acceleration of the centre of the sphere when it rolls without slipping down a plane inclined at 30° to the horizontal.

Before we can find the moment of inertia of a sphere, we need to find the moment of inertia of a thin circular disc. Consider a thin disc of radius a. Let the mass per unit area be m. The mass of a thin ring of width δx and radius x is then $2\pi m x \delta x$, and the moment of inertia of the disc about an axis through the centre perpendicular to the plane of the disc is

$$I_D = \lim_{x \to 0} \sum 2\pi m x \delta x . x^2$$

$$= \int_0^a 2\pi m x^3 dx$$

$$= \pi m a^4 / 2. \tag{1}$$

If the mass of the disc is M, then $M = \pi a^2 m$, and

$$I_D = \frac{M a^2}{2}.$$

This result is important in its own right—the moment of inertia of a disc of mass M and radius a about an axis through the centre perpendicular to the plane is $M a^2 / 2$.

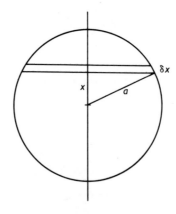

Fig. 149

We can now consider our sphere to be composed of a series of elementary discs. The moment of inertia of the sphere is then

$$I = \sum I_D.$$

If m is now the mass density of the sphere, then the moment of inertia of each disc, thickness δx distant x from the centre is $\pi m (a^2 - x^2)^2 \delta x / 2$ by equation (1). Thus

$$I = \frac{\pi m}{2} \int_{-a}^{a} (a^2 - x^2)^2 dx$$

$$= \pi m \int_{0}^{a} (a^4 - 2a^2 x^2 + x^4) dx$$

$$= \pi m (a^5 - \tfrac{2}{3}a^5 + \tfrac{1}{5}a^5)$$

$$= \frac{8\pi m a}{15}.$$

But the mass of the sphere M is $4\pi ma^3/3$, giving

$$I = \frac{2Ma^2}{5}.$$

The moment of inertia of a sphere of mass M and radius a about an axis of symmetry is $\dfrac{2Ma^2}{5}$.

Let the acceleration of the centre of the sphere rolling down the inclined plane be f. We consider the motion as it rolls from rest a distance s. Over this distance, let it attain a speed v, the angular speed ω then being v/a. By the principle of conservation of energy,

$$\tfrac{1}{2}Mv^2 + \tfrac{1}{2}I\omega^2 = Mgs \sin 30°.$$

Note that the kinetic energy now takes two forms—$\tfrac{1}{2}Mv^2$ is the energy due to translation, and $\tfrac{1}{2}I\omega^2$ is the energy due to rotation. From this equation

$$\frac{1}{2}Mv^2 + \frac{1}{2} \cdot \frac{2Ma^2}{5} \cdot \frac{v^2}{a^2} = \frac{Mgs}{2},$$

$$7v^2 = 5gs,$$

$$v^2 = 5gs/7.$$

But the equation of motion 2.3 gives

$$v^2 = 2fs.$$

Hence

$$2fs = 5gs/7,$$

$$f = \frac{5g}{14}.$$

The acceleration of the sphere down the plane is $5g/14$.

EXAMPLE 3   ABC *is an equilateral triangular lamina of uniform material, side 2a. E is the mid-point of* AC. *Find the moment of inertia of the lamina* (a) *about* BE, *and* (b) *about* AC.

In both instances we take the lamina to be composed of thin strips of width δx parallel to AC. The moment of inertia about BE, I_1, is the limit of the sum of the moments of inertia of all these strips about BE. Using

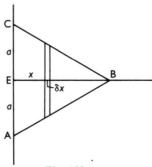

Fig. 150

the result of Example 1, the moment of inertia of one such strip distant x from AC is $ml^2/3$ where m is its mass and $2l$ its length. But if the mass per unit area is σ

$$m = 2l\sigma\delta x$$

and

$$l = a - x/\sqrt{3}.$$

The moment of inertia of one strip is thus

$$\tfrac{2}{3}(a-x/\sqrt{3})^3\sigma\delta x.$$

$$\therefore \; I_1 = \int_0^{\sqrt{3}a} \tfrac{2}{3}(a-x/\sqrt{3})^3\sigma dx$$

$$= \frac{2\sigma}{3}\int_0^{\sqrt{3}a}\left(a^3 - \sqrt{3}a^2x + ax^2 - \frac{x^3}{3\sqrt{3}}\right)dx$$

$$= \frac{2\sigma}{5}\left(\sqrt{3} - \frac{3\sqrt{3}}{2} + \sqrt{3} - \frac{\sqrt{3}}{4}\right)a^4$$

$$= \frac{\sigma a^4}{2\sqrt{3}}.$$

If the mass of the lamina is M, then $M = \sqrt{3}a^2\sigma$, giving

$$I_1 = \frac{Ma^2}{6}.$$

The moment of inertia of the lamina about BE is $Ma^2/6$.

Let the moment of inertia about AC be I_2. The moment of inertia of one strip about AC is mx^2. Thus

$$I_2 = 2\sigma \int_0^{\sqrt{3}a} (a - x/\sqrt{3})x^2 \, dx$$

$$= 2\left(\sqrt{3} - \frac{3\sqrt{3}}{4}\right)a^4\sigma$$

$$= \frac{\sigma\sqrt{3}a^4}{2}.$$

$$\therefore \ I_2 = \frac{Ma^2}{2}.$$

The moment of inertia of the lamina about AC is $Ma^2/2$.

Exercise 30

1 Find the moment of inertia of a uniform rod AB of mass M and length $2a$ about an axis through A perpendicular to the rod.

The rod is smoothly pivoted at A so as to turn freely in a vertical circle about A. It is gently displaced from equilibrium in which B is vertically above A. A second rod CD is light with a mass of magnitude M attached at D. The length of the rod is a, and it is similarly pivoted at C and displaced from equilibrium in which D is vertically above C. Show that the difference in angular speeds when passing through their lowest positions is

$$(2 - \sqrt{3})\sqrt{\frac{g}{a}}.$$

2 A uniform triangular lamina of mass m kg has sides of lengths 120 mm, 160 mm and 200 mm. Use the result of no. 1 to find the moments of inertia about the two shorter sides.

3 Show that the moment of inertia of a thin circular uniform ring of mass M and radius a about any diameter is $Ma^2/2$.

4 In Example 2 it was established that the moment of inertia of a uniform circular disc of radius a and mass M about an axis perpendicular to the disc through the centre is $Ma^2/2$. Use this result to show that the moment of inertia of a uniform solid cone of mass M base radius r and height h about the axis of symmetry is

$$\frac{3Mr^2}{10}.$$

5 Show that the moment of inertia of a uniform circular disc of mass M and radius a about a diameter is $Ma^2/4$.

6 The mass density of a straight rod AB increases uniformly from ρ at A to 2ρ at B. The total mass of the rod is M and its length is l. Find the moments of inertia of the rod about axes perpendicular to the rod (a) through A, and (b) through B.

Find the length of a uniform rod CD of mass M which will have the same moment of inertia about an axis through C perpendicular to CD, as the first rod has about A.

12.2 Theorem of parallel axes

There are an infinite number of axes about which we may require the moment of inertia of a body, and it is important that where possible we establish some relationship between them if we are to avoid repeated and complex integrations. There are two such theorems.

Let I_G be the moment of inertia of a body about an axis through the centre of mass G, and let I_A be the moment of inertia of the body about a parallel axis through a point A distant d from G such that GA lies in a

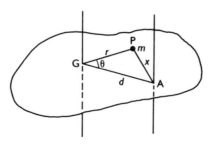

Fig. 151

plane perpendicular to the axes. Let P be an elementary particle of mass m in this plane such that GP $= r$ and AP $= x$. If angle AGP $= \theta$, the cosine rule in triangle AGP then gives

$$x^2 = r^2 + d^2 - 2rd \cos \theta.$$

It follows that considering all such particles P which make up the whole body,

$$\sum mx^2 = \sum mr^2 + \sum md^2 - \sum 2mrd \cos \theta,$$

i.e.
$$I_A = I_G + d^2 \sum m - 2d \sum mr \cos \theta.$$

But since G is the centre of mass, and $r \cos \theta$ is the distance of P from G in the direction GA, it follows that $\sum mr \cos \theta = 0$. Also, if the mass of the body is M, $\sum md^2 = Md^2$. Thus

$$I_A = I_G + Md^2.$$

This result is the *Theorem of Parallel Axes*. In words it states that: the moment of inertia of a body of mass M about a given axis is equal to the moment of inertia of the body about a parallel axis through the centre of mass plus Md^2 where d is the distance between the axes. Note that I_A must be greater than I_G; the moment of inertia increases as we move the axis away from the centre of mass, and decreases as we move towards it.

Consider a few illustrations.

The moment of inertia of a rod of length $2a$ about a perpendicular axis through the mid-point is $\dfrac{Ma^2}{3}$. About a parallel axis through the end of the rod the moment of inertia is

$$\frac{Ma^2}{3} + Ma^2 = \frac{4Ma^2}{3}.$$

(Compare Example 1 with Exercise 30 No. 1.)

The moment of inertia of a ring of radius a and mass M about a diameter is $\dfrac{Ma^2}{2}$. About a tangent the moment of inertia of the ring is

$$\frac{Ma^2}{2} + Ma^2 = \frac{3Ma^2}{2}.$$

The moment of inertia of a disc of radius a and mass M about a diameter is $\dfrac{Ma^2}{4}$. About a chord distant $a/3$ from the centre the moment of inertia of the disc is

$$\frac{Ma^2}{4} + \frac{Ma^2}{9} = \frac{13Ma^2}{36}.$$

12.3 Theorem of perpendicular axes

The second theorem concerns perpendicular axes, and applies only to plane laminas. Let OX, OY and OZ be three mutually perpendicular axes such that OX and OY lie in the plane of the lamina. Let the moments of inertia of the lamina about these axes be I_x, I_y and I_z respectively. Consider a point P of the lamina, distant y from OX, and x from OY. If P is an elementary particle of mass m then it follows that considering all such P,

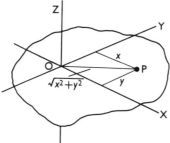

Fig. 152

$$I_x = \sum my^2,$$
and
$$I_y = \sum mx^2.$$

But it also follows from Pythagoras that

$$I_z = \sum m(x^2 + y^2)$$
$$= \sum my^2 + \sum mx^2,$$
i.e.
$$I_z = I_x + I_y.$$

This is the **Theorem of Perpendicular Axes**—if I_x and I_y are the moments of inertia of a plane lamina about two perpendicular axes in the plane of the lamina, then the moment of inertia about an axis perpendicular to and concurrent with these two axes is I_z where $I_z = I_x + I_y$.

EXAMPLE 4   *Show that the moment of inertia of a thin uniform circular ring of radius a and mass M about a diameter is $Ma^2/2$.*

We have already established this result in Exercise 30 No. 3 by integration. Integration is not necessary however if we apply the perpendicular axes theorem.

Let the moment of inertia of the ring about a diameter be I_d. Since every element of the ring is at a distance a from the centre, it follows that the moment of inertia of the ring about an axis through the centre perpendicular to the plane of the ring is Ma^2. Thus by the perpendicular axes theorem,

$$Ma^2 = I_d + I_d,$$

$$\Rightarrow I_d = \frac{Ma^2}{2}. \qquad\qquad \text{Q.E.D.}$$

We have also shown in Example 2 and Exercise 30 No. 5 that the moments of inertia of a uniform disc of radius a and mass M about the corresponding axes are $\frac{Ma^2}{2}$ and $\frac{Ma^2}{4}$. Note that either of these results can be deduced from the other by the theorem.

EXAMPLE 5   *A plane sector AOB is cut from a uniform disc of radius a and mass M so that angle AOB is 90°. OX, OY, OZ are mutually perpendicular axes where OX is an axis of symmetry and OY is also in the plane of the sector. Find the moments of inertia I_x, I_y, I_z about the respective axes.*

Since four such sectors make up a whole disc, and the moment of inertia of the disc about an axis through the centre perpendicular to the disc is $Ma^2/2$, it follows that

$$4I_z = Ma^2/2,$$

$$I_z = Ma^2/8.$$

(Note that if m is the mass of the sector, then this is $ma^2/2$, which is the same form as that of the disc itself.)

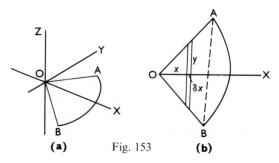

(a)   Fig. 153   (b)

We find I_x by integration, considering the sector to be composed of two parts: a triangle AOB, and a segment cut off by AB (Fig. 153(b)). Let the mass density be m. Using the fact that the moment of inertia of a uniform rod of mass M and length $2a$ about an axis perpendicular to the rod through the centre is $Ma^2/3$, the moment of inertia of an elementary strip parallel to OY about OX if it is of length $2y$ and width δx is

$$\frac{2my\delta x.y^2}{3}.$$

This is true if the strip is part of triangle AOB or part of the segment, but in the case of the triangle

$$y = x,$$

and in the case of the segment

$$y = (a^2 - x^2)^{\frac{1}{2}}.$$

For the triangle we integrate from $x = 0$ to $x = a/\sqrt{2}$, and for the segment from $x = a/\sqrt{2}$ to $x = a$. Substituting the appropriate expressions for y we have

$$I_x = \frac{2m}{3}\int_0^{a/\sqrt{2}} x^3 dx + \frac{2m}{3}\int^{a/\sqrt{2}}(a^2 - x^2)^{\frac{3}{2}}dx.$$

Let the second integral be I_s, and let $x = a \sin\theta$. Then

$$\frac{dx}{d\theta} = a\cos\theta$$

so that

$$I_s = \int_{\pi/4}^{\pi/2} a^4 \cos^4\theta\, d\theta.$$

Using the identity: $\cos^2\theta = \frac{1}{2}(1 + \cos 2\theta)$,

$$I_s = \int_{\pi/4}^{\pi/2} \frac{a^4}{4}(1 + \cos 2\theta)^2\, d\theta$$

$$= \frac{a^4}{4}\int_{\pi/4}^{\pi/2}(1 + 2\cos 2\theta + \cos^2 2\theta)d\theta$$

$$= \frac{a^4}{4}\int_{\pi/4}^{\pi/2}(\tfrac{3}{2} + 2\cos 2\theta + \tfrac{1}{2}\cos 4\theta)d\theta.$$

$$\therefore\ I_x = \frac{2m}{3}\left[\frac{x^4}{4}\right]_0^{a/\sqrt{2}} + \frac{2m}{3}\cdot\frac{a^4}{4}\left[\frac{3\theta}{2} + \sin 2\theta + \frac{1}{8}\sin 4\theta\right]_{\pi/4}^{\pi/2}$$

$$= \frac{2m}{3}\cdot\frac{a^4}{16} + \frac{ma^4}{6}\left(\frac{3\pi}{4} - \frac{3\pi}{8} - 1\right)$$

$$= ma^4\left(\frac{\pi}{16} - \frac{1}{8}\right).$$

But $\pi a^2 m = M$.

$$\therefore I_x = \frac{Ma^2}{16} - \frac{Ma^2}{8\pi},$$

$$I_x = \frac{Ma^2}{16\pi}(\pi - 2).$$

By the perpendicular axes theorem,

$$I_x + I_y = I_z.$$

$$\therefore I_y = \frac{Ma^2}{8} - \frac{Ma^2}{16\pi}(\pi - 2),$$

$$I_y = \frac{Ma^2}{16\pi}(\pi + 2).$$

EXAMPLE 6   *Calculate the moment of inertia of a uniform solid cylinder of circular cross-section radius r and length h about a diameter of an end face, if its total mass is M.*

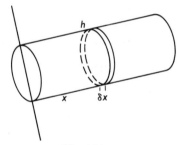

Fig. 154

Consider the cylinder as composed of a series of thin discs of thickness δx. The moment of inertia of such a disc of mass m about a diameter is $\frac{ma^2}{4}$. If the mass density of the cylinder is ρ then the moment of inertia of one of these discs about a diameter is

$$\frac{\rho \pi r^2 \delta x \cdot r^2}{4}.$$

By the theorem of parallel axes, if this disc is at a distance x from the end face of the cylinder, then its moment of inertia about a parallel diameter of the end face is

$$\frac{\rho \pi r^2 \delta x \cdot r^2}{4} + \rho \pi r^2 \delta x \cdot x^2.$$

Hence the moment of inertia I of the whole cylinder about a diameter of the end face is

$$\int_0^h \frac{\rho\pi r^4}{4}dx + \int_0^h \rho\pi r^2 x^2 dx = \frac{\rho\pi r^4}{4}\left[x\right]_0^h + \rho\pi r^2 \left[\frac{x^3}{3}\right]_0^h$$

$$= \frac{\rho\pi r^4 h}{4} + \frac{\rho\pi r^2 h^3}{3}.$$

But $M = \rho\pi r^2 h$.

$$\therefore \ I = M\left(\frac{r^2}{4} + \frac{h^2}{3}\right).$$

The Moment of Inertia of the cylinder about a diameter of the end face is

$$M\left(\frac{r^2}{4} + \frac{h^2}{3}\right).$$

EXAMPLE 7   *Two identical uniform rods AB, BC are rigidly attached to a circular disc centre B so tht angle ABC is a right-angle, and so that the rods lie in the same plane as the disc (Fig. 155). The system is free to turn*

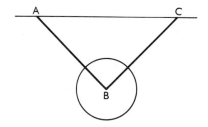

Fig. 155

about a horizontal axis through A and C. Each rod is of mass M and length 3a, and the disc is uniform of mass 4M and radius a. Find the moment of inertia of the system about AC.

We note the results already established for rods and discs. For a rod of length $2a$ and mass m about a perpendicular axis through the end it is $\frac{4ma^2}{3}$. For AB it follows that the moment of inertia about a perpendicular axis through A is

$$\frac{4}{3}M\left(\frac{3a}{2}\right)^2 = 3Ma^3.$$

By symmetry, the moment of inertia of AB about AC is the same as that about the vertical through A. Let this be I_1, then by the theorem of perpendicular axes

$$2I_1 = 3Ma^2,$$
$$I_1 = \tfrac{3}{2}Ma^2.$$

The moment of inertia of the disc about a diameter is

$$\frac{(4M)a^2}{4} = Ma^2.$$

Since the centre of the disc is a distance $3a/\sqrt{2}$ from AC, the theorem of parallel axes gives the moment of inertia I_2 of the disc about AC as

$$I_2 = Ma^2 + 4M\left(\frac{3a}{\sqrt{2}}\right)^2$$
$$= Ma^2 + 18Ma^2$$
$$= 19Ma^2.$$
$$\therefore\; 2I_1 + I_2 = 3Ma^2 + 19Ma^2$$
$$= 22Ma^2,$$

i.e. the moment of inertia of the system about AC is $22Ma^2$.

It will be evident that the moment of inertia is of the form Mk^2 where k is a length. The value of k for any particular case is referred to as the **radius of gyration**. So for example the radius of gyration of a uniform disc of mass M and radius a is $a/2$, since $\dfrac{Ma^2}{4} = M\left(\dfrac{a}{2}\right)^2$. Similarly the radius of gyration of the complete system in Example 7 about AC is $\sqrt{110a}/5$, since $22Ma^2 = 5M.\dfrac{110a^2}{25}$.

Exercise 31

1 A uniform plane lamina of mass M has moment of inertia I_x about an axis OX, O being a point of the lamina, OX being perpendicular to the plane of the lamina. Y and Z are two points in the lamina such that angle YOZ is a right-angle, and OY = OZ = 2 units. The centre of mass of the lamina is G where OYGZ is a square. Find expressions for the moments of inertia about the four sides of the square OYGZ, and about axes YX_1, ZX_2, GX_3 which are all parallel to OX, given that GO is an axis of symmetry.

2 A, B, C, D are four points of a plane lamina such that ABC is a straight line, angle BCD is 90°, AB = 2BC = CD = 2a, and B is the centre of mass. If the moment of inertia about ABC is $2Ma^2$, and about CD is $3Ma^2$, M being the mass of the lamina, find the moments of inertia about parallel axes perpendicular to the plane through each of the points A, B, C and D.

3 Using the result of Example 6, find the moment of inertia of a solid cylinder of mass m, base radius r and height $4r$, about an axis parallel to the base passing through the axis of symmetry at a distance r from the base.

4 Calculate the moment of inertia of a clock pendulum which is composed of a uniform straight rod AB of mass 50 g and length 120 mm and a uniform disc of mass 250 g. radius 45 mm. centre B if the pendulum swings about an axis through A perpendicular to the rod and the plane of the disc.

5 Calculate the moment of inertia of a hollow cylinder made of uniform material and closed at both ends if the mass is M. the base radius r and the length l. about an axis through the centre perpendicular to the generators.

6 Show that the moment of inertia of a uniform rectangular lamina measuring $2a \times 2b$. $a < b$. of mass M. about the axis of symmetry in the plane of the lamina parallel to the shorter side is $Mb^2/3$.

Hence find

(a) the moment of inertia about an axis perpendicular to the lamina through a vertex.

(b) the moment of inertia of a cuboid of mass M measuring $2a \times 2b \times 2c$ about an axis through the centre parallel to the edges of length $2a$.

(c) the moment of inertia of the cuboid in (b) about an edge of length $2c$.

7 A thin uniform circular disc of radius $4a$ has a circle cut out of radius a. the centre C of the circle being a distance a from the centre of the disc O. Find the moment of inertia of the disc with the hole (a) about CO. (b) about an axis in the plane of the disc perpendicular to CO through O. The mass of the disc before it was cut was $16M$.

8 A solid circular cone of mass M has base radius r and height h. Find the moment of inertia of the cone (a) about a diameter of the base. (b) about a parallel axis through the centre of mass. (c) about a parallel axis mid-way between the base and the vertex.

9 A uniform straight rod of mass m has ends A and B given by position vectors $\mathbf{a} = 0$ and $\mathbf{b} = 2x\mathbf{i}$ (with usual notation). Find the moment of inertia of the rod about the line $\mathbf{s} = 3t\mathbf{i} + (2 + 4t)\mathbf{j}$.

10 A uniform rod of length $5a$ and mass $2m$ is pivoted about a point distance a from one end so as to be free to swing in a vertical plane. A particle of mass $5m$ is attached to the end further from the pivot. and a particle of mass m' is attached to the other end. Find m' if the radius of gyration of the system is $2a$.

If the rod is held at an angle ϕ to the vertical with the $5m$ mass below the pivot and released. find the angular speed of the pendulum when subsequently at an angle θ to the vertical.

12.4 The vector product

We have already seen that we can multiply two vectors together resulting in a scalar—the scalar product. We now define the product of two vectors resulting in a vector—the vector (or cross) product. The **vector product** of two vectors **a** and **b** is defined by the equation

$$\mathbf{a} \wedge \mathbf{b} = |\mathbf{a}||\mathbf{b}| \sin \theta \mathbf{x}$$

where **x** is the unit vector perpendicular to both **a** and **b** in the sense satisfying the right-hand screw rule, and θ is the angle between **a** and **b**. Thus in Fig. 156 turning from **a** through θ to **b** is an anti-clockwise motion so that **x** acts upwards; a normal screw turned in that direction would move in the direction of **x**.

In Chapter 10 we defined angular velocity as a vector, but we went on to establish a scalar relationship between the angular velocity and linear

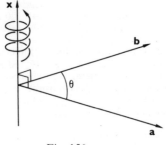

Fig. 156

velocity of a point, i.e. that $v = \omega r$. With corresponding notation we can now write this relation more accurately as $\mathbf{v} = \omega \wedge \mathbf{r}$ (Fig. 157).

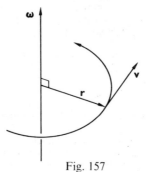

Fig. 157

Another concept which we have used in scalar form but is strictly a vector quantity is the moment of a vector $\mathbf{P}$ about a point. We can now define the moment of $\mathbf{P}$ about a point O as

$$\mathbf{r} \wedge \mathbf{P}$$

where $\mathbf{r}$ is the position vector of any point on the line of $\mathbf{P}$ relative to O. The value of the moment is unaffected by the choice of the point on the line.

Corresponding to this result, the moment of the vector $\mathbf{P}$ about a line is

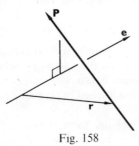

Fig. 158

the component of the moment of **P** about any point on the line in the direction of the line. Thus if the direction of the line is given by the unit vector **e**, the moment of **P** about the line is

$$((\mathbf{r} \wedge \mathbf{P}).\mathbf{e})\mathbf{e}$$

where **r** is the position vector of a point on the line of **P** relative to a point on the given line.

This last definition may appear to be very different to the definition given on p. 41. If however we write $\mathbf{P} = P_1\mathbf{e} + P_2\mathbf{e}_p$ and $\mathbf{r} = r_1\mathbf{e} + r_2\mathbf{e}_r$ where $\mathbf{e}_p$ and $\mathbf{e}_r$ are both unit vectors perpendicular to **e**, then the moment **M** about the line is

$$(((r_1\mathbf{e} + r_2\mathbf{e}_r) \wedge (P_1\mathbf{e} + P_2\mathbf{e}_p)).\mathbf{e})\mathbf{e}.$$

Assuming the distributive law holds for vector products this is

$$((r_1P_1\mathbf{e} \wedge \mathbf{e} + r_1P_2\mathbf{e} \wedge \mathbf{e}_p + r_2P_1\mathbf{e}_r \wedge \mathbf{e} + r_2P_2\mathbf{e}_r \wedge \mathbf{e}_p).\mathbf{e})\mathbf{e}.$$

But $\mathbf{e} \wedge \mathbf{e} = 0$, and since $\mathbf{e} \wedge \mathbf{e}_p$ is perpendicular to **e**,

$$(\mathbf{e} \wedge \mathbf{e}_p).\mathbf{e} = 0.$$

Similarly
$$(\mathbf{e}_r \wedge \mathbf{e}).\mathbf{e} = 0.$$

$$\therefore \ \mathbf{M} = ((r_2P_2\mathbf{e}_r \wedge \mathbf{e}_p).\mathbf{e})\mathbf{e}$$

$$= r_2P_2\mathbf{e},$$

which in vector form is the definition given on p. 41.

The following points should be noted:
(1) If $\theta = 0$, the vector product is zero, i.e. $\mathbf{a} \wedge \mathbf{a} = 0$.
(2) For the unit vectors **i**, **j**, **k** we have such results as $\mathbf{i} \wedge \mathbf{j} = \mathbf{k}$, but $\mathbf{j} \wedge \mathbf{i} = -\mathbf{k}$.
(3) $(a\mathbf{i} + b\mathbf{j} + c\mathbf{k}) \wedge (x\mathbf{i} + y\mathbf{j} + z\mathbf{k})$

$$= ay(\mathbf{i} \wedge \mathbf{j}) + az(\mathbf{i} \wedge \mathbf{k}) + bx(\mathbf{j} \wedge \mathbf{i}) + bz(\mathbf{j} \wedge \mathbf{k}) + cx(\mathbf{k} \wedge \mathbf{i}) + cy(\mathbf{k} \wedge \mathbf{j})$$

$$= ay\mathbf{k} - az\mathbf{j} - bx\mathbf{k} + bz\mathbf{i} + cz\mathbf{j} - cy\mathbf{i}$$

$$= (bz - cy)\mathbf{i} + (cx - az)\mathbf{j} + (ay - bx)\mathbf{k}.$$

12.5 Angular momentum

Consider a single particle of mass m and velocity v having position vector **r** relative to the origin O. We define the **moment of momentum**, which we also call **angular momentum**, of the particle about O to be

$$\mathbf{r} \wedge m\mathbf{v}.$$

Let the particle be moving in the **i**,**j**-plane. What we demonstrate here in two dimensions applies equally to three. Let $\mathbf{r} = x\mathbf{i} + y\mathbf{j}$, then $\mathbf{v} = \dot{x}\mathbf{i} + \dot{y}\mathbf{j}$, and

$$\mathbf{r} \wedge m\mathbf{v} = m(x\dot{y} - y\dot{x})\mathbf{k}.$$

$$\frac{d}{dt}(\mathbf{r} \wedge m\mathbf{v}) = m(\dot{x}\dot{y} + x\ddot{y} - \dot{y}\dot{x} - y\ddot{x})\mathbf{k}$$

$$= m(x\ddot{y} - y\ddot{x})\mathbf{k}$$

But this is $\mathbf{r} \wedge m\dot{\mathbf{v}}$, so that

$$\frac{d}{dt}(\mathbf{r} \wedge m\mathbf{v}) = \mathbf{r} \wedge \mathbf{F},$$

where $\mathbf{F}$ is the force on the particle. This demonstrates the **Principle of Angular Momentum for a Particle**:

> *The rate of change of angular momentum of a particle about a fixed point is equal to the moment of the impressed force about that point.*

We now extend our argument to rigid bodies. Since we are now to consider rotation about a line rather than a point, the position vector $\mathbf{r}_i$ of any elementary portion of mass m_i of the body must be understood to be perpendicular to the axis of rotation. The velocity $\mathbf{v}_i$ of this portion will lie in the same plane as $\mathbf{r}$ perpendicular to the axis, except in the case where there is translation along the axis. The angular momentum of the body is then

$$\sum(\mathbf{r}_i \wedge m_i\mathbf{v}_i).$$

But if the angular velocity of the body is ω, then

$$\mathbf{v}_i = \omega \wedge \mathbf{r}_i,$$

and the angular momentum $\mathbf{H}$ of the body is

$$\mathbf{H} = \sum(\mathbf{r}_i \wedge (m\omega \wedge \mathbf{r}_i)).$$

Now ω acts along the axis of rotation and is perpendicular to $\mathbf{r}_i$. Let $\mathbf{e}$

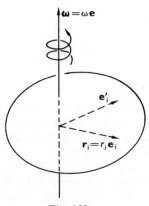

Fig. 159

be the unit vector along the axis so that $\boldsymbol{\omega} = \omega\mathbf{e}$, and $\mathbf{e}_i$ be the unit vector along $\mathbf{r}_i$ so that $\mathbf{r}_i = r_i\mathbf{e}_i$. Let $\mathbf{e}'_i = \mathbf{e} \wedge \mathbf{e}_i$, then

$$\boldsymbol{\omega} \wedge \mathbf{r}_i = \omega r_i(\mathbf{e} \wedge \mathbf{e}_i)$$
$$= \omega r_i\mathbf{e}'_i.$$
$$\therefore\ \mathbf{H} = \sum \mathbf{r}_i \wedge (m\omega r_i\mathbf{e}'_i)$$
$$= \sum m\omega r_i^2(\mathbf{e}_i \wedge \mathbf{e}'_i).$$

But $\mathbf{e}_i$ and $\mathbf{e}'_i$ are both perpendicular to $\mathbf{e}$.

$$\therefore\ \mathbf{H} = \sum m\omega r_i^2\mathbf{e} = I\omega\mathbf{e},$$

where I is the moment of inertia about the axis of rotation. In scalar terms we can define the angular momentum of a body as the product $I\omega$. By exactly the same argument as for a particle we can deduce the **Principle of Angular Momentum for a Rigid Body**:

> *The rate of change of the angular momentum of a rigid body about a given axis is equal to the sum of the moments of the impressed forces about that axis, and is equal to $I\dot{\omega}$, where I is the moment of inertia of the body about the axis and $\dot{\omega}$ is the angular acceleration.*

As with linear motion, we have a very important corollary; if the sum of the moments of the impressed forces about the axis is zero, then the angular momentum is constant—**the Principle of Conservation of Angular Momentum**.

12.6 Applications

Problems concerning the rotational motion of rigid bodies will be solved by applying one of the two principles: the Conservation of Energy and that of Angular Momentum. The Conservation of Energy is more appropriate to those examples which do not take account of time; problems which do involve time must be approached by the Principle of Angular Momentum.

There are a few examples which can be approached by either principle. Example 2 was such a problem. In the last stage of the Example we applied the Conservation of Energy in order to calculate the acceleration of the sphere as it rolled down the inclined plane. With the same notation as before, consider how we would solve this by the Principle of Angular Momentum. By this principle,

$$I\dot{\omega} = Mga \sin \theta$$

where in this case $\theta = 30°$. Thus

$$\left(\frac{2Ma^2}{5} + Ma^2\right)\dot{\omega} = Mga/2,$$
$$\tfrac{7}{5}a\dot{\omega} = g/2.$$

But $f = \dot{\omega}a$.

$$\therefore \; \tfrac{7}{5}f = g/2,$$

$$f = \frac{5g}{14}.$$

in this case a shorter solution.

EXAMPLE 8   *A wheel of mass 4M in the form of a disc of radius r m is accelerated from rest about a fixed axis through the centre by a constant tangential force of magnitude Mg N for 10 s. Calculate the speed of the wheel after this time and the angle through which it will have turned.*

Since time is involved we apply the Principle of Angular Momentum to obtain our equation of motion. It is of the simplest possible form:

$$\frac{d^2\theta}{dt^2} = \text{constant.}$$

The moment of the force about the axis (the torque) is Mgr N m, and the moment of inertia is

$$I = \frac{(4M)r^2}{2}$$

$$= 2Mr^2.$$

$\therefore$ the Principle of Angular Momentum gives

$$2Mr^2\frac{d^2\theta}{dt^2} = Mgr,$$

$$\frac{d^2\theta}{dt^2} = \frac{g}{2r}.$$

Integrating with respect to t,

$$\frac{d\theta}{dt} = \frac{gt}{2r} + c.$$

Since the wheel starts from rest, $\dfrac{d\theta}{dt} = 0$ when $t = 0$, giving $c = 0$.

$$\therefore \; \frac{d\theta}{dt} = \frac{gt}{2r}.$$

Integrating again with respect to t,

$$\theta = \frac{gt^2}{4r} + k.$$

But $\theta = 0$ when $t = 0$, so that $k = 0$.

$$\therefore \ \theta = \frac{gt^2}{4r}.$$

When $t = 10$,
$$\frac{d\theta}{dt} = 5g/r,$$

and
$$\theta = 25g/r.$$

$\therefore$ after 10 s, the speed of the wheel is $5g/r$ rad/s, and it has turned through $25g/r$ radians.

EXAMPLE 9   *A pulley wheel of mass m and radius r is rotating at a steady speed of Ω rad/s when it is suddenly subjected to a braking torque proportional to the speed. As a result the speed is halved in T s. Find the magnitude of the torque at ω rad/s, and the angle through which it turns in this time.*

Let n be the constant such that the torque at ω rad/s is $n\omega$, then the Principle of Angular Momentum gives

$$I\dot{\omega} = -n\omega$$

where I is the moment of inertia. Hence

$$\frac{1}{\omega}\frac{d\omega}{dt} = -\frac{n}{I},$$

$$\int \frac{d\omega}{\omega} = -\frac{n}{I}\int dt$$

$$\Rightarrow \log_e \omega = -\frac{n}{I}t + c.$$

When $t = 0$, $\omega = \Omega$, giving $c = \log_e \Omega$.

$$\therefore \ \log_e \frac{\omega}{\Omega} = -\frac{nt}{I},$$

$$\omega = \Omega e^{-nt/I}. \tag{1}$$

After T s, $\omega = \Omega/2$.

$$\therefore \tfrac{1}{2} = e^{-nT/I},$$

$$\Rightarrow nT/I = \log_e 2,$$

or
$$n = \frac{I}{T}\log_e 2.$$

But $I = mr^2/2$, so that

$$n = \frac{mr^2}{2T}\log_e 2.$$

The torque at ω rad/s is $\dfrac{mr^2\omega}{2T}\log_e 2$.

To find the angle through which it has turned we integrate equation (1) giving

$$\theta = -\frac{\Omega I}{n}e^{-nt/I} + c.$$

Putting $\theta = 0$ when $t = 0$, $c = \dfrac{\Omega I}{n}$, and

$$\theta = \frac{\Omega I}{n}(1 - e^{-nt/I}).$$

∴ when $t = T$,

$$\theta = \frac{\Omega I}{n}(1 - e^{-nT/I}),$$

$$= \frac{\Omega T}{\log_e 2}(1 - \tfrac{1}{2})$$

$$= \frac{\Omega T}{2\log_e 2}.$$

In T s it has turned through $\dfrac{\Omega T}{2\log_e 2}$ radians.

EXAMPLE 10   *A pulley of mass m and radius r has a light rope of length 7r wrapped round the circumference. It is attached by one end to a point on the rim, and a weight of 2mg is attached to the other. The system is held at rest with the rope completely in contact with the pulley and the weight on the same level as the horizontal axis through the centre, assumed to be smooth. The rope will fall free from the pulley immediately it is unwound. If the system is released find the maximum speed of the pulley.*

If in fact the angular speed is half this value due to friction, calculate the work done against friction.

Since time is not involved we shall apply the Principle of Conservation of Energy. Let I be the moment of inertia of the pulley, v the speed of the weight as the rope falls free, and ω the angular speed of the pulley. Then by this principle,

$$\tfrac{1}{2}.2mv^2 - 7r.2mg + \tfrac{1}{2}I\omega^2 = 0.$$

Hence

$$m\omega^2 r^2 + \tfrac{1}{2}\frac{mr^2}{2}\omega^2 = 14mgr,$$

$$\frac{5}{4}r\omega^2 = 14g,$$

$$\omega^2 = \frac{56g}{5r},$$

$$\omega = 2\sqrt{\frac{14g}{5r}}.$$

The maximum speed attained is $2\sqrt{\dfrac{14g}{5r}}$.

If however $\omega = \sqrt{\dfrac{14g}{5r}}$, then by the Conservation of Energy the work done against friction is W where

$$m\omega^2 r^2 + \tfrac{1}{2}.\frac{mr^2}{2}\omega^2 + W = 14mgr.$$

Hence

$$W = 14mgr - \frac{5}{4}mr^2\omega^2$$

$$= 14mgr - \frac{5}{4}mr^2.\frac{14g}{5r}$$

$$= 14mgr - \frac{7}{2}mgr$$

$$= 21mgr/2.$$

The work done against friction is $21mgr/2$.

12.7 The compound pendulum

A body free to swing about a horizontal axis is called a **compound pendulum**. Let such a body be of mass m and have centre of mass G, O being a point on the axis such that O and G are always in the same vertical plane. Let OG $= h$, then the Principle of Angular Momentum gives

$$\frac{d}{dt}(I\omega) = -mgh \sin \theta$$

where θ is the angle OG makes with the vertical (Fig. 160). Since I, the moment of inertia about O, is constant it follows that

$$I\dot{\omega} = -mgh \sin \theta$$

i.e.

$$I\frac{d^2\theta}{dt^2} = -mgh \sin \theta$$

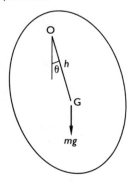

Fig. 160

If θ is sufficiently small then

$$\frac{d^2\theta}{dt^2} = -\frac{mgh}{I}\theta,$$

which is simple harmonic motion of period $2\pi\sqrt{\dfrac{I}{mgh}}$.

It is sometimes relevant to write this equation of motion in a form directly associated with the moment of inertia of the body about the centre of mass. Let the radius of gyration about the centre of mass be k, then by the Theorem of Parallel Axes

$$I = mk^2 + mh^2.$$

Substituting in the equation of motion:

$$\frac{d^2\theta}{dt^2} = -\frac{gh}{k^2+h^2}\sin\theta,$$

$$= -\frac{gh}{k^2+h^2}\theta \text{ for } \theta \text{ small.}$$

In this latter case, the period of the motion is $2\pi\sqrt{\dfrac{k^2+h^2}{gh}}$.

EXAMPLE 11   *A uniform straight rod of length 0·6 m and mass 0·25 kg is smoothly pivoted about a point 0·04 m from one end so as to turn freely in a vertical plane. Find the period of small oscillations about the pivot.*

The moment of inertia of a uniform rod length $2a$ and mass M about the centre is $\dfrac{Ma^2}{3}$, so that applying the theorem of parallel axes and putting $M = 0\cdot25$, $a = 0\cdot3$, the moment of inertia about the pivot is

$$I = \frac{0\cdot25 \times 0\cdot3^2}{3} + 0\cdot25 \times 0\cdot26^2$$

$$= 0\cdot0075 + 0\cdot0169$$

$$= 0\cdot0244.$$

From the above argument, the equation of motion of the pendulum for small oscillations is

$$\frac{d^2\theta}{dt^2} = -\frac{mgh}{I}\theta,$$

where $m = 0\cdot25$ and $h = 0\cdot26$. It follows that the period of small oscillations is

$$2\pi\sqrt{\frac{I}{mgh}} = 2\pi\sqrt{\frac{0\cdot0244}{0\cdot25 \times 0\cdot26g}}$$

$$= 2\pi \times 0\cdot1967$$

$$= 1\cdot23 \text{ s.}$$

Period of small oscillations is $1\cdot23$ s (to 3 significant figures).

EXAMPLE 12   *A uniform rod of mass m and length 2a is pivoted about a point distant x from the centre so as to swing in a vertical plane. Find the length of the equivalent simple pendulum, and show that this length is least when $x = k$, the radius of gyration of the rod about the mass centre.*

The moment of inertia of the rod about the pivot, by the theorem of parallel axes, is $m(k^2 + x^2)$ where $k^2 = a^2/3$. By the principle of angular momentum

$$I\frac{d^2\theta}{dt^2} = -mgx \sin\theta,$$

i.e.

$$\frac{d^2\theta}{dt^2} = -\frac{gx}{k^2 + x^2} \sin\theta,$$

and for small oscillations this becomes

$$\frac{d^2\theta}{dt^2} = -\frac{gx}{k^2 + x^2}\theta.$$

This motion is equivalent to a simple pendulum of length l if this equation corresponds to the equation of motion

$$\frac{d^2\theta}{dt^2} = -\frac{g}{l}\theta.$$

Hence
$$\frac{g}{l} = \frac{gx}{k^2 + x^2}.$$

$$\Rightarrow l = \frac{k^2 + x^2}{x}.$$

Length of equivalent simple pendulum is $\dfrac{a^2 + 3x^2}{3x}$.

Now if
$$l = \frac{k^2 + x^2}{x},$$

then
$$\frac{dl}{dx} = \frac{2x^2 - (k^2 + x^2)}{x^2}$$

$$= \frac{x^2 - k^2}{x^2}.$$

$$\therefore \frac{dl}{dx} = 0 \text{ when } x = \pm k.$$

This corresponds to a minimum value for l, taking $x > 0$, since there is only one stationary value for $x > 0$, and $l \to \infty$ for both $x \to 0$ and $x \to \infty$.

Length of equivalent simple pendulum is least when $x = k$.

Exercise 32

1 Evaluate the following products:
   (a) $(2i+3j+k) \wedge (2i-3j-k)$,
   (b) $(3i+4k) \wedge (4i-3k)$,
   (c) $((i+j+k) \wedge (2i-3j+4k)) \cdot (i-j-2k)$.

2 Write down in terms of the vector product an expression for the moment of a vector $\mathbf{F}$ about a point with position vector $\mathbf{p}$ if $\mathbf{F}$ acts through a point with position vector $\mathbf{q}$.
   Evaluate this moment if
   (a) $\mathbf{F} = 6i$; $\mathbf{p} = 3j$; $\mathbf{q} = 4k$;
   (b) $\mathbf{F} = 2i+j$; $\mathbf{p} = 2i-j$; $\mathbf{q} = -j-2k$;
   (c) $\mathbf{F} = 3i+2j+k$; $\mathbf{p} = 4i+k$; $\mathbf{q} = i+j$.

3 Evaluate the sum of the moments of the three forces
$$\mathbf{F} = 2i+j, \quad \mathbf{F}_2 = 3i-j+2k \quad \text{and} \quad \mathbf{F}_3 = 3j+k$$

if they act through the points $\mathbf{i}, \mathbf{j}$ and $\mathbf{k}$ respectively, (i) about the point $i+j-k$, and (2) about the line $i+j-k+s(2i-j)$.

4 Show that the moment of momentum of a particle of mass m moving with velocity $\dot{\mathbf{p}} = x\mathbf{i}+y\mathbf{j}$ at the position $\mathbf{p} = xt\mathbf{i}+yt\mathbf{j}+z\mathbf{k}$ about the origin is
$$mz(-y\mathbf{i}+x\mathbf{j}).$$

A system of four particles with masses $m, 2m, 3m, 4m$ move each with constant speed V along the lines $i+sj, j+sk, k-si, k-sj$. $s = 0$ when time $t = 0$ in each instance. Find the angular momentum of the system.

5 At time t, a particle of mass m has position vector

$$\mathbf{r} = r \cos \phi \mathbf{i} + r \sin \phi \mathbf{j}.$$

Show that if the angular momentum about the origin is $c\mathbf{k}$ at any time t where c is constant, then

$$\phi = \frac{ct}{mr^2}.$$

6 Find the angular acceleration of a pulley of mass 50 g and radius 15 mm under a torque of magnitude 0·001 N m.

7 A flywheel of mass 200 kg and radius 280 mm is rotating at a steady speed of 600 rev/min. Calculate its kinetic energy.

The flywheel now begins to slow down under the effect of a frictional torque of magnitude 5 N m. Calculate the time taken for the flywheel to come to rest.

8 An electric motor starts from rest under a constant torque of 6 N m. Frictional torques are equal to 0·1ω N m at a speed of ω rad/s. Calculate the maximum speed of the motor.

Calculate the effective power of the motor when working at maximum capacity at a steady speed of 30 rad/s.

9 A flywheel of mass M and radius a rotates at a constant speed ω_1 rad/s when it is suddenly acted upon by a torque of magnitude $\frac{1}{5}(Mga + 2\omega)$ where ω is the speed of rotation at any instant. Calculate the time that will elapse before it comes to rest.

10 A rigid body is made to rotate about a fixed axis by a constant couple. Deduce three equations of motion for rotational motion to correspond to the three equations of motion *2.1–2.3* relating to linear motion under a constant force.

11 A uniform solid sphere is released from the top of a rough inclined plane of length l m and angle of inclination α to the horizontal. If it takes t s to reach the foot of the plane, show that

$$l = \frac{5g}{14} \sin \alpha t^2.$$

12 An outboard motor will fire if made to turn at 240 rev/min, but exerts a constant resistance before starting of 0·3 N m. It is started with a rope of length 1 m wrapped round the flywheel which is of mass 5 kg and radius 120 mm. Assuming the moment of inertia of other rotating parts to be small compared with the flywheel, find the minimum steady pull on the rope required to start the motor.

13 A pulley of mass 200 g and radius 45 mm is smoothly pivoted about a fixed horizontal axis through the centre. A light inelastic string passing over the pulley has weights of masses 50 g and 250 g attached to the ends. If the string does not slip, find the angular acceleration of the pulley. (Hint: Note that the tensions in the two free portions of the string are not equal. Apply the principle: force = mass × acceleration to the weights, and the principle of angular momentum to the pulley.)

14 A pulley of radius a, smoothly pivoted about a fixed horizontal axis through the centre, is of mass m. A light inextensible string passes over it, and masses of magnitudes $2m$ and $3m$ are attached to the ends. If the system is released from rest with the string taut, and if it does not slip, show that the acceleration of either mass is $2g/11$.

15 A uniform solid sphere of radius r and mass $5m$ has a rod AB rigidly attached to a point B on its surface, BA being radial to the sphere. The rod is uniform, of length $2a$ and mass $3m$. Find the period of small oscillations about a fixed smooth horizontal axis through A.

16 A thin uniform rod AB of length $2a$ and mass m has masses $4m$ and $4m$ attached to the ends. When pivoted about a point C on AB it can oscillate in a vertical plane with a motion equivalent to a simple pendulum of length $28a/9$. Find the distance of C from A if it is less than a.

17 A hoop of radius r and mass m has three weights each of mass m attached to points on the hoop so that they are equally spaced round the circumference. If AB is a diameter such that one weight is attached at A, show that the moments of inertia about A and B, axes perpendicular to the plane of the hoop, are equal. Prove further that the moment of inertia of the system about any other parallel axis through a point on the hoop also has this value.

Find the period of small oscillations in a vertical plane about a point on the rim.

18 An equilateral triangle is made out of uniform wire of length $6a$ and mass $3m$ bent into the appropriate shape with no part overlapping. It is freely suspended from one vertex, and it makes small oscillations in its own plane about this vertex. Show that the length of the equivalent simple pendulum is $\sqrt{3}a$.

If the triangle is now made to oscillate about an axis through the vertex parallel to the opposite side, find the length of the new equivalent simple pendulum.

12.8 Rotation and translation

We have already inferred that the motion of a body can be considered in two parts—translation and rotation. Let this rotation be about an axis through the centre of mass G. This will cause no loss of generality, but it requires that our translation be such that G is translated directly from its initial position A to its final position B, irrespective of the moment of rotation. If the rotation is after translation then it will be about B, as illustrated in Fig. 161.

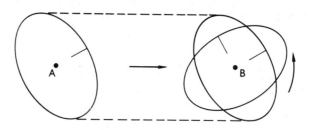

Fig. 161

Consider the energy of this rigid body at a given instant of time. Let the instantaneous centre be C, and the angular velocity be ω. The energy of the body due to motion is then

$$E = \tfrac{1}{2}I_c\omega^2,$$

where I_c is the moment of inertia about C. But if CG is of length x, then by the Theorem of Parallel Axes,

$$I_c = I_g + Mx^2,$$

where I_g is the moment of inertia about G. Thus

$$E = \tfrac{1}{2}I_g\omega^2 + \tfrac{1}{2}Mx^2\omega^2.$$

But $\omega x = v$, the linear speed of G.

$$\therefore\ E = \tfrac{1}{2}I_g\omega^2 + \tfrac{1}{2}Mv^2.$$

We conclude that:

> the kinetic energy of a rigid body is equal to the kinetic energy due to rotation about the mass centre together with the kinetic energy due to translation of the entire mass, assumed to be concentrated at the centre of mass.

In a similar way, we consider the angular momentum of the same rigid body about the instantaneous centre C. It is

$$\mathbf{H} = I_c\omega$$
$$= I_g\omega + Mx^2\omega.$$

But $\qquad \mathbf{x}\wedge(\boldsymbol{\omega}\wedge\mathbf{x}) = x^2\boldsymbol{\omega},$

and also $\qquad \mathbf{x}\wedge(\boldsymbol{\omega}\wedge\mathbf{x}) = \mathbf{x}\wedge\mathbf{v},$

i.e. $\qquad Mx^2\boldsymbol{\omega} = M\mathbf{x}\wedge(\boldsymbol{\omega}\wedge\mathbf{x})$

$$= \mathbf{x}\wedge M\mathbf{v}.$$

$$\therefore\ \mathbf{H} = I_g\boldsymbol{\omega} + \mathbf{x}\wedge M\mathbf{v}.$$

We conclude that:

> the angular momentum of the body about the instantaneous centre is equal to the angular momentum about the centre of mass together with the moment of the linear momentum (angular momentum) of the total mass, assumed to be concentrated at the mass centre, about the instantaneous centre.

12.9 Impulse on a rigid body

Consider now the effect of an impulse acting on a rigid body. Let the impulse be

$$\mathbf{J} = \int_0^{\delta t} \mathbf{F}\,dt$$

where δt is small, acting at a point A having position vector $\mathbf{a}$ relative to the axis of rotation. Let G be the centre of mass of the body with position vector $\mathbf{x}$ relative to O in the axis, where OG is perpendicular to the axis. We shall assume $\mathbf{J}$, $\mathbf{a}$ and $\mathbf{x}$ to be in the same vertical plane.

If the axis is fixed, then in general there must be an impulsive reaction at O of magnitude $\mathbf{K}$ say. If the velocity of G changes from $\mathbf{v}_1$ to $\mathbf{v}_2$ due to the impulse, and the mass of the body is M, then the principle of linear momentum gives

$$\mathbf{J} - \mathbf{K} = M\mathbf{v}_2 - M\mathbf{v}_1. \qquad\qquad 12.1$$

The principle of angular momentum gives

$$\int_0^{\delta t} \mathbf{a}\wedge\mathbf{F}\,dt = I_o\boldsymbol{\omega}_2 - I_o\boldsymbol{\omega}_1,$$

where ω_1 and ω_2 are the angular velocities before and after the impulse, and I_0 is the moment of inertia about O. Since $\mathbf{a}$ is fixed, this becomes

$$\mathbf{a} \wedge \mathbf{J} = I_0\omega_2 - I_0\omega_1. \qquad 12.2$$

Thus:

> *the moment of the impulse about* O *is equal to the change in angular momentum about* O.

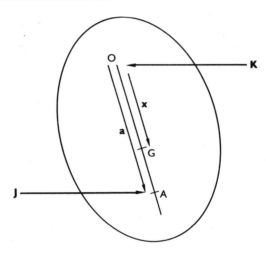

Fig. 162

We can of course apply the principle of angular momentum about any point of the body, but this would necessarily introduce $\mathbf{K}$. There is one case when this would be a reasonable step, i.e. when $\mathbf{K} = 0$. This will happen (a) if the axis is not fixed, and (b) if a fixed axis happens to coincide with the instantaneous axis so that it begins to move as if it were not fixed. In such cases *12.1* and *12.2* become

$$\mathbf{J} = M\mathbf{v}_2 - M\mathbf{v}_1, \qquad 12.3$$

and applying the principle of angular momentum about the centre of mass,

$$(\mathbf{a} - \mathbf{x}) \wedge \mathbf{J} = I\omega_2 - I\omega_1,$$

i.e.

$$\mathbf{m} \wedge \mathbf{J} = I\omega_2 - I\omega_1, \qquad 12.4$$

where $\mathbf{m}$ is the position vector of A relative to the mass centre and I is the moment of inertia about the mass centre.

We conclude that, for a fixed axis we apply the principles of linear and angular momentum in the form of equations *12.1,2*, but for a free axis then we apply the principles in the form of the equations *12.3,4*.

EXAMPLE 13   *A uniform rod of length 2a and mass m is smoothly pivoted in a vertical plane about a point O distance x(< a) from one end. The rod hangs at rest in stable equilibrium when an impulse of magnitude J is applied horizontally in the plane at the lower end. Find the impulsive reaction at O, and deduce the value of x for which this reaction is zero.*

Let the impulsive reaction at O be K, then by the principle of linear momentum

$$J - K = mv, \tag{1}$$

where v is the initial speed of the centre of mass G.

By the principle of angular momentum,

$$J(2a - x) = \left\{ \frac{ma^2}{3} + m(a - x)^2 \right\} \omega$$

where ω is the angular speed. Hence

$$J = m\omega(4a^2 - 6ax + 3x^2)/3(2a - x). \tag{2}$$

From (1)

$$K = J - mv$$

$$= J - m(a - x)\omega.$$

Substituting from (2),

$$K = \frac{m\omega}{3(2a - x)} \{ 4a^2 - 6ax + 3x^2 - 3(a - x)(2a - x) \}$$

$$= \frac{m\omega}{3(2a - x)} (3ax - 2a^2).$$

∴ the impulsive reaction at O is $\dfrac{ma\omega(3x - 2a)}{3(2a - x)}$.

Hence the reaction is zero when $x = 2a/3$.

EXAMPLE 14   *A uniform rod AB of length a and mass m lies at rest on a smooth horizontal table when it is struck by a horizontal impulse of magnitude mv perpendicular to AB at the point a/4 from B. Find the initial angular velocity and the instantaneous centre.*

By the Conservation of Linear Momentum, the velocity of the mass centre will be v.

By the Conservation of Angular Momentum about the mass centre,

$$mv\frac{a}{4} = I\omega,$$

where ω is the initial angular velocity, and I is the moment of inertia about the mass centre. But

$$I = \frac{1}{3}m\left(\frac{a}{2}\right)^2$$

$$= ma^2/12.$$

$$\therefore \frac{mva}{4} = \frac{ma^2\omega}{12},$$

$$\omega = \frac{3v}{a}.$$

The initial angular velocity is $3v/a$.

Let the instantaneous centre C be a distance x from the point of impulse. By the Conservation of Angular Momentum about C,

$$mvx = \left\{\frac{ma^2}{12} + m\left(x - \frac{a}{4}\right)^2\right\}\omega.$$

Putting $\omega = 3v/a$,

$$mvx = \frac{3mv}{a}\left(\frac{a^2}{12} + x^2 - \frac{ax}{2} + \frac{a^2}{16}\right),$$

$$ax = \frac{7a^2}{16} + 3x^2 - \frac{3ax}{2},$$

$$48x^2 - 40ax + 7a^2 = 0.$$

$$(12x - 7a)(4x - a) = 0,$$

$$x = 7a/12 \quad \text{or} \quad a/4.$$

$x = a/4$ coincides with the centre of mass, and since this moves with speed v it cannot be the instantaneous centre.

$\therefore$ the instantaneous centre is $7a/12$ from the impulse.

EXAMPLE 15   *A uniform rod AB of mass m and length 5a is free to rotate on a smooth horizontal table about a pivot through P, a point on AB such that AP = a. A particle of mass 2m moving on the table strikes AB perpendicularly at the point 2a from P with speed v, the rod being at rest. If the coefficient of restitution between them is 1/4, determine their speeds immediately after the impact.*

Let the point of impact be Q, and let the velocities of Q and the particle after the impact be v_q and v_p respectively in the senses shown in Fig. 163.

We have three principles to apply: Conservation of Linear Momentum, Conservation of Angular Momentum, and Newton's Law of Restitution.

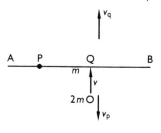

Fig. 163

Linear Momentum however will involve the impulsive reaction at P, and unless we wish to find this we avoid using this principle.

By Newton's Law of Restitution,

$$v_p + v_q = v/4. \tag{1}$$

By the Conservation of Angular Momentum, the effective impulse on the rod at Q is equal to the change in momentum of the particle, and so

$$(2mv + 2mv_p) = I_p \omega,$$

where I_p is the moment of inertia about P.

$$I_p = \frac{1}{3}m\left(\frac{5a}{2}\right)^2 + m\left(\frac{3a}{2}\right)^2$$

$$= \frac{13ma^2}{3}.$$

$$\therefore \quad 4ma(v + v_p) = \frac{13ma^2}{3}\omega,$$

$$12(v + v_p) = 13a\omega. \tag{2}$$

But also the angular velocity of the rod, ω, is such that

$$v_q = 2a\omega. \tag{3}$$

Substituting for v_p from (1) into (2),

$$12(v + v/4 - v_q) = 13a\omega,$$

$$12(5v/4 - 2a\omega) = 13a\omega, \text{ from (3)}.$$

$$15v - 24a\omega = 13a\omega,$$

$$\omega = \frac{15v}{37a}.$$

Substituting back in (1)

$$v_p = \frac{v}{4} - 2a \cdot \frac{15v}{37a}$$

$$= \frac{v}{4} - \frac{30v}{37}$$

$$= -\frac{83v}{148}.$$

The angular speed of the rod is $\frac{15v}{37a}$, and the speed of the particle is $\frac{83v}{148}$ after the impact.

Exercise 33

1 Two particles, each of mass m are joined together by a light rod of length d, and lie at rest on a smooth horizontal table. The rod receives a blow perpendicular to its length at a point $d/3$ from one end. Find the distance of the instantaneous centre from the point of the impulse.

2 A smooth uniform disc of radius a and mass m lies on a smooth horizontal table when it is struck tangentially by an impulse of magnitude mv. Find the distance of the instantaneous centre from the centre of the disc immediately after the blow, and calculate the energy imparted to the disc.

3 A uniform rod AB of length $2a$ and mass $2m$ is suspended freely at A and hangs vertically at rest when a particle of mass m is fired horizontally with speed v to strike the rod at its mid-point. If the particle is brought to rest by the impact, find
  (a) the impulsive reaction at A,
  (b) the initial angular speed of the rod, and
  (c) the maximum angle the rod makes with the vertical in the subsequent motion.

4 A uniform square lamina ABCD of side a and mass m lies on a smooth horizontal table. It is smoothly pivoted about a fixed point through the mid-point of AB. It is struck by an impulse of magnitude J at B along BC. Find J if it begins to turn about the pivot with angular speed ω.

5 A uniform rod of mass $4m$ and length a is smoothly pivoted at one end to a fixed point on a smooth horizontal table. A particle of mass m strikes the rod (which is at rest) perpendicularly with speed v at the end opposite to the pivot. If the coefficient of restitution between the rod and the particle is e, show that the rod begins to move with angular speed

$$\frac{3v}{7a}(1+e).$$

If the particle is brought to rest by the impact, find the value of e, and calculate the speed of the particle after the next impact.

6 A uniform rod of mass $2m$ has a weight of mass $3m$ attached to one end and is suspended by a smooth fixed pivot at the other end. Determine the point at which the rod must be struck by a horizontal impulse so that the impulsive reaction at the pivot is zero.

If in fact the reaction at the pivot is half the impulse and acts in the opposite sense, determine where the rod is struck.

7 A uniform rod of length $2r$ and mass m is rotating in a horizontal plane about a smooth fixed pivot through the centre at a steady speed of ω rad/s. A particle of mass m moving with speed $\omega r/4$ strikes an end of the rod perpendicularly. The rod and particle are moving towards each other, and the coefficient of restitution is $1/2$. Calculate the impulsive reaction at the pivot, and the new speed of the rod.

8 Project Example:

Examine the motion following the impact of two rough spheres.

9 Project Example:

It is said that a sailing dinghy will sail faster, particularly in a swell, if its moment of inertia is made as small as possible. Consider and discuss this hypothesis.

13 Vector Geometry

13.1 Two and three dimensional curves

We have seen under a number of circumstances how easy it is to use vector notation when a vector has been expressed in terms of its components in mutually perpendicular directions. When we form a vector equation to represent a curve in two or three dimensions we have to introduce a scalar variable—a parameter. This parameter will generally be a direct link with the cartesian equation of the curve, since the same parameter can be used to represent x, y and z. We have already met this in the case of the circle. A circle of radius r and centre (a,b) is represented in parametric form by the relations

$$x = a + r \cos \theta,$$
$$y = b + r \sin \theta.$$

This translates to the corresponding vector equation:

$$\mathbf{p} = (a + r \cos \theta)\mathbf{i} + (b + r \sin \theta)\mathbf{j}.$$

It will now be evident to the reader familiar with the other conics that the vector equations of the standard forms with centres at the origin are:

the parabola: $\qquad \mathbf{p} = at^2\mathbf{i} + 2at\mathbf{j},$

the ellipse: $\qquad \mathbf{p} = a \cos \theta\mathbf{i} + b \sin \theta\mathbf{j},$

the hyperbola: $\qquad \mathbf{p} = a \sec \theta\mathbf{i} + b \tan \theta\mathbf{j}.$

It is possible to deduce the equations of quite complicated loci from these and similar two dimensional forms. One important example is the helix, which is a curve in the surface of a cylinder with a fixed angle to the generators (Fig. 164). Let the axis of the cylinder lie along the $\mathbf{k}$-axis, then the projection of the curve on the $\mathbf{i},\mathbf{j}$-plane is a circle, of radius a, say. The $\mathbf{k}$-component of a point on the helix is directly proportional to θ, the angle turned through in the $\mathbf{i},\mathbf{j}$-plane, and so the helix has equation

$$\mathbf{r} = a \cos \theta\mathbf{i} + a \sin \theta\mathbf{j} + c\theta\mathbf{k}.$$

Since the curve is such that the $\mathbf{k}$-component increases uniformly with θ, the angle the curve makes with the $\mathbf{i},\mathbf{j}$-plane is

$$\tan^{-1} \frac{c\theta}{a\theta} = \tan^{-1} \frac{c}{a}.$$

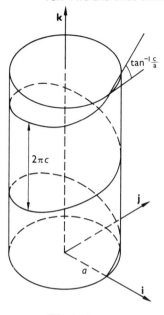

Fig. 164

We refer to the value of $2\pi c$ as the **pitch**, this being the distance between two points on the curve separated by one complete rotation about the **k**-axis—i.e. the respective values of the parameter θ differ by 2π.

The first Example illustrates how vector theory can be used to establish the equation of a locus composed of several motions.

EXAMPLE 1 *P is a point on the rim of a circular disc of radius a. The disc rolls without slipping on the circle*

$$\mathbf{r} = 4a \cos \theta \mathbf{i} + 4a \sin \theta \mathbf{j}$$

*so that the plane of the disc is always perpendicular to the **i,j**-plane and lies in the positive **k** direction of space. Find an equation to represent the locus of P if it starts from the point 4a**i**.*

Let the position vectors of the centre of the disc and of P be **c** and **p** relative to the origin respectively. When the disc has rotated through an angle ϕ about its centre,

$$\mathbf{p} - \mathbf{c} = -a \sin \phi \mathbf{e} - a \cos \phi \mathbf{k}$$

where **e** is a unit vector parallel to the **i,j**-plane in the plane of the disc.
But

$$\mathbf{c} = 4a \cos \theta \mathbf{i} + 4a \sin \theta \mathbf{j} + a\mathbf{k}.$$

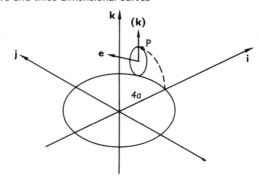

Fig. 165

Equating the arc on the disc to the arc described on the circle,

$$4a\theta = a\phi \Rightarrow \phi = 4\theta.$$

$$\therefore \ \mathbf{p} - \mathbf{c} = -a \sin 4\theta \mathbf{e} - a \cos 4\theta \mathbf{k}.$$

But also $\mathbf{e}$ makes an angle θ with $\mathbf{j}$ so that

$$\mathbf{e} = -\sin \theta \mathbf{i} + \cos \theta \mathbf{j}.$$

$$\therefore \ \mathbf{p} - \mathbf{c} = a \sin \theta \sin 4\theta \mathbf{i} - a \cos \theta \sin 4\theta \mathbf{j} - a \cos 4\theta \mathbf{k},$$

and

$$\mathbf{p} = a(4 \cos \theta + \sin \theta \sin 4\theta)\mathbf{i} + a(4 \sin \theta - \cos \theta \sin 4\theta)\mathbf{j}$$
$$+ a(1 - \cos 4\theta)\mathbf{k}.$$

The second Example is based on the helix, and can be solved quite easily by treating it as a static problem of equilibrium in three dimensions. The reader may care to solve it in this way in order to compare the merits of such a method with the vector approach which follows.

EXAMPLE 2   *A bead of mass m is threaded onto a wire in the shape of the circular helix*

$$\mathbf{p} = a \cos \theta \mathbf{i} + a \sin \theta \mathbf{j} + 2a\theta \mathbf{k}.$$

*The **k**-axis is directed vertically upwards, and the bead slides down the wire under gravity at constant speed. Determine the frictional force acting on the bead.*

Since the bead moves with constant speed, $d\theta/dt = -\omega$, a constant. $d\theta/dt$ is negative since the bead is sliding down the wire. If we take $\theta = 0$ when $t = 0$, then $\theta = -\omega t$. The position of the bead after time t is then

$$\mathbf{p} = a \cos \omega t \mathbf{i} - a \sin \omega t \mathbf{j} - 2a\omega t \mathbf{k}.$$

It follows that

$$\dot{\mathbf{p}} = -a\omega \sin \omega t \mathbf{i} - a\omega \cos \omega t \mathbf{j} - 2a\omega \mathbf{k},$$

and
$$\ddot{\mathbf{p}} = -a\omega^2 \cos \omega t \mathbf{i} + a\omega^2 \sin \omega t \mathbf{j}.$$

Let the normal reaction between the bead and the wire on the bead be N, and the frictional force on the bead be F, then

$$\mathbf{N} + \mathbf{F} - mg\mathbf{k} = m\ddot{\mathbf{p}}.$$

But the frictional force must act in the opposite direction to the velocity $\dot{\mathbf{p}}$. Thus if c is a constant then

$$\mathbf{F} = -mc\dot{\mathbf{p}},$$

and so

$$\mathbf{N} = m\ddot{\mathbf{p}} + mc\dot{\mathbf{p}} + mg\mathbf{k}.$$

But since F and N are perpendicular,
$$\mathbf{F}.\mathbf{N} = 0.$$
$$\therefore \quad -mc\dot{\mathbf{p}}.(m\ddot{\mathbf{p}} + mc\dot{\mathbf{p}} + mg\mathbf{k}) = 0,$$
$$\dot{\mathbf{p}}.\ddot{\mathbf{p}} + c\dot{\mathbf{p}}.\dot{\mathbf{p}} + g\dot{\mathbf{p}}.\mathbf{k} = 0,$$
$$\Rightarrow 0 + c(a^2\omega^2 + 4a^2\omega^2) - 2ag\omega = 0,$$
$$5ca\omega = 2g,$$
$$c = \frac{2g}{5a\omega}.$$

$\therefore$ the frictional force is

$$\mathbf{F} = \frac{2mg}{5}(\sin \omega t \mathbf{i} + \cos \omega t \mathbf{j} + 2\mathbf{k}).$$

It will be evident that we could now find a similar expression for N, but it is not so concise as the vector F. We do know however that $|\mathbf{N}|$ is constant, and so by taking a particular value for θ we can determine the magnitude of N relatively easily.

13.2 The distance of a point from a line

Let p be the position vector of a fixed point P relative to some origin O, and let $\mathbf{r} = \mathbf{q} + s\mathbf{t}$ be the equation relative to O of a straight line not passing through P, q and t being constant. Let N, with position vector n, be the

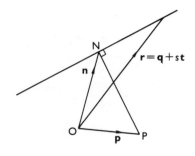

Fig. 166

point on the line such that PN is the shortest distance from P to the line, and let

$$n = q + s_n t.$$

PN is perpendicular to the line. Since PN is represented by $n-p$, and the direction of the line is t, it follows that

$$(n-p).t = 0.$$

Hence we can evaluate s_n, and then use the relation

$$PN = |n-p|.$$

EXAMPLE 3   *Calculate the distance of the point $2i-j+k$ from the line $r = (i-j) + s(i+2j+3k)$.*

Let $r_1 = (i-j) + s_1(i+2j+3k)$ be the point on the line nearest to the point $p = 2i-j+k$, then

$$(r_1 - p).(i+2j+3k) = 0.$$

$$\therefore \; \{(s_1-1)i + 2s_1 j + (3s_1 - 1)k\}.(i+2j+3k) = 0,$$

$$(s_1-1) + 4s_1 + 3(3s_1 - 1) = 0,$$

$$14s_1 - 4 = 0,$$

$$s_1 = \tfrac{2}{7}.$$

$$\therefore \; r_1 - p = -\tfrac{5}{7}i + \tfrac{4}{7}j - \tfrac{1}{7}k,$$

and

$$|r_1 - p| = \tfrac{1}{7}\sqrt{25 + 16 + 1}$$

$$= \tfrac{\sqrt{42}}{7} = \sqrt{\tfrac{6}{7}}.$$

The distance of $2i-j+k$ from r is $\sqrt{\tfrac{6}{7}}$ units.

An alternative method of solving the same problem is to use the vector product. In an earlier chapter we defined the moment of a vector **F** about a point P to be

$$\mathbf{F} \wedge \mathbf{r}$$

where **r** is the position vector of a point on the line of **F** relative to P. But we also deduced that

$$|\mathbf{F} \wedge \mathbf{r}| = |\mathbf{F}|\,\text{PN}$$

where PN is the perpendicular from P to the line. Thus the alternative solution to Example 3 runs as follows.

The line given by the equation

$$\mathbf{r} = (\mathbf{i} - \mathbf{j}) + s(\mathbf{i} + 2\mathbf{j} + 3\mathbf{k})$$

passes through the point **q** = **i**−**j**, and the vector **F** = **i**+2**j**+3**k** acts along the line. Therefore if the position vector of 2**i**−**j**+**k** is **p**,

$$|\mathbf{F} \wedge (\mathbf{q} - \mathbf{p})| = |\mathbf{F}|\,\text{PN}$$

where PN is the shortest distance from P to the line.

$$\therefore \; |(\mathbf{i} + 2\mathbf{j} + 3\mathbf{k}) \wedge (-\mathbf{i} - \mathbf{k})| = |\mathbf{i} + 2\mathbf{j} + 3\mathbf{k}|\,\text{PN},$$
$$|-2\mathbf{i} - 2\mathbf{j} + 2\mathbf{k}| = |\mathbf{i} + 2\mathbf{j} + 3\mathbf{k}|\,\text{PN},$$
$$\sqrt{12} = \sqrt{14}\,\text{PN},$$
$$\text{PN} = \sqrt{\tfrac{6}{7}}, \text{ as before.}$$

13.3 The distance between two skew lines

It is a brief extension to the method using the scalar product which enables us to calculate the distance between two skew lines in space. Let two such lines be $\mathbf{r}_1 = \mathbf{a} + s\mathbf{b}$ and $\mathbf{r}_2 = \mathbf{c} + t\mathbf{d}$. Let P on the first line and Q on the second be the points such that PQ is perpendicular to both lines—PQ is then the shortest distance between the two lines. Let P and Q have position vectors

$$\mathbf{p} = \mathbf{a} + s_1\mathbf{b} \quad \text{and} \quad \mathbf{q} = \mathbf{c} + t_1\mathbf{d}$$

respectively, then

$$(\mathbf{p} - \mathbf{q}).\mathbf{b} = (\mathbf{p} - \mathbf{q}).\mathbf{d} = 0,$$

giving both s_1 and t_1. Hence we can determine $|\mathbf{p} - \mathbf{q}|$, the distance between the skew lines.

EXAMPLE 4   *Calculate the shortest distance between the two skew lines* $s(\mathbf{i} + \mathbf{j} - 2\mathbf{k})$ *and* $\mathbf{i} + 2\mathbf{j} + t(\mathbf{i} - \mathbf{j} - 3\mathbf{k})$.

Let A be the point **a** on the first line for which $s = s_1$ and B the point **b** on the second such that $t = t_1$, so that AB is the shortest distance between the lines. Then AB is perpendicular to both lines.

$$\therefore \ (\mathbf{a}-\mathbf{b}).(\mathbf{i}+\mathbf{j}-2\mathbf{k}) = (\mathbf{a}-\mathbf{b}).(\mathbf{i}-\mathbf{j}-3\mathbf{k}) = 0.$$

Hence

$$\{(s_1-1-t_1)\mathbf{i}+(s_1-2+t_1)\mathbf{j}+(3t_1-2s_1)\mathbf{k}\}.(\mathbf{i}+\mathbf{j}-2\mathbf{k}) = 0.$$
$$\therefore \ s_1-1-t_1+s_1-2+t_1-6t_1+4s_1 = 0,$$
$$6s_1-6t_1-3 = 0,$$
$$2s_1 = 2t_1+1. \quad (1)$$

Similarly

$$\{(s_1-1-t_1)\mathbf{i}+(s_1-2+t_1)\mathbf{j}+(3t_1-2s_1)\mathbf{k}\}.(\mathbf{i}-\mathbf{j}-3\mathbf{k}) = 0.$$
$$\therefore \ s_1-1-t_1-s_1+2-t_1-9t_1+6s_1 = 0,$$
$$6s_1 = 11t_1-1. \quad (2)$$

Eliminating s_1 from (1) and (2)

$$6t_1+3 = 11t_1-1,$$
$$5t_1 = 4,$$
$$t_1 = 4/5.$$
$$\therefore \ s_1 = 13/10.$$
$$\therefore \ \mathbf{a}-\mathbf{b} = -\tfrac{1}{2}\mathbf{i}+\tfrac{1}{10}\mathbf{j}-\tfrac{1}{5}\mathbf{k},$$

and

$$|\mathbf{a}-\mathbf{b}| = \tfrac{1}{10}|-5\mathbf{i}+\mathbf{j}-2\mathbf{k}|$$
$$= \sqrt{0.3}.$$

The shortest distance between the two lines is $\sqrt{0.3}$ units.

As before, there is an alternative method which applies the vector product. Let the two lines be $\mathbf{r}_1 = \mathbf{a}+s\mathbf{b}$ and $\mathbf{r}_2 = \mathbf{c}+t\mathbf{d}$, with P and Q

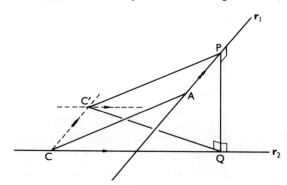

Fig. 167

being the points on the lines such that PQ is the shortest distance between them (as above). Then since PQ is perpendicular to both $\mathbf{r}_1$ and $\mathbf{r}_2$, it follows that the vector $\mathbf{n} = \mathbf{b} \wedge \mathbf{d}$ is parallel to PQ. Let A and C be the points on the lines given by the vectors $\mathbf{a}$ and $\mathbf{c}$, then the projection of AC onto PQ is the length of PQ (Fig. 167). This will be evident from the figure in which C′P is equal and a parallel to CA. C′QP is a right-angle. But CA is represented by the vector $\mathbf{c} - \mathbf{a}$, and the projection of this onto PQ is

$$\frac{(\mathbf{c} - \mathbf{a}) . \mathbf{n}}{|\mathbf{n}|}.$$

Thus the distance between the two lines is

$$\frac{|(\mathbf{c} - \mathbf{a}) . (\mathbf{b} \wedge \mathbf{d})|}{|\mathbf{b} \wedge \mathbf{d}|}.$$

In Example 4, the solution would then be as follows. The direction of the shortest line PQ is

$$\mathbf{n} = (\mathbf{i} + \mathbf{j} - 2\mathbf{k}) \wedge (\mathbf{i} - \mathbf{j} - 3\mathbf{k})$$
$$= -\mathbf{k} + 3\mathbf{j} - \mathbf{k} - 3\mathbf{i} - 2\mathbf{j} - 2\mathbf{i}$$
$$= -5\mathbf{i} + \mathbf{j} - 2\mathbf{k}.$$

Points on the respective lines are $\mathbf{O}$ and $\mathbf{i} + 2\mathbf{j}$. and so the line joining these two points is given by $\mathbf{i} + 2\mathbf{j}$. The projection of this line on PQ is of length

$$\frac{|(\mathbf{i} + 2\mathbf{j}) . (-5\mathbf{i} + \mathbf{j} - 2\mathbf{k})|}{|-5\mathbf{i} + \mathbf{j} - 2\mathbf{k}|} = \frac{|-5 + 2|}{\sqrt{30}}$$
$$= \sqrt{0 \cdot 3} \text{ as before.}$$

13.4 The vector equation of a plane

We can express the equation of a plane in two different ways. The first we describe is the most obvious and follows on from the equation of a straight line, but it is not always the most convenient as it requires two scalar variables.

Let A be a point on the plane with position vector $\mathbf{a}$, and let B and C be two further points in the plane such that A, B, C are not collinear. Let their position vectors relative to A be $\mathbf{b}_a$ and $\mathbf{c}_a$ respectively. Then the position $\mathbf{p}$ of any point in the plane is then given by the equation

$$\mathbf{p} = \mathbf{a} + s\mathbf{b}_a + t\mathbf{c}_a,$$

where s and t are the two scalar variables. This is the first form of the equation of a plane.

Now the direction of any normal to a particular plane is unique. Since $\mathbf{b}_a$ and $\mathbf{c}_a$ lie in the plane, it follows that

$$\mathbf{n} = \mathbf{b}_a \wedge \mathbf{c}_a$$

is a vector in the direction of the normal.* Let $\mathbf{e}_n$ be the unit vector in this direction so that $\mathbf{n} = n\mathbf{e}_n$.

Let N be the foot of the normal which passes through the origin O, then

$$\mathbf{ON} . \mathbf{a} = \mathbf{ON}^2.$$

$$\therefore \; \mathbf{e}_n . \mathbf{a} = \mathbf{ON}$$

$$= d, \text{ say.}$$

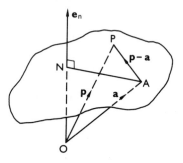

Fig. 168

If the position of any point in the plane is $\mathbf{p}$, then $\mathbf{p} - \mathbf{a}$ must be perpendicular to $\mathbf{e}_n$, and so it follows that

$$(\mathbf{p} - \mathbf{a}) . \mathbf{e}_n = 0.$$

$$\therefore \; \mathbf{p} . \mathbf{e}_n - \mathbf{a} . \mathbf{e}_n = 0,$$

$$\mathbf{p} . \mathbf{e}_n = d.$$

This is the second form of the equation of a plane, in which d is the distance of the plane from the origin, and $\mathbf{e}_n$ is the unit vector normal to the plane.

Using the directions of the normals we can calculate the angle at which two planes intersect. If $\mathbf{n}_1$ is normal to plane P_1 and $\mathbf{n}_2$ normal to plane P_2, then the two planes will intersect at an angle θ given by

$$\mathbf{n}_1 . \mathbf{n}_2 = |\mathbf{n}_1| |\mathbf{n}_2| \cos \theta.$$

Similarly a line with direction $\mathbf{l}$ will cut the plane P_1 at an angle ϕ where

$$n_1 . \mathbf{l} = |\mathbf{n}_1| |\mathbf{l}| \cos \left(\frac{\pi}{2} - \phi \right).$$

---

* $\mathbf{n}$ can also be found using the scalar product. Since both $\mathbf{b}_a$ and $\mathbf{c}_a$ are perpendicular to $\mathbf{n}$ we can solve the simultaneous equations: $\mathbf{n} . \mathbf{b}_a = \mathbf{n} . \mathbf{c}_a = 0$.

13.5 The distance of a point from a plane

Let Q be a point with position vector $\mathbf{q}$ relative to the origin O such that Q is not in the plane given by the equation

$$\mathbf{p} . \mathbf{e}_n = d.$$

The projection of OQ onto ON (defined as above) is then

$$\mathbf{q} . \mathbf{e}_n.$$

Thus the distance of the point Q from the plane is

$$|d - \mathbf{q} . \mathbf{e}_n|.$$

EXAMPLE 5   *The vertices A, B, C, D of a tetrahedron have position vectors $\mathbf{a} = \mathbf{i} + 2\mathbf{j} + \mathbf{k}$, $\mathbf{b} = \mathbf{i} - 2\mathbf{j} - \mathbf{k}$, $\mathbf{c} = -\mathbf{i} + 2\mathbf{j} - \mathbf{k}$, $\mathbf{d} = 2\mathbf{i}$ respectively. Determine the distance of D from the face ABC. If G (position vector $\mathbf{g}$) is the centroid of triangle ABC, find the angle DG makes with the face ABC.*

We find the equation of the face ABC. Let $\mathbf{e}_n$ be the unit vector normal to this face. The vector $\mathbf{n}$ is in the direction of $\mathbf{e}_n$ where

$$\begin{aligned} \mathbf{n} &= (\mathbf{a} - \mathbf{b}) \wedge (\mathbf{a} - \mathbf{c}) \\ &= (4\mathbf{j} + 2\mathbf{k}) \wedge (2\mathbf{i} + 2\mathbf{k}) \\ &= -8\mathbf{k} + 8\mathbf{i} + 4\mathbf{j} \\ &= 4(2\mathbf{i} + \mathbf{j} - 2\mathbf{k}). \\ \therefore \quad \mathbf{e}_n &= \tfrac{1}{3}(2\mathbf{i} + \mathbf{j} - 2\mathbf{k}). \end{aligned}$$

Hence
$$\begin{aligned} \mathbf{a} . \mathbf{e}_n &= \tfrac{1}{3}(\mathbf{i} + 2\mathbf{j} + \mathbf{k}) . (2\mathbf{i} + \mathbf{j} - 2\mathbf{k}) \\ &= \tfrac{1}{3}(2 + 2 - 2) \\ &= \tfrac{2}{3}. \end{aligned}$$

Thus the equation of the plane is

$$\mathbf{p} . (2\mathbf{i} + \mathbf{j} - 2\mathbf{k}) = 2.$$

The distance of D from the face ABC is

$$\begin{aligned} (\mathbf{a} - \mathbf{d}) . \mathbf{e}_n &= (-\mathbf{i} + 2\mathbf{j} + \mathbf{k}) . \tfrac{1}{3}(2\mathbf{i} + \mathbf{j} - 2\mathbf{k}) \\ &= \tfrac{1}{3}(-2 + 2 - 2) \\ &= -\tfrac{2}{3}. \end{aligned}$$

$\therefore$ the vertex D is 2/3 unit from the face ABC.

The centroid of ABC has position $\tfrac{1}{3}(\mathbf{a} + \mathbf{b} + \mathbf{c})$.

$$\therefore \quad \mathbf{g} = \tfrac{1}{3}(\mathbf{i} + 2\mathbf{j} - \mathbf{k}).$$

The direction of DG is then that of

$$3(\mathbf{g}-\mathbf{d}) = (\mathbf{i}+2\mathbf{j}-\mathbf{k})-6\mathbf{i}$$
$$= -5\mathbf{i}+2\mathbf{j}-\mathbf{k}.$$

Let the angle between DG and the face ABC be ϕ, then

$$\tfrac{1}{3}(2\mathbf{i}+\mathbf{j}-2\mathbf{k}).(-5\mathbf{i}+2\mathbf{j}-\mathbf{k}) = |-5\mathbf{i}+2\mathbf{j}-\mathbf{k}|\cos\left(\frac{\pi}{2}-\phi\right),$$

$$\tfrac{1}{3}(-10+2+2) = \sqrt{30}\cos\left(\frac{\pi}{2}-\phi\right),$$

$$\cos\left(\frac{\pi}{2}-\phi\right) = -\frac{2}{\sqrt{30}}.$$

The acute angle between the normal and DG is $\cos^{-1}(2/\sqrt{30})$,

i.e.
$$\frac{\pi}{2}-\phi = 68°\,36'.$$

$$\therefore\ \phi = 21°\,24'.$$

The angle between DG and the face ABC is $21°\,24'$.

At this stage we are using unit vectors more frequently, and they have an important characteristic when written in terms of mutually perpendicular unit vectors $\mathbf{i}$, $\mathbf{j}$ and $\mathbf{k}$. Let $\mathbf{e}$ be a unit vector such that

$$\mathbf{e} = e_1\mathbf{i}+e_2\mathbf{j}+e_3\mathbf{k},$$

then it follows that

$$\mathbf{e}.\mathbf{i} = e_1.$$

But since $\mathbf{e}$ and $\mathbf{i}$ are both unit vectors, it follows that

$$e_1 = \cos\theta,$$

where θ is the angle between $\mathbf{e}$ and the i-axis. Similarly e_2 and e_3 are the cosines of the angles $\mathbf{e}$ makes with the j- and k-axes respectively, and so e_1, e_2 and e_3 are commonly referred to as the **direction cosines** of $\mathbf{e}$, and also of any multiple of $\mathbf{e}$, $k\mathbf{e}$.

Exercise 34

1 Find the equation of the helix of pitch π which passes through the point $9\mathbf{i}+3\mathbf{j}$ if its projection on the $\mathbf{i},\mathbf{j}$-plane is a circle with centre $5\mathbf{i}$.

2 The position of a particle at a given instant is

$$\mathbf{p} = a\cos\theta\mathbf{i}+a\sin\theta\mathbf{j}+c\theta\mathbf{k}.$$

Prove that if $\ddot{\mathbf{p}}.\mathbf{k} = 0$ then $d\theta/dt$ is constant. Hence show that if $\ddot{\mathbf{p}}.\mathbf{k} = 0$ that $\dot{\mathbf{p}}.\ddot{\mathbf{p}} = 0$ also.

3 A bead moves on the helix

$$\mathbf{p} = a\cos\theta\mathbf{i} + a\sin\theta\mathbf{j} + 2a\theta\mathbf{k}$$

so that its position after time t is given by $\theta = \pi t$. A second bead slides down a straight wire with equation

$$\mathbf{p} = 8\pi a\mathbf{k} + s(a\mathbf{i} - 8\pi a\mathbf{k})$$

so that its position after time t is given by $s = t^2/4$. Find the relative position, velocity and acceleration vectors after time t of the second bead to the first.

Hence find the value of t, $0 < t < 4$, such that the magnitude of the relative acceleration is a maximum, and determine this maximum value.

4 A sphere of radius a lies between two parallel rough planes distant $2a$ apart. One plane P_1 is fixed and corresponds to the $\mathbf{i},\mathbf{j}$-plane. The second plane P_2 cuts the $\mathbf{k}$-axis at $2a\mathbf{k}$. P_2 moves so that the point A in the plane has position $a\cos\theta\mathbf{i} + a\sin\theta\mathbf{j} + 2a\mathbf{k}$, and B in the plane has position $2a\mathbf{i}$ relative to A for all θ. When $\theta = 0$, the sphere touches P_2 at B. Determine the locus of the centre C of the sphere and also the locus of the point of contact between the sphere and P_2 relative to B.

5 A particle P moves in a spiral such that its position after time t relative to a fixed point O is

$$\mathbf{p} = e^t\cos\omega t\mathbf{i} + e^t\sin\omega t\mathbf{j} + \omega t\mathbf{k}$$

where ω is constant and $\mathbf{i},\mathbf{j},\mathbf{k}$ are mutually perpendicular unit vectors. Prove that $\dot{\mathbf{p}}$ is at right-angles to $\mathbf{p}$ if $e^{2t} + \omega^2 t = 0$, and by sketching appropriate graphs show that this equation has only one real root, and that this root is less than zero. Determine the speed of P at time t.

Prove also that if $\omega = 1$ then

$$\ddot{\mathbf{p}} = 2\dot{\mathbf{p}} - 2\mathbf{p} + 2(t-1)\mathbf{k}.$$

6 Calculate the least distance between the two skew lines

$$\mathbf{i} + 2\mathbf{j} + s(\mathbf{i} - \mathbf{j} + 3\mathbf{k}) \quad \text{and} \quad 2\mathbf{i} - \mathbf{j} - \mathbf{k} + s(3\mathbf{i} + \mathbf{j} + \mathbf{k}).$$

7 Find the equation of the shortest line joining the two skew lines

$$5\mathbf{i} + 6\mathbf{j} + \mathbf{k} + s(2\mathbf{i} + 2\mathbf{j} - \mathbf{k}) \quad \text{and} \quad 6\mathbf{i} - 9\mathbf{j} + 6\mathbf{k} + t(4\mathbf{i} - 8\mathbf{j} + 7\mathbf{k}).$$

8 Three mutually perpendicular lines L_1, L_2, L_3 meet in the point $\mathbf{a} = \mathbf{i} + 2\mathbf{j} - \mathbf{k}$. L_1 has the direction of $\mathbf{i} + \mathbf{j} + \mathbf{k}$, and L_2 passes through the point $3\mathbf{i} + 3\mathbf{j} - 4\mathbf{k}$. Find the equations of the three lines.

Find also which line is nearest to the point $\mathbf{i} + \mathbf{j} + 3\mathbf{k}$, and determine the distance from the line in this case.

9 Determine the moment of inertia of a system of four particles of masses m, $2m$, $2m$ and $3m$ at the points $\mathbf{i} + \mathbf{j}$, $\mathbf{i} + \mathbf{j} + 2\mathbf{k}$, $2\mathbf{i} + 3\mathbf{j} - \mathbf{k}$ and $2\mathbf{j} - 3\mathbf{k}$ respectively about the line $\mathbf{i} + \mathbf{j} + \mathbf{k} + s(\mathbf{i} - \mathbf{j} + 2\mathbf{k})$.

10 Show that the area of a triangle XYZ with vertices given by $\mathbf{x}$, $\mathbf{y}$ and $\mathbf{z}$ respectively has area $\left|\frac{1}{2}(\mathbf{x} - \mathbf{y}) \wedge (\mathbf{z} - \mathbf{y})\right|$. Does it make sense to say that the area is $\frac{1}{2}(\mathbf{x} - \mathbf{y}) \wedge (\mathbf{z} - \mathbf{y})$?

Use this expression to find the centre of mass of a hollow tetrahedron made of uniform material with vertices at the points $\mathbf{i}$, $2\mathbf{j}$, $3\mathbf{k}$ and $-\mathbf{i}$.

11 Two ships travelling at steady velocities have positions

$$\mathbf{a} = \mathbf{p} + t\mathbf{u}$$

and

$$\mathbf{b} = \mathbf{q} + t\mathbf{v}$$

respectively after time t. Show that their shortest distance apart is d where

$$d = \left| \frac{(\mathbf{u} - \mathbf{v}) \wedge (\mathbf{p} - \mathbf{q})}{|\mathbf{u} - \mathbf{v}|} \right|.$$

Hence show that they are closest together when

$$t = \frac{(\mathbf{q}-\mathbf{p}).(\mathbf{u}-\mathbf{v})}{|\mathbf{u}-\mathbf{v}|^2}.$$

12 Find the equation of the plane passing through the three points $\mathbf{i}+\mathbf{j}+\mathbf{k}$, $2\mathbf{i}-\mathbf{j}-4\mathbf{k}$ and $3\mathbf{i}-4\mathbf{j}+5\mathbf{k}$.

13 Determine which of the two points $\mathbf{a} = 3\mathbf{i}+2\mathbf{j}-\mathbf{k}$ and $\mathbf{b} = 2\mathbf{i}-\mathbf{j}+3\mathbf{k}$ is nearer to the plane

$$\mathbf{p}.(\mathbf{i}-\mathbf{j}+\mathbf{k}) = 3\sqrt{3}.$$

What is this shortest distance?

14 A tetrahedron ABCD has vertices $\mathbf{a} = \mathbf{i}+\mathbf{j}$, $\mathbf{b} = 6\mathbf{i}+3\mathbf{j}+3\mathbf{k}$, $\mathbf{c} = -5\mathbf{i}-\mathbf{j}-3\mathbf{k}$ and $\mathbf{d} = \mathbf{i}+4\mathbf{j}+3\mathbf{k}$. Determine the angle between the faces ABC and ABD.

Find also the volume of the tetrahedron.

15 Find the line of intersection of the two planes

$$\mathbf{p}.(\mathbf{i}+\mathbf{j}-\mathbf{k}) = 3,$$

and $\qquad\qquad \mathbf{p}.(2\mathbf{i}+\mathbf{j}+2\mathbf{k}) = 6.$

13.6 Radial and transverse components of acceleration

The cartesian coordinate system and its corresponding vector equivalent of mutually perpendicular unit vectors $\mathbf{i}$, $\mathbf{j}$, $\mathbf{k}$ are not always the most convenient methods of defining position. One alternative system which may already be familiar to the reader is that of polar coordinates. A useful vector system exists which is based on the same variables—the radius vector and the angle it makes with a fixed line of reference.

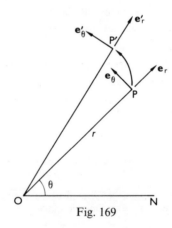

Fig. 169

Consider a point P in a plane, O being the fixed point of reference in the plane. Let ON be a fixed line of reference in the plane, and angle PON $= \theta$. OP $= r$. The polar coordinate system then defines the position of P in terms of θ and r.

Let $\mathbf{e}_r$ be the unit vector along OP, and $\mathbf{e}_\theta$ the unit vector perpendicular to OP in the positive sense of θ, positive being conventionally anticlockwise (Fig. 169). The position of P relative to O is then

$$\mathbf{p} = r\mathbf{e}_r.$$

Suppose that P is now displaced a small distance to the point P'. The directions, but not the magnitudes, of the vectors $\mathbf{e}_r$ and $\mathbf{e}_\theta$ will have changed, let us say, to $\mathbf{e}'_r$ and $\mathbf{e}'_\theta$, and it follows that neither $\dot{\mathbf{e}}_r$ nor $\dot{\mathbf{e}}_\theta$ are zero. Let $\mathbf{i}$ and $\mathbf{j}$ be unit vectors along and perpendicular to ON, then

$$\mathbf{e}_r = |\mathbf{e}_r|(\cos\theta\mathbf{i}+\sin\theta\mathbf{j})$$
$$= \cos\theta\mathbf{i}+\sin\theta\mathbf{j}.$$
$$\therefore \dot{\mathbf{e}}_r = -\sin\theta\dot\theta\mathbf{i}+\cos\theta\dot\theta\mathbf{j}.$$

Similarly

$$\mathbf{e}_\theta = |\mathbf{e}_\theta|(-\sin\theta\mathbf{i}+\cos\theta\mathbf{j})$$
$$= -\sin\theta\mathbf{i}+\cos\theta\mathbf{j}.$$
$$\therefore \dot{\mathbf{e}}_\theta = -\cos\theta\dot\theta\mathbf{i}-\sin\theta\dot\theta\mathbf{j}.$$

It follows that

$$\dot{\mathbf{e}}_r = \dot\theta\mathbf{e}_\theta,$$

and

$$\dot{\mathbf{e}}_\theta = -\dot\theta\mathbf{e}_r.$$
$$\therefore \mathbf{p} = r\mathbf{e}_r$$
$$\Rightarrow \dot{\mathbf{p}} = \dot{r}\mathbf{e}_r+r\dot{\mathbf{e}}_r,$$
$$\dot{\mathbf{p}} = \dot{r}\mathbf{e}_r+r\dot\theta\mathbf{e}_\theta. \qquad 13.1$$

Differentiating again,

$$\ddot{\mathbf{p}} = \ddot{r}\mathbf{e}_r+\dot{r}\dot{\mathbf{e}}_r+\dot{r}\dot\theta\mathbf{e}_\theta+r\ddot\theta\mathbf{e}_\theta+r\dot\theta\dot{\mathbf{e}}_\theta$$
$$= (\ddot{r}-r\dot\theta^2)\mathbf{e}_r+(2\dot{r}\dot\theta+r\ddot\theta)\mathbf{e}_\theta. \qquad 13.2$$

$(\ddot{r}-r\dot\theta^2)$ and $(2\dot{r}\dot\theta+r\ddot\theta)$ are referred to as the radial and transverse components of acceleration respectively. The equation for $\ddot{\mathbf{p}}$ can also be written in the form:

$$\ddot{\mathbf{p}} = (\ddot{r}-r\dot\theta^2)\mathbf{e}_r+\frac{1}{r}\frac{d}{dt}(r^2\dot\theta)\mathbf{e}_\theta. \qquad 13.2a$$

This is equivalent to saying that the change in angular momentum is proportional to the moment of the impressed force. The moment of the impressed force is

$$r.\frac{m}{r}\frac{d}{dt}(r^2\dot\theta) \quad \text{about 0,}$$

$$= \frac{d}{dt}(mr^2\dot\theta)$$

$$= \frac{d}{dt}(I\omega)$$

with usual notation.

EXAMPLE 6   *The position of a point P is given by the vector* $\mathbf{p} = r\mathbf{e}_r$, *where* $r = e^t$ *and* $\theta = t^2 - 1$ *after time t. Form expressions for* $\dot{\mathbf{p}}$ *and* $\ddot{\mathbf{p}}$ *and show that* $\dot{\mathbf{p}}$ *and* $\ddot{\mathbf{p}}$ *are perpendicular for only one finite value of t.*

If $r = e^t$, then $\dot{r} = e^t = \ddot{r}$.
If $\theta = t^2 - 1$, then $\dot{\theta} = 2t$ and $\ddot{\theta} = 2$.
From equation *13.1*,

$$\dot{\mathbf{p}} = \dot{r}\mathbf{e}_r + r\dot{\theta}\mathbf{e}_\theta.$$

$$\therefore \quad \dot{\mathbf{p}} = e^t\mathbf{e}_r + 2te^t\mathbf{e}_\theta.$$

Similarly from *13.2*,

$$\ddot{\mathbf{p}} = (\ddot{r} - r\dot{\theta}^2)\mathbf{e}_r + (2\dot{r}\dot{\theta} + r\ddot{\theta})\mathbf{e}_\theta$$

$$= e^t(1 - 4t^2)\mathbf{e}_r + e^t(4t + 2)\mathbf{e}_\theta.$$

If $\dot{\mathbf{p}}$ and $\ddot{\mathbf{p}}$ are perpendicular then $\dot{\mathbf{p}} \cdot \ddot{\mathbf{p}} = 0$. But

$$\dot{\mathbf{p}} \cdot \ddot{\mathbf{p}} = e^{2t}(1 - 4t^2) + 2te^{2t}(4t + 2)$$

$$= e^{2t}(1 + 4t^2 + 4t).$$

Thus if $\dot{\mathbf{p}} \cdot \ddot{\mathbf{p}} = 0$, either

$$e^{2t} = 0, \Rightarrow t \text{ not finite,}$$

or

$$4t^2 + 4t + 1 = 0.$$

$$\therefore \quad (2t + 1)^2 = 0,$$

$$t = -\tfrac{1}{2} \text{ (twice).}$$

Thus there is only one value of t such that $\dot{\mathbf{p}}$ and $\ddot{\mathbf{p}}$ are perpendicular.

EXAMPLE 7   *A uniform rod of mass m and length 2a oscillates in a vertical plane about a smooth horizontal axis through one end. If the maximum angular velocity of the rod is* ω, *form an expression for the reaction at the axis when the rod makes an angle* θ *with the downward vertical.*

By the principle of angular momentum

$$I\ddot{\theta} = -mgh \sin \theta$$

where the moment of inertia $I = \tfrac{4}{3}ma^2$ and $h = a$. Substituting

$$\tfrac{4}{3}ma^2\ddot{\theta} = -mga \sin \theta,$$

$$\ddot{\theta} = -\frac{3g}{4a} \sin \theta.$$

By the Conservation of Energy

$$\tfrac{1}{2}I\omega^2 = \tfrac{1}{2}I\dot{\theta}^2 + mga(1 - \cos \theta).$$

$$\therefore \quad \frac{2ma^2}{3}\dot{\theta}^2 = \frac{2ma^2}{3}\omega^2 - mga(1-\cos\theta),$$

$$\dot{\theta}^2 = \omega^2 - \frac{3g}{2a}(1-\cos\theta).$$

We consider the motion of the centre of the rod relative to the axis. In terms of equation *13.1*, $r = a$, and $\dot{r} = \ddot{r} = 0$. Thus equation *13.2* will become

$$\ddot{\mathbf{p}} = -a\dot{\theta}^2\mathbf{e}_r + a\ddot{\theta}\mathbf{e}_\theta.$$

Substituting for $\dot{\theta}$ and $\ddot{\theta}$,

$$\ddot{\mathbf{p}} = \left\{-a\omega^2 + \frac{3g}{2}(1-\cos\theta)\right\}\mathbf{e}_r - \frac{3g}{4}\sin\theta\mathbf{e}_\theta.$$

This vector is relative however, and does not account for the reaction to the weight of the rod. If **k** is the vertical unit vector then the force on the pivot is

$$-mg\mathbf{k} - m\ddot{\mathbf{p}}.$$

But $\mathbf{k} = -\cos\theta\mathbf{e}_r + \sin\theta\mathbf{e}_\theta$. Therefore the force on the pivot is

$$\left\{mg\cos\theta + ma\omega^2 - \frac{3mg}{2}(1-\cos\theta)\right\}\mathbf{e}_r + \left(-mg\sin\theta + \frac{3g}{4}m\sin\theta\right)\mathbf{e}_\theta$$

$$= m\left\{\omega^2 a + \frac{g}{2}(5\cos\theta - 3)\right\}\mathbf{e}_r - \frac{mg}{4}\sin\theta\mathbf{e}_\theta.$$

13.7 Motion in a conic

An important result applicable to planetary motion can now be demonstrated. Newton's Law of Gravitation states that the force of attraction between two bodies is inversely proportional to the square of the distance between them (see **2.4**). It is possible by appropriate substitution in equations *13.1* and **13.2a** to show that the corresponding path must be a conic, but this involves further knowledge of calculus which we shall not assume at this point; this is considered more fully in **14.4**. We can however demonstrate the converse, i.e. that any body the locus of which is a conic, moves under the action of a force which is inversely proportional to the square of its distance from a fixed point (the focus of the conic) and which is directed through that point.

We define a conic as the locus of a point P such that its distance from a fixed point O (the focus) and its distance from a fixed line (the directrix) are in a fixed ratio. Let N be the foot of the perpendicular from P to the directrix, then

$$\frac{\text{OP}}{\text{NP}} = e$$

where e is a constant (eccentricity).

Let X be the foot of the perpendicular from O to the directrix and OX $= d$. Let angle POX $= \theta$, then

$$e = r/(d - r \cos \theta).$$

Hence $\qquad\qquad r(1 + e \cos \theta) = ed, \qquad\qquad\qquad$ 13.3

which is the polar equation of a conic.

We assume that the force acting on a body at P due to a mass at O is radial. From equation 13.2a it follows that

$$\frac{1}{r}\frac{d}{dt}(r^2\dot\theta) = 0,$$

$$\Rightarrow r^2\dot\theta = h, \text{ a constant.}$$

Differentiating equation 13.3 with respect to time,

$$\dot r(1 + e \cos \theta) - re \sin \theta\dot\theta = 0,$$

i.e. $\qquad\qquad \dot r de - r^2 e \sin \theta\dot\theta = 0.$

$$\dot r d - r^2 \sin \theta\dot\theta = 0.$$

Substituting for $\dot\theta$,

$$\dot r d - h \sin \theta = 0.$$

Differentiating again,

$$\ddot r d - h \cos \theta\dot\theta = 0,$$

$$\Rightarrow \ddot r d - \frac{h^2}{r^2} \cos \theta = 0.$$

Now from equation 13.2a, the acceleration is

$$\ddot{\mathbf p} = (\ddot r - r\dot\theta^2)\mathbf{e}_r$$

$$= \left(\frac{h^2}{dr^2} \cos \theta - \frac{h^2}{r^3}\right)\mathbf{e}_r$$

$$= \frac{h^2}{r^2}\left(\frac{1}{d} \cos \theta - \frac{1}{r}\right)\mathbf{e}_r.$$

But from 13.3

$$\cos \theta = \frac{d}{r} - \frac{1}{e}.$$

$$\therefore \quad \ddot{\mathbf p} = \frac{h^2}{r^2}\left(\frac{1}{r} - \frac{1}{de} - \frac{1}{r}\right)\mathbf{e}_r$$

$$= -\frac{h^2}{der^2}\mathbf{e}_r$$

which is inversely proportional to r^2.

The question which now arises is, what will determine the nature of the conic in a particular situation. We know that it will be an ellipse for $e < 1$, a parabola if $e = 1$, and a hyperbola if $e > 1$. In the physical situation the value of e will depend on the angular momentum of the body about O. The reader is encouraged to find this relation for himself by considering Examples 5, 6 and 7 in Exercise 35.

The question of the nature of the orbit is closely allied to the problem of launching satellites from orbits round the Earth into suitable paths to reach other planets. In order to escape from an elliptical orbit, the satellite must be given an increase in velocity. The value of the new velocity which will just cause the satellite to escape occurs when $e = 1$, and is sometimes referred to as the critical velocity. In practice a satellite is given a greater velocity than this, and will thus pursue a hyperbolic path away from the planet.

Exercise 35

1 Without reference to the text, deduce the radial and transverse components of velocity of a particle in terms of r, θ and their derivatives.

Hence deduce the acceleration vector of a point

$$\mathbf{p} = r\mathbf{e}_r \quad \text{if} \quad r = t^2 \quad \text{and} \quad \theta = 2t.$$

2 If $\theta = ct^2$ where c is a constant, and

$$r = 1 + \sin\theta,$$

find the velocity and acceleration of a point P with position $r\mathbf{e}_r$ in terms of r, c and time t.

3 A particle of mass m moves on the curve $\mathbf{p} = r\mathbf{e}_r$ where

$$r = 2a + a\sin\omega t$$

in which $\dfrac{d\theta}{dt} = \omega = $ constant. Determine the magnitude of the force acting on the particle. Sketch also the locus of P.

4 A particle moves under the action of a varying force so that its polar equation is

$$r = a\sin\theta \text{ where } \theta = \omega t, \text{ and } \omega \text{ is constant.}$$

Show that the acceleration vector is

$$\ddot{\mathbf{p}} = 2\omega^2(-r\mathbf{e}_r + a\cos\omega t\mathbf{e}_\theta).$$

Sketch the locus of the particle, and determine the period of a complete cycle of its motion.

5 A satellite moves in orbit round a planet of mass M on the path $\mathbf{p} = r\mathbf{e}_r$ where

$$r(1 + e\cos\theta) = ed.$$

When $\theta = 0$, $r = a$ and $\dot{\mathbf{p}} = v\mathbf{e}_\theta$. Show that the velocity v when $\theta = 0$ must be less than $\sqrt{2GM/a}$ if the orbit is to be elliptical, where G is the universal gravitational constant.

6 A space capsule of mass m moves in a circular orbit of radius R under the effect of a central force of magnitude μ/R^2. Form an expression for the speed V of the craft.

If the speed of the capsule is now increased to $V + v$, show that the eccentricity of the new orbit is

$$\frac{R}{\mu}(V + v)^2 - 1.$$

7 A space craft is in a circular orbit of altitude 400 km round the Earth. Show that the speed of the craft is approximately 461 km/min.

Over a very brief time the speed of the space craft is increased by 100 km/min. Show that the eccentricity of the new orbit is approximately 0·48. (Take G as $6·67 \times 10^{-11}$ and the mass of the Earth as $5·98 \times 10^{24}$ kg.)

8 A particle of mass m moves in the path $\mathbf{p} = r\mathbf{e}_r$ where $\mathbf{e}_r$ is the unit radial vector and $r^3 \cos 3\theta = a^3$ under the action of a force directed through the origin. Show that this force is given by

$$\mathbf{F} = -\frac{2mh^2}{a^6} r^3 \mathbf{e}_r$$

where $h = r^2\dot{\theta}$.

14 Differential Equations

14.1 Method of separation of the variables

In Chapter 11, where we deduced the equations *11.3* and *11.4* relative to simple harmonic motion from the definitive equation $\dfrac{d^2x}{dt^2} = -\omega^2 x$, we assumed a method of integration which has a much wider application. The method is commonly referred to as integration by separation of the variables, and in this section we introduce some further applications of this method in mechanics.

The method of separation of the variables is applicable to any differential equation which can be expressed in the form

$$f(x)\frac{dx}{dz} = g(y)\frac{dy}{dz}. \qquad\qquad 14.1$$

If $f(x)$ is the derivative of $F(x)$ with respect to x, then $f(x)\dfrac{dx}{dz}$ is the derivative of $F(x)$ with respect to z. It follows that

$$\int f(x)\frac{dx}{dz}dz \equiv \int f(x)dx.$$

Similarly,

$$\int g(y)\frac{dy}{dz}dz \equiv \int g(y)dy.$$

Thus we can integrate the equation *14.1* with respect to z giving

$$\int f(x)dx = \int g(y)dy.$$

In practice Equation *14.1* will often occur in the simpler form

$$f(x)\frac{dx}{dz} = g(z),$$

but in this case the same argument gives, integrating with respect to z,

$$\int f(x)dx = \int g(z)dz.$$

EXAMPLE 1   *Find the general solution of the equation* $\dfrac{dy}{dx} = y^2$.

Rearranging the equation

$$\frac{1}{y^2}\frac{dy}{dx} = 1.$$

Integrating with respect to x,

$$\int\frac{1}{y^2}\frac{dy}{dx}dx = \int dx,$$

$$-\frac{1}{y} = x+c,$$

or $\qquad\qquad xy+cy+1 = 0.$

EXAMPLE 2   *Solve the equation* $(1+t)\dfrac{dv}{dt}+t^2 = 3t^2v.$

We rearrange the equation first as

$$(1+t)\frac{dv}{dt} = t^2(3v-1),$$

then separating the variables,

$$\frac{1}{(3v-1)}\frac{dv}{dt} = \frac{t^2}{1+t}.$$

Integrating with respect to t,

$$\int\frac{1}{(3v-1)}dv = \int\frac{t^2}{1+t}dt.$$

$$\tfrac{1}{3}\log_e(3v-1) = \int\left(t-1+\frac{1}{1+t}\right)dt$$

$$= \tfrac{1}{2}t^2-t+\log_e(1+t)+c,$$

i.e. $\log_e k\dfrac{(3v-1)^{\frac{1}{3}}}{1+t} = t(t-1)/2,$

where $-\log_e k = c$, the constant of integration.

EXAMPLE 3   *Integrate the equation* $x^2\dfrac{dx}{dt}+y^2\dfrac{dy}{dt} = 1.$

The equation is already in the appropriate form. Integrating with respect to t gives

$$\frac{x^3}{3}+\frac{y^3}{3} = t+c,$$

i.e. $\qquad\qquad x^3+y^3 = 3t+k.$

We consider now the application of the method to examples in mechanics. They most frequently arise where the force acting on a particle is related either to position or to velocity. It is helpful to note the two cases.

(1) If $\ddot{x} = f(x)$, then we can only put

$$v\frac{dv}{dx} = f(x)$$

and integrate with respect to x.

(2) If $\ddot{x} = f(v)$, then we can deduce two equations. The first comes by writing

$$\frac{dv}{dt} = f(v),$$

separating the variables and integrating with respect to t. The second comes as before by writing

$$v\frac{dv}{dx} = f(v),$$

but separating the variables in this case, and integrating with respect to x.

EXAMPLE 4   *A body moving in a straight line has velocity proportional to its distance from a fixed point* O *on that line and directed towards* O. *If* $t = 0$ *when the body is 1 m from* O, *and* $t = 1$ *when it is 0.5 m from* O, *find* t *when it reaches the point 0.01 m from* O.

If the distance from O at time t is x then

$$\frac{dx}{dt} = -kx.$$

$$\therefore \frac{1}{x}\frac{dx}{dt} = -k.$$

Integrating with respect to t,

$$\log_e x = -kt+c.$$

But $x = 1$ when $t = 0$.

$$\therefore c = 0,$$

and

$$\log_e x = -kt.$$

When $x = 0.5$, $t = 1$.

$$\therefore \log_e \tfrac{1}{2} = -k,$$

$$k = \log_e 2.$$

$$\therefore \log_e x = -t \log_e 2.$$

Putting $x = 0\cdot01$,

$$\log_e 0\cdot01 = -t \log_e 2,$$
$$\Rightarrow -2 \log_e 10 = -t \log_e 2,$$
$$t = \frac{2 \log_e 10}{\log_e 2}$$
$$= 2 \log_2 10.$$

The particle is $0\cdot01$ m from O after time $2 \log_2 10$.

EXAMPLE 5   *A particle is projected vertically upwards with speed V and attains a maximum height h above the point of projection. If air resistance is kv^2 per unit mass, where v is the speed and k is a constant, show that*

$$e^{2hk} = 1 + \frac{k}{g}V^2.$$

If the particle returns through the starting point with speed V', find the ratio $V^2 : V'^2$.

At time t after projection at a height x above the point of projection

$$\frac{d^2x}{dt^2} = -g - kv^2 \tag{1}$$

until the particle reaches its highest point. Thereafter

$$\frac{d^2x}{dt^2} = -g + kv^2. \tag{2}$$

It is because the equation of motion alters in this way that $V \neq V'$.
For the first stage of the motion, equation (1) gives

$$v\frac{dv}{dx} = -(g + kv^2).$$

We integrate with respect to x. As x increases from zero, and v decreases from V, we can insert the limits of integration immediately. Thus

$$\int_V^v \frac{v\,dv}{g + kv^2} = -\int_0^x dx.$$

$$\frac{1}{2k}\left[\log_e (g + kv^2)\right]_V^v = -x,$$

$$x = \frac{1}{2k} \log_e \left(\frac{g + kV^2}{g + kv^2}\right).$$

But when $x = h$, $v = 0$.

$$\therefore \ h = \frac{1}{2k} \log_e \left(\frac{g + kV^2}{g} \right),$$

$$e^{2hk} = 1 + \frac{k}{g} V^2. \qquad \qquad \underline{\text{Q.E.D.}}$$

In practice, we can find the value of k by drawing graphs of $y = e^{2hk}$ and $y = 1 + \frac{k}{g} V^2$.

After reaching the maximum height equation (2) becomes the equation of motion. Thus

$$v\frac{dv}{dx} = kv^2 - g.$$

Integrating with respect to x between the limits at the maximum height and the instant it passes through the point of projection,

$$\int_0^{V''} \frac{v \, dv}{kv^2 - g} = \int_h^0 dx.$$

$$\frac{1}{2k} \left[\log_e (kv^2 - g) \right]_0^{V''} = -h,$$

$$h = \frac{1}{2k} \log_e \left(\frac{-g}{kV''^2 - g} \right).$$

$$\therefore \ e^{2hk} = 1 \Big/ \left(1 - \frac{k}{g} V''^2 \right),$$

$$e^{-2hk} = 1 - \frac{k}{g} V''^2.$$

Comparing this with the corresponding result for the first part of the motion we get

$$V^2 : V''^2 = (e^{2hk} - 1) : (1 - e^{-2hk}).$$

Exercise 36

1 Find the general solutions of the following:

   (a) $xy\frac{dy}{dx} = y^2 + 1$,

   (b) $\frac{dy}{dx} = (1 - y)^{\frac{1}{2}}$,

   (c) $x\frac{dy}{dx} + y^2(x - 1) = 0$,

   (d) $\frac{dy}{dx} = xe^y$.

2 The motion of a particle is given by the equation

$$\frac{d^2x}{dt^2} = x^{3/2},$$

with usual notation. If the speed $v = 0$ when $x = 0$, and if $t = 0$ when $x = 25$, show that

$$x = 400(t-2)^{-4}.$$

3 A particle P moves so that its acceleration when at a distance x from a fixed point O is given by

$$\ddot{x} = -k/x^2.$$

If it is launched directly away from O when $x = a$ with speed V, show that it will return through O unless

$$V \geqslant \sqrt{\frac{2k}{a}}.$$

4 A body of mass m is accelerated from rest at a point X distance 1 unit from O to strike an inelastic object distance 3 units from O on OX produced. The acceleration of the body is kx^2, where x is its distance from O and k is a constant. Determine the magnitude of the blow imparted to the object.

5 The rate of radioactive decay of a particular substance is given by the formula

$$\frac{dN}{dt} + kN = 0$$

where N is the number of atoms not yet decayed. If the half-life of the substance (i.e. the time in which N is reduced to $N/2$) is 100 days, find k, and hence show that just over 330 days will elapse before the number of active atoms is reduced to a tenth.

6 The acceleration of a particle is inversely proportional to the square of its distance x from a fixed point O and is directed towards O. If the velocity can be assumed to be zero for x sufficiently large, form a general equation for x in terms of time t.

If the particle is projected from a point distant 1 unit from O, away from O with velocity 10^4 units/s, show that its speed is less than 10^2 units/s when $x > 10^4$ and $t > \frac{200}{3}(1 - 10^{-6})$.

7 The acceleration of a particle is given by the equation

$$\frac{d^2x}{dt^2} = -v^2.$$

When $x = 0$, $t = 0$, and when $x = 10$, $v = 1$. Show that when $x = 10$,

$$t = 1 - e^{-10}.$$

8 A particle is falling through a liquid under gravity so that its acceleration is given by the equation

$$\frac{dv}{dt} = g - kv.$$

At the instant when $t = 0$, $v = 3g/k$. Show that after a further time t

$$v = \frac{g}{k}(1 + 2e^{-kt}).$$

9 A particle is projected vertically upwards from a point O with speed u, and is subject to air resistance equal to kv^2 per unit mass where k is a constant and v is the speed after time t. If it reaches its maximum height h after time T, show that

$$u = \sqrt{\frac{g}{k}} \tan(\sqrt{gk}\,T).$$

10 The acceleration of a particle is given by the equation

$$\frac{dv}{dt} = a - bv^2$$

where a and b are constants. Show that if $v = 0$ when $t = 0$, then

$$2\sqrt{ab}\,t = \log_e \frac{\sqrt{a} + \sqrt{b}\,v}{\sqrt{a} - \sqrt{b}\,v}.$$

By writing $\dfrac{dv}{dt}$ as $v\dfrac{dv}{dx}$, integrate the original equation with respect to x and so form an expression for v in terms of x, assuming $v = 0$ when $x = 0$.

11 A body falling under gravity is subject to a resisting force proportional to the square of its speed. If the maximum speed it can attain from rest is 50 m/s, find the speed at which it would strike the ground and the time taken before it does so if released from rest at a height of 120 m above the ground.

12 A particle of unit mass is projected vertically upwards with initial speed 200 m/s, and is subject to air resistance of kv^2 N where k is a constant and v is the speed t s after projection. The maximum height attained above the point of projection is 1800 m. Show that

$$4 \cdot 0 \times 10^{-5} < k < 9 \cdot 0 \times 10^{-5}.$$

Draw appropriate graphs to find k to two significant figures.
(Take g as $9 \cdot 8$ m/s².)

14.2 Damped oscillations

A particle oscillating with simple harmonic motion obeys the equation

$$\frac{d^2x}{dt^2} = -\omega^2 x$$

where x is the distance from the centre of the oscillation. In practice the particle may be acted upon by further forces, and in particular we consider the effect of a damping force proportional to $\dfrac{dx}{dt}$, and also the effect of a disturbing force of simple harmonic form which may initiate, or force, the oscillations.

In the former case, referred to as damped oscillations, the equation of motion takes the form

$$\ddot{x} = -\omega^2 x - 2a\dot{x},$$

which is

$$\frac{d^2x}{dt^2} + 2a\frac{dx}{dt} + \omega^2 x = 0. \qquad 14.2$$

All equations of the form

$$\frac{d^2x}{dt^2} + a\frac{dx}{dt} + bx = 0.$$

have solutions of the form $x = ke^{nt}$, and substituting in the differential equation gives us that n must satisfy

$$n^2 + an + b = 0.$$

If n_1 and n_2 are the roots of this equation, then it follows that the general solution is

$$x = k_1 e^{n_1 t} + k_2 e^{n_2 t}.$$

Let the solution of Equation *14.2* be $x = ke^{nt}$, then by substituting in *14.2*,

$$n^2 k e^{nt} + 2ank e^{nt} + \omega^2 k e^{nt} = 0,$$

i.e. $$n^2 + 2an + \omega^2 = 0.$$

The roots of this equation are n_1 and n_2 where

$$n_1 = -a + \sqrt{a^2 - \omega^2},$$

and $$n_2 = -a - \sqrt{a^2 - \omega^2},$$

The general solution of *14.2* is then

$$x = k_1 e^{n_1 t} + k_2 e^{n_2 t}.$$

In practice two distinct cases of damping can occur. They correspond to the values of n_1, n_2 being real or complex.

If n_1, n_2 are real, then $a^2 > \omega^2$. Let $\sqrt{a^2 - \omega^2} = c$, then

$$x = k_1 e^{-at + ct} + k_2 e^{-at - ct}$$
$$= e^{-at}(k_1 e^{ct} + k_2 e^{-ct}).$$

The main characteristic of the motion in this case is that the oscillation quickly ceases. We can show this more clearly by considering $\dot{x}$.

$$\dot{x} = -ae^{-at}(k_1 e^{ct} + k_2 e^{-ct}) + e^{-at}(ck_1 e^{ct} - ck_2 e^{-ct})$$
$$= e^{-at}((c-a)k_1 e^{ct} - (c+a)k_2 e^{-ct}).$$

Hence $\dot{x} = 0$ when

$$(c-a)k_1 e^{ct} = (c+a)k_2 e^{-ct},$$

$$e^{2ct} = \frac{(c+a)k_2}{(c-a)k_1}.$$

Since the right-hand side is a constant, and e^{2ct} is a steadily increasing function with t, the speed $\dot{x}$ is zero for not more than one value of t. It will be evident from a practical consideration as well as algebraically that such a motion occurs when the damping force, $2ma\dot{x}$, is the dominant force, and we refer to such a case as **heavy damping**. Fig. 170 illustrates the basic forms the motion can take.

The alternative to this type of damping is the case in which $a^2 < \omega^2$,

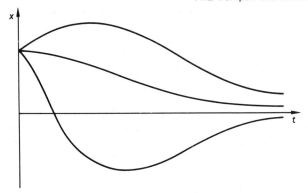

Fig. 170

and the damping force is comparatively light. n_1 and n_2 are now complex. Let $\sqrt{a^2 - \omega^2} = ci$, then the solution of Equation *14.2* is

$$x = k_1 e^{-at + cti} + k_2 e^{-at - cti}$$
$$= e^{-at}(k_1 e^{cti} + k_2 e^{-cti}),$$

where k_1 and k_2 are complex constants. But

$$e^{cti} = \cos ct + i \sin ct,$$

and $\qquad e^{-cti} = \cos ct - i \sin ct.$

$$\therefore \quad x = e^{-at}((k_1 + k_2) \cos ct + (k_1 - k_2)i \sin ct)$$
$$= e^{-at}(A \cos ct + B \sin ct).$$

Since we are considering a physical situation we are only interested in those

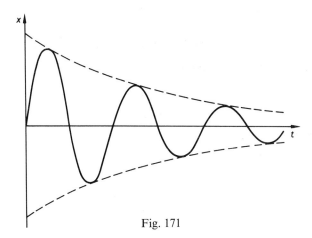

Fig. 171

solutions in which both A and B are real. In this case we can choose constants p and ε such that

$$x = pe^{-at} \cos (ct+\varepsilon).$$

Further, if we choose $t = 0$ when $x = p$ then

$$x = pe^{-at} \cos ct. \qquad\qquad 14.3$$

This equation is very similar to that of simple harmonic motion— $x = p \cos ct$. It has the same frequency as the simple harmonic motion, but the amplitude diminishes as e^{-at}. We refer to this effect as **light damping**, and such motion is illustrated by Fig. 171.

14.3 Forced oscillations

An oscillatory motion of the simple harmonic form can also be modified by other forces, and in general we may have to solve an equation of the form

$$\frac{d^2x}{dt^2} + a\frac{dx}{dt} + bx = f(t). \qquad\qquad 14.4$$

An equation of this form is solved by finding a particular solution x_1, referred to as the **particular integral**, and adding the **complementary function** x_2 which is the solution of

$$\frac{d^2x}{dt^2} + a\frac{dx}{dt} + bx = 0.$$

We illustrate the method by considering instances which arise in mechanics.

Suppose that

$$\frac{d^2x}{dt^2} + \omega^2 x = d,$$

where d is constant. If x_1 is constant then we note that $\dfrac{d^2x}{dt^2}$ is zero, and so the particular integral is given by

$$\omega^2 x = d.$$

Thus $\qquad\qquad\qquad\qquad x_1 = d/\omega^2.$

The complementary function is

$$x_2 = a \sin \omega t,$$

since

$$\frac{d^2x}{dt^2} + \omega^2 x = 0$$

defines simple harmonic motion, and we can choose t so that $x_2 = 0$ when $t = 0$. The complete solution is then

$$x = \frac{d}{\omega^2} + a \sin \omega t.$$

This is simple harmonic motion, but about the point distant d/ω^2 from the origin.

Consider now the case in which $f(t)$ is itself a harmonic function, so that

$$\frac{d^2x}{dt^2} + \omega^2 x = b \cos ct. \qquad 14.5$$

The particular integral in this case is found by assuming it to be of the form

$$x = A \cos ct.$$

Substitution in Equation 14.5 gives

$$-Ac^2 \cos ct + A\omega^2 \cos ct = b \cos ct.$$

Hence

$$A = \frac{b}{\omega^2 - c^2},$$

and the complete solution to 14.5 is

$$x = \frac{b}{\omega^2 - c^2} \cos ct + a \cos (\omega t + \varepsilon).$$

If $\omega^2 - c^2$ is small, then the amplitude of the motion becomes very large— the condition referred to as resonance.

Since a damping force will almost invariably apply to a physical oscillatory motion, it is pertinent to ask whether an oscillation can be sustained by applying an additional harmonic force of this kind. The equation of motion would then become

$$\frac{d^2x}{dt^2} + 2a\frac{dx}{dt} + \omega^2 x = b \cos ct. \qquad 14.6$$

We have already found the complementary function which is the solution of Equation 14.2. We assume the particular integral to be of the form

$$x_1 = A \cos ct + B \sin ct.$$

Substitution for x_1 into 14.6 will determine the constants A and B. In general however x_1 can also be written in the form

$$x_1 = A' \cos (ct + \varepsilon).$$

This is of simple harmonic form and continues indefinitely. We know from **14.2** that the complementary function is the equation of a damping motion, and whether heavy or light it diminishes with time. Thus initially the motion is composed of the sum of two distinct oscillations, but one diminishes in time so that the motion tends to that of the particular integral given by

$$x_1 = A' \cos (ct + \varepsilon).$$

If this forced oscillation has the same frequency as that of the complementary function the final motion will be identical to the free oscillation, but the determination of the constants is such that they will not be in phase—in this case there is a difference of $\pi/2$ in the phase.

14.4 Planetary motion

As a further application of these methods to physical situations, we can now consider gravitational motion starting from the force equation. If the position of a body relative to a centre of attraction is $\mathbf{p}$, then from Equation *13.2*

$$\ddot{\mathbf{p}} = (\ddot{r} - r\dot{\theta}^2)\mathbf{e}_r + \frac{1}{r}\frac{d}{dt}(r^2\dot{\theta})\mathbf{e}_\theta$$

$$= -\frac{k}{r^2}\mathbf{e}_r.$$

$$\therefore \ \ddot{r} - r\dot{\theta}^2 = -\frac{k}{r^2}, \tag{1}$$

and $$r^2\dot{\theta} = h, \text{ a constant.*} \tag{2}$$

Let $r = \dfrac{1}{u}$, then from (2)

$$\dot{\theta} = hu^2.$$

Thus $$\dot{r} = \frac{d}{dt}\left(\frac{1}{u}\right)$$

$$= -\frac{1}{u^2}\frac{du}{d\theta}\frac{d\theta}{dt}$$

$$= -h\frac{du}{d\theta}.$$

Differentiating again,

$$\ddot{r} = -h\frac{d}{dt}\left(\frac{du}{d\theta}\right)$$

---

* It is relevant to note that $\frac{1}{2}r^2\dot{\theta}$ is the area swept out by the radius vector for a small rotation θ, and so $\frac{1}{2}r^2\dot{\theta}$ can be referred to as the areal velocity. It is a feature of planetary motion that the areal velocity is constant, as shown by equation (2).

$$= -h\frac{d^2u}{d\theta^2}\frac{d\theta}{dt}$$

$$= -h^2u^2\frac{d^2u}{d\theta^2}.$$

$$\therefore \ \ddot{r}-r\dot{\theta}^2 = -h^2u^2\frac{d^2u}{d\theta^2}-h^2u^3$$

$$= -h^2u^2\left(\frac{d^2u}{d\theta^2}+u\right).$$

Substituting in (1) gives

$$-h^2u^2\left(\frac{d^2u}{d\theta^2}+u\right) = -ku^2.$$

$$\frac{d^2u}{d\theta^2}+u = k/h^2.$$

The particular integral of this equation is $u = k/h^2$, and the complementary function is

$$u = Ae^{i\theta} + Be^{-i\theta},$$

or $$u = C\cos(\theta+\varepsilon),$$

where C and ε are constants suitably related to the constants A and B. Thus the full solution is

$$u = C\cos(\theta+\varepsilon)+k/h^2,$$

which is

$$1 = Cr\cos(\theta+\varepsilon)+kr/h^2.$$

By a suitable choice of base line, $\varepsilon = 0$, so that

$$1 = Cr\cos\theta+kr/h^2.$$

Hence $$r\left(1+\frac{Ch^2}{k}\cos\theta\right) = \frac{h^2}{k}.$$

This is the equation of a conic of eccentricity Ch^2/k. (Cf. Equation *13.3*.)

Exercise 37

1 Find the general solutions of the following:

    (a) $\ddot{x}+5\dot{x}+6x = 0$,

    (b) $\ddot{x}+\dot{x}+2x = 0$,

    (c) $\ddot{x}+k\dot{x}+x = 2t$,   where $0 < k < 2$.

2 Find x, the distance of a particle from O, after time t if

    (a) $\ddot{x}+7\dot{x}+12x = 0$,   and when $t = 0, x = 2$ and $\dot{x} = -4$,

    (b) $\ddot{x}+\dot{x}+4x = \cos 2\pi t$ if when $t = 0, x = \frac{1}{2}$ and $\dot{x} = 1$.

3 A simple pendulum slows down under the effect of a force of magnitude kv per unit mass, and it is noted that it takes 300 seconds to cause the amplitude to halve. Assuming the frequency to be relatively large, show that k is approximately $3 \cdot 14 \times 10^{-3}$.

4 A particle of unit mass moves along the straight line AOB so that its acceleration is composed of two parts:

    (i) one of magnitude $n^2 x$ directed towards O where x is the distance of the particle from O, and

    (ii) one of magnitude k times the speed causing the particle to slow down, $k < 2n$.

If the particle starts from A where $x = -a$ and when $t = 0$, form an expression for x after time t, and hence show that the amplitude of the motion is halved in time $\dfrac{2}{k} \log_e 2$.

5 A particle moves according to the equation

$$\frac{d^2 x}{dt^2} + 2k \frac{dx}{dt} + n^2 x = 0$$

where $k > n$. When $t = 0$, $x = a$. If $b = \sqrt{k^2 - n^2}$, find x in terms of a, b and k given that $\dot{x} = 0$ when $t = 0$.

If, instead, $\dot{x} = 0$ when $t = -1/2b$, show that

$$x = Ce^{-kt}((a+b)e^{1+bt} - (a-b)e^{-bt})$$

where
$$C = \frac{a}{a(e-1) + b(e+1)}$$

6 Solve the equation

$$\ddot{x} + 4\dot{x} + 2x = 2t + 3$$

given that the particular integral takes the form $at + b$, and that $x = \dot{x} = 0$ when $t = 0$.

7 A particle moves according to the equation

$$\ddot{x} + 2k\dot{x} + n^2 x = kt^2.$$

Assuming the particular integral to be a quadratic function of t, form the general solution when $k^2 < n^2$.

If $k = 1$ and $n = 2$, and $x = a$ when $t = 0$, show that when $t = n\pi$

$$x = ae^{-n\pi} + \frac{n\pi}{4}(n\pi - 1).$$

8 An elastic string AB of natural length a and modulus λ has a particle attached to the end B. B is held at a depth a vertically below A. As B is released, A begins to move vertically so that its displacement from its initial position after time t is y where $\ddot{y} = -\omega^2 y$. Show that the displacement x of the particle after time t is given by

$$\ddot{x} + \frac{\lambda x}{ma} = \frac{\lambda C}{ma} \sin \omega t - g$$

where C is the amplitude of the motion of A, A is assumed to move upwards initially, and the string never goes slack.

If $\lambda = mg$ and $C = a/2$, show that the particular integral is of the form $p \sin \omega t - q$, and deduce that

$$x = a \cos \omega t - a.$$

Support Exercise E

Miscellaneous examples which may be worked concurrently with Chapters 12–14

1 A uniform rod AB of mass $4m$ and length $2a$ has three masses each of magnitude m attached at A, B and the mid-point. It is smoothly pivoted on a fixed axis perpendicular to the rod through the mid-point. Calculate the kinetic energy of the system when rotating at 50 rev/s.

If the rod is accelerated from rest to this speed and turns through 25π rad in the process the actual work done is $20\,000ma^2\pi^2$. Show that the average frictional torque is $400ma^2\pi/3$.

Through what angle will it turn in coming to rest from 50 rev/s under the effect of this frictional torque?

2 A, B, C are three points in a straight line on a smooth horizontal plane such that $AB = BC$ and ABC is perpendicular to a vertical wall at C. A particle of mass $3m$ lies at rest at B when it is struck by a second particle of mass m moving with speed v from A towards C. After the impact the first particle strikes the wall and rebounds to strike the second particle at A. If the coefficient of restitution at the wall is $\frac{1}{2}$, find the coefficient of restitution e between the particles.

Find the speeds of the particles after the second impact.

3 Prove that a *solid* tetrahedron with vertices A, B, C, D given by the position vectors $\mathbf{a} = 2\mathbf{i}+2\mathbf{j}$, $\mathbf{b} = -\mathbf{i}+\mathbf{j}+3\mathbf{k}$, $\mathbf{c} = 2\mathbf{i}-3\mathbf{j}+6\mathbf{k}$ and $\mathbf{d} = -2\mathbf{i}+6\mathbf{j}-3\mathbf{k}$ respectively, has centre of mass

$$\mathbf{m} = \tfrac{1}{4}\mathbf{i}+\tfrac{3}{2}\mathbf{j}+\tfrac{3}{2}\mathbf{k}.$$

X, Y, Z are the mid-points of the edges AD, BD, CD respectively. If the tetrahedron is cut into two parts by the plane XYZ, find the centre of mass of the larger portion.

($\mathbf{i}$, $\mathbf{j}$, $\mathbf{k}$ are mutually perpendicular unit vectors.)

4 Define the moment of inertia of a body.

A thin rod AB of length d is such that its mass density increases uniformly from ρ at A to 4ρ at B, its total mass being M. Show that the moment of inertia of the rod about an axis through A perpendicular to AB is $13Md^2/30$.

If this axis through A is horizontal, and AB can turn freely in a vertical plane about A, show that the maximum speed it attains after being released from a position making an angle ϕ with the downward vertical is

$$6\sqrt{\frac{g}{13d}(1-\cos\phi)}.$$

5 A rigid rod AB of length $2a$ is firmly fixed at A with B above A at an angle of $45°$ with the horizontal. A particle of mass m is suspended from B on a light inextensible string of length a. If the mass is given a horizontal velocity in the vertical plane of the rod when it is vertically below B, the string being taut, show that the moment of the tension about A when it makes an angle θ with the vertical is

$$2a \sin (45° + \theta)\left\{\frac{mv^2}{a} + mg(3 \cos \theta - 2)\right\}.$$

Show that if $v^2 = 5ga$, then the moment is maximum when $\theta = \pi/6$ and is approximately $10\cdot8mga$.

6 ABCD is an isosceles trapezium such that AB $= 2a$, BC $=$ CD $=$ DA $= a$. Forces of magnitudes P, $2Q$, $3Q$, $4Q$ act along the sides AB, BC, CD, DA in the senses indicated by the order of the letters. Find the point at which the resultant cuts AB, produced if necessary. **Hence** find P if the resultant passes through D.

If a couple of magnitude M is added to the system so as to cause the resultant to pass through C, find M. If the forces along AB and CD are altered so as to incorporate this couple, find the new values of the forces acting along these two sides.

7 State the principle known as the triangle of vectors.

A uniform plane lamina ABC is in the shape of an isosceles triangle with AB $=$ BC and has weight W. It is suspended in a vertical plane with AC horizontal and B below AC. It is held in this position by the reaction of a rough vertical wall at A and a string CD joining C to a point D on the wall vertically above A; 3AC $=$ 2CD. A further weight W is attached at C and the system is in limiting equilibrium. Show that the angle of friction at A is $\cos^{-1}(6/\sqrt{41})$, and determine the reaction at A and the tension in the string.

8 A particle of unit mass lying at rest at the origin of perpendicular unit vectors $\mathbf{i}$ and $\mathbf{j}$ is acted upon by a force $\mathbf{F}_1 = \mathbf{i} + 2\mathbf{j}$ for 2 s, and then by a force $\mathbf{F}_2$ for a further 2 s, after which time the particle is at the point $10\mathbf{i} + 2\mathbf{j}$. No other forces act. Find $\mathbf{F}_2$, and find the velocity of the particle as it passes through the point $10\mathbf{i} + 2\mathbf{j}$.

Find also the total work done.

9 A triangular lamina ABC has AB $=$ AC, BC $= 2a$ and angle ABC $= 64\frac{2}{7}°$. If it is uniform of mass m, show that the moment of inertia of the lamina about an axis perpendicular to its plane through A is $131ma^2/57$ on the assumption that $\sin 64\frac{2}{7}° = 0\cdot9$.

Hence find the moment of inertia of a uniform lamina of mass m in the form of a regular septagon, about an axis perpendicular to its plane through any vertex, if the sides are each of length $2a$.

10 Two particles A and B, of masses M and m respectively are attached to the ends of a light spring of modulus λ and natural length l, the whole lying at rest on a smooth horizontal plane with the spring straight and AB $= l$. If B is now projected directly away from A, show that, when the length of the spring is $l + x$ and the displacement of A is y,

$$m\left(\frac{d^2x}{dt^2} + \frac{d^2y}{dt^2}\right) = -T,$$

where T is the tension. Write down the equation of motion for A and deduce that the motion of B relative to A is simple harmonic and of amplitude u/ω, where

$$\omega^2 = \frac{(M+m)\lambda}{Mml},$$

u is the initial speed of B and the amplitude is assumed to be less than l. Find y as a function of t and briefly describe the motion of A.   (JMB)

11 B is a small hole in a smooth horizontal table and A is a fixed point vertically below B such that AB $= a/2$. A light elastic string of natural length a and modulus of elasticity mg is attached by one end to A, passes through B and is attached by the other end to a particle P of mass m lying on the table. A light marker C is attached to the string a quarter of the way along its length from A. Determine the length AC when P is made to rotate in a circle about B with constant angular speed ω, and deduce the value of ω when CA $= a/2$.

If now C is assumed to have mass $m/2$, find the new values of ω such that (1) CA $= a/4$, and (2) CA $= a/2$.

12 Fig. 172 illustrates a framework ABCDEFG of eleven light rods smoothly jointed together. Rods AG, GC, FD are each $\sqrt{5}$ units long, GF, FE, AB, BC and CD are 1 unit long, and GB, FC, ED are 2 units long. The frame is smoothly

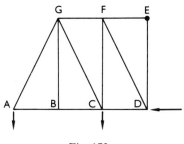

Fig. 172

pivoted to a fixed point at E and is kept with AD horizontal by a horizontal force at D, loads of masses 20 t and 5 t being suspended from A and C respectively. Apply the method of sections to determine the stresses in GF, GC and BC.

Find also the force required at D and the reaction at E.

13 A regular hexagon ABCDEF is composed of 12 uniform rods of length 4 m and mass 5 kg—AB, BC, CD, DE, EF, FA and AO, BO, CO, DO, EO, FO where O is the centre of the hexagon. The frame is pivoted about an axis through O perpendicular to ABCDEF. Find the moment of inertia about O.

If the hexagon is spinning at 600 rev/min, calculate the number of revolutions it will make before coming to rest against a frictional couple of magnitude 48 N m.

14 Two particles A and B both of mass m lie at rest on a smooth horizontal table a distance a apart. A straight line CD is drawn on the table through A perpendicular to AB. The particles are connected by a light inextensible string of length $2a$. If A is given an impulse of magnitude mv in the direction of CD, find the impulsive tension in the string when it becomes taut.

Find also the velocities of both A and B when the string is first parallel to CD.

15 A motorist wishing to stop from a speed of 50 km/h in a distance of 28 m discovers that he is on a patch of ice covering the first 20 m of road. Find the co-efficient of friction between the car and the ice (assumed constant) if his speed is only reduced to 45 km/h on the ice.

His maximum retardation on a normal road is 8 m/s². Show that he will not manage to stop in time, and calculate the magnitude of the impact with a stationary vehicle at the point he wishes to stop at if the mass of his car is 950 kg.

16 From the fact that the moment of inertia of a uniform rod of mass m and length $2a$ about a perpendicular axis through the mid-point is $\dfrac{ma^2}{3}$, deduce that the moment of inertia of a uniform equilateral triangular lamina of side $3a$ and mass m about an axis through the centroid perpendicular to the plane of the lamina is $3ma^2/4$.

If two equilateral triangles of side a are cut from two of the vertices, calculate the moment of inertia of the remnant about an axis perpendicular to the lamina through the remaining vertex.

17 Show that the work done by a couple of moment C in turning a body through θ radians about its axis of rotation is $C\theta$.

A flywheel of radius r has moment of inertia I about its horizontal axis, and its rotation about the axis is resisted by a constant frictional couple C. A light string wrapped round the flywheel supports a mass m. When the system is released from rest, the mass m descends a distance h vertically before reaching the ground. The string does not interfere with the subsequent motion of the flywheel, which comes to rest in a further time T and makes a further n rotations.

(i) Find the maximum angular velocity of the flywheel in terms of T and n,

(ii) Show $CT^2 = 4\pi n I$.

(iii) Eexpress I in terms of m, r, h, T and n.   (S)

18 A cylinder of weight W lies against two planes both inclined at 30° to the horizontal with their intersection horizontal and parallel to the axis of the cylinder. The coefficient of friction at both lines of contact is μ. A force P is applied horizontally to the top of the cylinder in a direction perpendicular to the generators. Find the minimum value of P to cause the cylinder to roll without slipping, assuming μ to be sufficiently large. If for this value of P it is also about to slip, find μ.

If $\mu = \frac{1}{4\sqrt{3}}$, calculate the value of P which will just cause the cylinder to slip.

19 Find the moment of inertia of a uniform hollow sphere of mass m having internal radius $r/2$ and external radius r about an axis through the centre.

Two spheres, both of mass m, are held at the top of a rough inclined plane of length d and angle $\sin^{-1} \frac{1}{5}$ to the horizontal. Both spheres are of radius r, but one is solid and the other is hollow with uniform thickness and internal radius $\frac{1}{2}r$. If they are released simultaneously show that the solid sphere will reach the bottom first, in which time the hollow sphere has rolled a distance

$$\frac{98d}{101}.$$

(The moment of inertia of a solid sphere of mass m and radius r about an axis through the centre is $\frac{2}{5}ma^2$.)

20 A particle is projected from a point A, the foot of a smooth plane inclined at an angle α to the horizontal, with speed V at an angle of elevation θ to the line of greatest slope of the plane. The particle strikes the plane normally at a point B $2r$ from A, and subsequently strikes the plane at the point C mid-way between A and B. Show that

$$V^2 \sin \theta \cos (\alpha + \theta) = rg \cos^2 \alpha$$

where $2 \tan \theta \tan \alpha = 1$.

Hence show that the value of e, the coefficient of restitution between the particle and the plane, is $1/\sqrt{2}$.

21 A sphere A of mass M has velocity vector $4\mathbf{i} - 3\mathbf{j}$ and a sphere B of mass m has velocity vector $4\mathbf{j}$. They are both smooth, and the coefficient of restitution between them is e. They collide with their line of centres in the direction of $\mathbf{j}$, and B is left stationary by the impact. Find the ratio $m:M$, and the angle through which A is deflected.

Show that the total loss in kinetic energy due to the impact is $\frac{7}{2}M(3 + 4e - 7e^2)$.

22 A uniform circular disc is free to rotate in a horizontal plane about a fixed vertical axis through its centre. It has a rough upper surface. When it is rotating with angular velocity Ω a second disc of the same moment of inertia is laid gently on top of it and concentrically so that initially the upper disc has no angular velocity. Prove that when the frictional couple between the discs has brought their two angular velocities to the same value this value is $\frac{1}{2}\Omega$.

Prove also that, if the frictional couple is constant and the angles through which the upper and lower discs have at that moment rotated are α and β, then $\beta = 3\alpha$.   (O&C)

23 A car of mass 1000 kg is moving on a level road at a steady speed of 100 km/h with its engine working at 60 kW. Calculate in newtons the total resistance to motion, which may be assumed to be constant.

The engine is now disconnected, the brakes are applied, and the car comes to rest in 100 metres. Assuming that the total resistance remains the same, show that the retarding force of the brakes is about 1700 newtons.

If the engine is still disconnected, find the distance the car would run up a hill of inclination $\sin^{-1} \frac{1}{10}$ before coming to rest, starting at 100 km/h, when the same resistance and braking force are operating.   (C)

24 O and A are two fixed points at a distance a apart, with A vertically below O. A particle P of mass m is attached to one end of a light inelastic string of length a, the other end of which is attached to O. P is also attached to one end of a light elastic string of natural length a and modulus of elasticity mg, the other end of which is attached to A. The inelastic string OP is taut and P is describing a horizontal circle of radius $a \sin \alpha$ ($\alpha > 0$) with constant speed $a\omega \sin \alpha$.

   (i) If the string AP is slack, show that $g < a\omega^2 < 2g$, and find α in terms of a, ω and g.

   (ii) If both strings are taut and $\alpha = 2 \sin^{-1} \frac{3}{5}$, find ω in terms of a and g, and also the tension in each string.   (W)

25 A lamina of mass m is free to rotate in its own plane, which is vertical, about a fixed point O of itself. Its centre of mass G is at a distance h from O, and its moment of inertia about an axis through O perpendicular to its plane is I.

If θ is the angle between OG and the downward vertical, find $d^2\theta/dt^2$ in terms of θ and show that it is the same as if θ were the deflection from the vertical of the string of a simple pendulum of length I/mh. (The motion is *not* to be supposed small in either case.)

Show also that if the speed of G is V when G is vertically below O, then the greatest value of θ attained is

$$\cos^{-1} \left(1 - \frac{IV^2}{2mgh^3}\right)$$

if $4mgh^3 > IV^2$.

Describe the motion of the lamina if $4mgh^3 < IV^2$.   (W)

26 Sphere A of mass $3m$ has a velocity vector $3\mathbf{i}+3\mathbf{j}$ and sphere B of mass m has velocity vector $-\mathbf{i}+2\mathbf{j}$. Both are smooth, and they collide with their line of centres in the direction of $\mathbf{i}$. If the coefficient of restitution is e, find their velocities after impact.

Show that it is impossible for their kinetic energies after impact to be equal, and that it is also impossible for the kinetic energy of A after impact to equal the kinetic energy of B before impact.

If $e = \frac{1}{2}$, find the ratio of kinetic energies after impact.

27 Prove that the centre of mass of a uniform solid cone of base radius r and height h is a distance $h/4$ from the base.

The cone, of mass m, rests in limiting equilibrium with its plane face in contact with a rough plane which makes an angle α with the horizontal. The cone is then placed on the plane so that its curved surface is in contact with the plane and the vertex above the base. The angle of the plane in limiting equilibrium is now β. (The angle of friction is greater than both α and β.) Show that

$$\tan (\alpha+\beta)+4 \cot \alpha = 0.$$

Find the value of β if $h = 3r$.

28 Two identical uniform rods AB, BC are smoothly hinged at B, and rest in limiting equilibrium in a vertical plane with A and C in contact with a rough plane inclined at 30° to the horizontal so that AC is in the line of greatest slope and C above A. Angle ABC is a right-angle. If the normal reactions at A and C are R and S, and the frictional forces at A and C are xR and yS, find x and y, and deduce the coefficient of friction between the rods and the plane.

29 A lamina has centre of gravity G and radius of gyration k about an axis through G perpendicular to the lamina. A and B are two points of the lamina such that $AG \neq BG$, but such that the period of small oscillations about a horizontal axis through A perpendicular to the lamina is the same as the period of small osciila- tions about a similar axis through B. Show that $k^2 = AG.BG$.

A uniform rod PQ is of length $4a$ and mass m, and X and Y are two points on the rod such that $PX = QY = a$. A particle of mass m is attached to the rod at distance x ($\neq 0$) from the centre. If the periods of small oscillations of the com- bined body about horizontal axes perpendicular to the rod through X and Y are the same, show that $x^2 = \frac{2}{3}a^2$. (C)

30 Forces of magnitudes 5, 4, 3 and F act along the lines AC, BC, CD and at M parallel to CB where M is the mid-point of CD and ABCD is a rectangular lamina. $AB = 4$ units and $BC = 3$ units. The force F is to be adjusted so that the lamina can be fixed by a smooth pin through some point within triangle ABD. Show that $F < 1\frac{1}{2}$ or $F > 12\frac{1}{2}$. Show also that of all such cases the resultant of the system cuts AD internally only if $12\frac{1}{2} < F < 14$.

31 In Fig. 173, AB is a smooth, fixed, vertical rail. CD and DE are light rods smoothly hinged together at D. The end C is constrained to move without friction along AB and the end E is smoothly hinged to a fixed point. Give a geometrical con- struction for the instantaneous centre of rotation of CD.

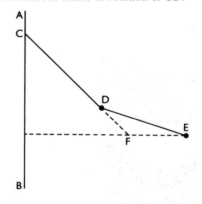

Fig. 173

Use the principle of virtual work to prove that, if a weight W is suspended from C, the couple that must be applied to DE to maintain equilibrium is FE.W, where F is the point of intersection of CD produced with the line through E at right-angles to the rail. (O)

32 A uniform circular disc rolls, without slipping, in a vertical plane down the line of greatest slope of a rough, fixed plane, inclined to the horizontal at an angle α. Prove that its acceleration is $\frac{2}{3}g \sin \alpha$ and that the coefficient of friction between the disc and the plane must be at least $\frac{1}{3} \tan \alpha$. (O)

33 Find, from first principles, the moment of inertia of a uniform circular lamina of radius a and mass m about a diameter.

The lamina is free to rotate about one of its tangents, which is fixed horizontally. It is released from rest in a horizontal position, and is brought to rest again by an inelastic peg fixed at a distance a vertically below the point of contact of the fixed tangent. Find the impulsive reaction at the moment of impact. (O)

34 Find the length of the simple pendulum equivalent to the motion of a point P which oscillates simple harmonically between two points A and B distant $2a$ apart and has a speed of $\sqrt{3}an$ at the point $a/2$ from A.

If such a pendulum is made a length $\dfrac{kg}{4n^2}$ too long, show that the percentage error of the period is $25k(4-k)/2$ neglecting terms of order higher than k^2.

35 Show that if a lies in the same plane as the two non-parallel unit vectors $\mathbf{e}_1$ and $\mathbf{e}_2$, then $\mathbf{a}$ can be represented uniquely by $\mathbf{a} = \alpha\mathbf{e}_1 + \beta\mathbf{e}_2$.

The two vectors $\mathbf{a} = \mathbf{e}_1 - 2\mathbf{e}_2$ and $\mathbf{b} = 7\mathbf{e}_1 + 2\mathbf{e}_2$ are perpendicular. Find the angle between the vectors $\mathbf{e}_1$ and $\mathbf{e}_2$, and hence calculate the resolutes of $\mathbf{a}$ and $\mathbf{b}$ in the directions of $\mathbf{e}_1$ and $\mathbf{e}_2$.

Find the work done by a force $3\mathbf{a}$ (newtons) which moves a particle slowly from the point $(\mathbf{b}-\mathbf{a})$ to the point $2\mathbf{a}$ (distances in metres).

36 A uniform rod AB of length $4a$ and mass $3m$ is rigidly attached to a point on the rim of a uniform disc of mass $8m$ and radius a so that AB produced passes through the centre of the disc. The system is suspended from A and is free to turn about A in the plane perpendicular to the disc. The system is hanging at rest when a particle of mass m is fired with velocity V to strike the disc perpendicularly at the centre. The coefficient of restitution is $\frac{1}{2}$.

(1) Find the initial angular velocity of the disc after impact.
(2) Show that the maximum angle θ AB makes with the vertical in the subsequent motion is approximately

$$\cos^{-1}(1 - 0.002\,26V^2/ag).$$

Hence calculate the speed of the particle to two significant figures if $\theta = \pi/6$, $a = 100$ mm and $g = 9.8$ m/s^2.

37 The power of a car engine at x rev/min is

$$7x^2(6000-x)/(4\times10^6)\text{ W}.$$

When in top gear the car travels at $x/100$ m/s. If the resistance to motion is kx^2 N, where k is constant, and if the maximum speed is 162 km/h, show that

$$k = 7/(12\times10^4).$$

Hence form an expression for the accelerating force F at x rev/min in top gear, and draw accurately to an appropriate scale a graph of F against x. Deduce the speed in km/h at which the car will have maximum acceleration.

38 A particle of mass m is attached to one end of a light inextensible string of length a, the other end of which is attached to a fixed point O. The particle is projected horizontally from O with speed V where $V^2 = \sqrt{3}ag$. Show that the impulsive tension in the string as it becomes taut is

$$\frac{4m\sqrt{ag}}{(4+2\sqrt{3})^{\frac{1}{2}}}.$$

Show also that the particle continues immediately after this instant with speed $V(2-\sqrt{3})$.

39 Find the moment of inertia about its axis of symmetry of a uniform solid right circular cone having mass M, and a base of radius a.

The cone is suspended from the ceiling by a wire which is attached to its vertex. The cone is given a twist about the vertical axis and released. If the restoring couple is $\lambda\theta$ where λ is a constant and θ the angular displacement from the equilibrium position, obtain the equation of motion for the cone and hence find the period of the simple harmonic oscillations about the vertical axis.   (NI)

40 A compound pendulum of mass M oscillates avout a smooth fixed horizontal axis. Its moment of inertia about an axis through its centre of gravity G, parallel to the fixed axis, is Mk^2. The centre of gravity moves in a vertical plane which cuts the fixed axis at O, and $OG = a$. Show that for small oscillations the period of the pendulum is the same as that of a simple pendulum of length l, and find l in terms of k and a.

If the pendulum is held with OG horizontal and is then released find its angular velocity when it reaches the position where OG is vertical.

At this instant a stationary particle of mass M adheres to the pendulum at G. Find the angular velocity of the combined body immediately afterwards.

Subsequently it first comes to rest with OG making an angle ϕ with the vertical. Show that

$$\cos \phi = \frac{k^2 + 3a^2}{2k^2 + 4a^2}.$$

(C)

41 A bead moves on an elliptical helix so that its position after time t is given by the equation

$$\mathbf{r} = a \cos \omega t \mathbf{i} - b \sin \omega t \mathbf{j} + (4\pi - \omega t)\mathbf{k}$$

where ω is constant. Find the value of t when at the point $\mathbf{r} = a\mathbf{i}$, and its speed at this point.

The $\mathbf{k}$-axis is vertically upwards, and a second bead slides from rest down a smooth straight wire with equation

$$\mathbf{r} = 4\pi\mathbf{k} + s(4\pi \tan \alpha \mathbf{i} - 4\pi\mathbf{k})$$

from the point $4\pi\mathbf{k}$ to the $\mathbf{i},\mathbf{j}$-plane in the same time as the first bead, so that they arrive in that plane at the same instant. Determine the value of α, and the relative velocity of the second bead to the first when they meet the $\mathbf{i},\mathbf{j}$-plane.

42 A uniform rod AB of weight W and length $3a$ is smoothly hinged at A. The rod rests in equilibrium against a fixed smooth sphere of radius a, the centre of which is $2a$ from A on the same horizontal level as A, and in the same vertical plane as the rod. Find the reaction between the rod and the sphere.

If $R = (25 - 12\sqrt{3})^{\frac{1}{2}}$, show that the reaction at A is $RW/4$, and find the angle this reaction makes with the vertical.

43 A gun fires shots at a target on level ground, firing always with the same muzzle velocity. When shots are fired at inclinations α and β with the horizontal, one shot overshoots while the other undershoots by the same amount. Prove that the inclination θ that is required to hit the target is given by

$$2 \sin 2\theta = \sin 2\alpha + \sin 2\beta.$$

Prove also that a shot at the inclination $\frac{1}{2}(\alpha + \beta)$ will always overshoot.

(O&C)

44 Water is pumped at the rate of 1·2 cubic metres per minute from a large tank on the ground up to a point 8 metres above the level of the water in the tank. It emerges as a horizontal jet from a pipe of cross-section 5 cm². If the efficiency of the apparatus is 60%, find, correct to the nearest 1/10 kW, the power supplied to the pump.

If the jet of water is immediately directed at right angles on to a vertical wall, find the force in newtons exerted on the wall, assuming that the water does not rebound.

(C)

45 The position vector at time t of a particle of mass m moving under the action of a variable force $\mathbf{F}$ is given by

$$\mathbf{r} = a \cos nt\mathbf{i} + a \sin nt\mathbf{j} + bt\mathbf{k}$$

where a, b, n are positive constants. Find the angle between the velocity vector and the acceleration vector at time t.

Show that if P is the position of the particle and Q is the point whose position vector is $bt\mathbf{k}$, then the force $\mathbf{F}$ on the particle at time t is proportional to $\overrightarrow{PQ}$, the constant of proportionality being independent of t.

Show that the vector $\overrightarrow{PQ}$ is of constant length and rotates parallel to the plane of $\mathbf{i}$ and $\mathbf{j}$ with a constant angular speed. (JMB)

46 A force $\mathbf{F} = 3\mathbf{i}+2\mathbf{j}+\mathbf{k}$ acts at a point P with position $\mathbf{p} = \mathbf{i}+\mathbf{j}$. Q is the point $\mathbf{q} = 2\mathbf{j}+\mathbf{k}$. Find the moment $\mathbf{M}$ of $\mathbf{F}$ about Q.

The line L passes through Q and has the direction of $\mathbf{e} = \frac{1}{\sqrt{3}}(\mathbf{i}-\mathbf{j}+\mathbf{k})$. Find the least distance d between L and the line of action of $\mathbf{F}$.

Verify that

$$|\mathbf{F}-(\mathbf{F}.\mathbf{e})\mathbf{e}|\,d = \mathbf{M}.\mathbf{e}.$$

47 A particle of mass m is attached to one end of a light inelastic cord of length l. The other end of the cord is held fixed at a height h(less than l) above a smooth horizontal table. If the particle is held on the table with the cord fully extended and projected along the table so that it moves in a horizontal circle with uniform speed v, prove that the force R that it exerts on the table is given by

$$R = m\left(g-\frac{v^2h}{l^2-h^2}\right).$$

Find an expression for T, the tension of the cord, in terms of m, v, l, h.

If $h = 0.3$ and $l = 0.5$ (both in metres) and $m = 2$ (kg),

(i) evaluate the force R, stating the units, when the speed is 1 m/s;
(ii) find the maximum velocity for which the particle will remain on the table, and the corresponding tension of the string. (S)

48 A smooth sphere of mass M is suspended at rest from a fixed point by an inextensible string. A second sphere of mass m falls vertically and strikes the first sphere with speed u, the line of centres at the moment of impact making an angle α with the vertical. If the sphere of mass M has initial speed v as a result of the impact, find the coefficient of restitution e. (NI)

49 A ship A has position $-4\mathbf{i}+3\mathbf{j}$ (nautical miles) relative to the origin of unit vectors $\mathbf{i}$ and $\mathbf{j}$ at 1000 hours. $\mathbf{i}$ is east and $\mathbf{j}$ is north. The velocity of A is $20\mathbf{i}+15\mathbf{j}$ (knots).

A launch B is at the point $2\mathbf{i}-4\mathbf{j}$ at 1000 hours and sets off to intercept A. If it does so at the point $4\mathbf{i}+9\mathbf{j}$, determine the speed and course of B.

Due to a mechanical fault, B has to reduce speed by 20% at 1012 hours. Determine when A and B are closest together and the magnitude of the distance between them to the nearest 1/10th of a nautical mile.

50 Deduce from first principles the radial and transverse components of velocity and acceleration of a particle with position $\mathbf{p} = r\mathbf{e}_r$ after time t.

A particle lies on a rough disc centre O at a point P such that $OP = d$. The coefficient of friction between the particle and the disc is μ. The disc is accelerated from rest at a rate θ. Show that the particle will begin to move relative to the disc when

$$d^2(\theta+\theta^4) = \mu^2g^2.$$

Deduce at what angle to OP the particle will begin to move if $\ddot\theta = k$, a constant.

51 Determine the equation of the plane in which lie the points $\mathbf{r}_1 = 2\mathbf{i}-\mathbf{j}, \mathbf{r}_2 = \mathbf{i}-2\mathbf{j}$, $\mathbf{r}_3 = -2\mathbf{j}+2\mathbf{k}$ in the form $\mathbf{p}.\mathbf{e}_n = d$, and hence show that the point $\mathbf{r}_4 = \mathbf{i}+2\mathbf{j}+8\mathbf{k}$ also lies in the plane.

Four parallel forces $\mathbf{F}_1, \mathbf{F}_2, \mathbf{F}_3, \mathbf{F}_4$ act through $\mathbf{r}_1, \mathbf{r}_2, \mathbf{r}_3, \mathbf{r}_4$ respectively all in the same sense. If $\mathbf{F}_1 = 2\mathbf{F}_2 = \mathbf{F}_3 = 3\mathbf{F}_4$, determine where their resultant cuts the plane.

52 The gravitational attraction between two members of the solar system is given by $\gamma m_1 m_2/r^2$ where m_1, m_2 are their masses, r is the distance between them and γ is a constant.

Assuming that the Moon and the Earth travel with constant speeds in circular orbits round the Earth and the Sun respectively, show that

$$\left(\frac{R'}{R}\right)^3 = \frac{m}{M}\left(\frac{T'}{T}\right)^2$$

where

m = mass of Earth

M = mass of Sun,

R' = distance of Moon from Earth,

R = distance of Earth from Sun,

T' = time taken by Moon to make 1 revolution round Earth,

T = time taken by Earth to make 1 revolution round Sun.

Hence calculate the distance of the Moon from the Earth given that $T' = 27\cdot3$ days, $T = 365$ days, $R = 150 \times 10^6$ kilometres and $m/M = 3 \times 10^{-6}$.   (NI)

53 A space craft is moving in an elliptical orbit of eccentricity $\frac{3}{4}$ about the Earth. Its speed when nearest to the Earth is V. At this instant it is retarded to a speed of $(V-v)$. Determine v if the new orbit is to be circular.

54 A plane smooth uniform disc of radius a and mass m is sliding over a smooth horizontal table, the plane of the disc being the same as that of the table. The motion of the disc is purely translational and is of speed v. A nail is now fired into the disc so as to pin the disc as by a smooth pivot to the table at a point $a/2$ from the centre of the disc, the line joining the nail to the centre being perpendicular to the motion at that instant. Show that the disc spins round the nail with speed $2v/3a$, and determine (a) the impulsive reaction on the nail, and (b) the subsequent reaction on the nail.

55 A particle P of mass m when distant x from a fixed point O is subject to a force of magnitude mk^2/x^5 directed towards O, where K is a constant. P is initially at a distance a from O and is projected with a velocity u directly away from O. Show that provided $u^2 < k^2/(2a^4)$, the particle comes instantaneously to rest at a point given by

$$x^4 = k^2a^4/(k^2 - 2a^4u^2).$$

If $u^2 > k^2/(2a^4)$, show that the particle slows down but never stops, and that its speed v when at a greater distance from O is given by

$$v^2 = u^2 - k^2/(2a^4).$$

If $u^2 = k^2/(2a^4)$, find an expression for the displacement x after time t.   (C)

56 The average speed over the period of a complete oscillation of a particle performing rectilinear simple harmonic motion is 2 cm/s. If the particle attains this speed when it is at a point P whose distance from the centre O is 4 cm, determine
  (i) the amplitude,
  (ii) the periodic time of the motion,
expressing your answers in terms of π.

Show also that the least time taken by the particle to travel from O to P is given by

$$\frac{4}{\sqrt{\pi^2-4}}\,\sin^{-1}\left(\frac{1}{\pi}\sqrt{\pi^2-4}\right).$$ (NI)

57 The position of a particle P at time t is given as

$$\mathbf{p} = at\cos\pi t\,\mathbf{i} + at\sin\pi t\,\mathbf{j} + t\mathbf{k}.$$

Describe the path of P.

At time t a second particle Q has position

$$\mathbf{q} = at\cos\pi t\,\mathbf{i} - at\sin\pi t\,\mathbf{j} + (2a-t)\mathbf{k}.$$

Find the condition on a that they should not collide.

If $a = 2\frac{1}{2}$ show that they are *not* at a minimum distance apart when $t = a$.

If P started from O, the origin of unit vectors **i, j, k**, find angle OPQ when $t = 1$ and $a = 2\frac{1}{2}$.

58 The gravitational force on a particle of mass m can be written as mgd^2/x^2 where g is the gravitational acceleration at the Earth's surface, d is the radius of the Earth, and x is the distance of the particle from the centre of the Earth. Determine W the work done in lifting the particle from rest on the Earth's surface to an altitude h and speed v.

If the particle then continues directly away from the Earth without further aid show that the minimum value of W is independent of both v and h if it is to escape from the Earth's gravitational field.

59 A light inelastic string is attached by one end to a fixed point from which it passes down under a rough uniform pulley in the form of a disc of radius r and mass M. It then passes up over a smooth light fixed pulley, and has a weight of mass m attached to the free end. All parts of the string not in contact with the pulleys are vertical. Show that the acceleration of the heavy pulley is

$$\frac{2(M-2m)g}{3M+8m},$$

and find the tensions in the string.

60 The figure illustrates a uniform pylon AB supporting a chair-lift. The tension in the cable under full load is $5W$, and the weight of the pylon is W. Above and

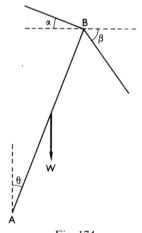

Fig. 174

below B, the cable makes angles α and β with the horizontal respectively. Show that if there is to be no moment about A, then the pylon makes an angle θ with the vertical where

$$\tan \theta = \frac{10\,(\cos \alpha - \cos \beta)}{10\,(\sin \beta - \sin \alpha) + 1}.$$

If AB is 6 metres, W is 1·2 kilonewtons, $\alpha = \sin^{-1}(7/25)$ and $\beta = \sin^{-1}(3/5)$, find the moment about A when the lift is not loaded, in which case the tension throughout the cable is reduced by one third but the angles remain unchanged.

61 A pendulum consists of a uniform straight thin rod AB of mass $3m$ and length

$2a$ with a particle of mass $3m$ fixed to B. The pendulum is free to rotate about A, which is fixed, in a fixed vertical plane. The pendulum is released from rest with AB making an angle α with the downward vertical.

(a) If α is small, find the period of small oscillations.

(b) If $\alpha = \frac{1}{2}\pi$, find the magnitude of the reaction at the pivot when B is vertically below A.   (W)

62 The velocity of a particle moving in a straight line is v when its distance from a fixed point O of the line is x. Prove that the acceleration of the particle is $\frac{1}{2}d(v^2)/dx$.

The mass of the particle is m and the only forces acting on it are

(a) a force of magnitude $\frac{1}{2}mlx$ towards O, and

(b) a resisting force, in the direction opposite to that of its velocity and of magnitude $\frac{1}{2}mkv^2$,

where l and k are positive constants. If the particle is released from rest at a distance a from O, prove that when it reaches O

$$v^2 = \frac{l}{k^2}\left\{1 - (1 + ak)e^{-ak}\right\}. \tag{O}$$

63 A solid uniform sphere of mass m and radius r is projected without initial rotation with speed V over a rough horizontal plane, coefficient of friction being μ. By applying the principles of angular and linear momentum show that it ceases to slide after a time $2V/(3\mu g)$, and find the speed of the sphere at this instant. Deduce how far it has travelled whilst sliding.

64 A particle of mass m is suspended from a fixed point by a spring of natural length a and modulus λ, and a periodic force equal to $mf \sin pt$ acts downwards on it. The motion of the particle is resisted by a force equal to k times its speed. If x is the downward displacement from the equilibrium position at time t, show that

$$\frac{d^2x}{dt^2} + \frac{k}{m}\frac{dx}{dt} + \frac{\lambda}{ma}x = f \sin pt.$$

If $k = 4m$ and $\lambda = 5ma$, show that the amplitude of the periodic forced oscillations is

$$\frac{|f|}{\sqrt{((5-p^2)^2 + 16p^2)}}.$$

Show that this amplitude decreases steadily as p^2 increases.   (JMB)

65 Show that the line

$$\mathbf{r}_1 = \mathbf{i} + \mathbf{j} + s(\mathbf{i} + \mathbf{j} + 4\mathbf{k})$$

is parallel to the plane P_1:

$$\mathbf{p}.(2\mathbf{i} + 2\mathbf{j} - \mathbf{k}) = 6.$$

A second plane P_2 passes through $\mathbf{i} + \mathbf{j}$ and is perpendicular to $\mathbf{r}_1$. A and B are two points 2 units apart on the intersection of P_1 and P_2 and are equidistant from $\mathbf{i} + \mathbf{j}$. Find A and B, and show that the area of the triangle with A, B and $\mathbf{i} + \mathbf{j}$ as vertices is 2/3 units^2.

Find the equation of P_2.

66 A small bead is released from a point A in still viscous liquid and falls under gravity through points B and C 1 m and 2 m below A respectively. The acceleration of the bead is

$$\frac{dv}{dt} = g - 0 \cdot 2v.$$

Deduce expressions for t and for x in terms of v where x is the distance below A at time t.

By drawing suitable graphs, find the speeds of the bead as it passes through B and C.

(Take g as $9 \cdot 8$ m/s^2.)

Support Exercise F

Examination examples

1 A uniform wire of total weight W and length $4x+2y$ is bent to form three sides of a rectangle AB, BC, CD where AB $=$ CD $=2x$ and BC $=2y$. It is suspended in a vertical plane from a smooth joint at A.

    (i) If a horizontal force F is applied to the wire at D and maintains equilibrium with AC vertical and C lower than A prove that

$$F = \frac{Wx}{2(2x+y)}.$$

    (ii) If this force is removed prove that the side AB will make an angle

$$\tan^{-1} \frac{y(2x+y)}{2x(x+y)}$$

with the vertical when the wire is hanging freely at rest. (A.E.B.)

2 State Hooke's Law.

    A uniform beam ACB, of weight W, is suspended by three vertical elastic strings, each of natural length l and modulus kW, which are attached at the ends A and B and at the mid-point C. Calculate, in terms of l and k, the extension in each string when the beam hangs at rest in a horizontal position.

    A weight W is now attached to the beam at the mid-point of CB. Assuming that the strings remain vertical, calculate the tension in each string, and the total energy stored in the three elastic strings when the beam hangs in equilibrium. (A.E.B.)

3 In a uniform rectangular lamina ABCD, the lengths AB and BC are $4a$ and $3a$ respectively and E is the point in CD such that CE $= \lambda a$. The portion BCE is removed. Find the distance of the centroid of the remainder from (i) AD, (ii) AB.

    When this remainder is freely suspended from the corner A, the line AM, where M is the mid-point of BE, is vertical. Find the value of λ. (A.E.B.)

4 Three ships A, B and C are sailing at constant speeds on steady courses. To an observer on B, which is sailing due east at 12 knots, A appears to be sailing due south. To an observer on C, which is sailing at 8 knots on a course of $030°$, A appears to be on a course of $150°$. Find the speed of A and the course on which it is sailing.

    If B and C maintain their speeds and courses they will collide in 15 minutes. Find the bearing and the distance of C from B. (A.E.B.)

5 If a particle moves in a circle of radius r with constant angular speed ω, prove that the acceleration of the particle is $r\omega^2$ directed towards the centre of the circle.

    A small ring is threaded on to a rough wire which is bent into the form of a circle of radius a and centre O. The wire rotates about a diameter which is vertical. When the ring is at a point P of the wire and PO makes an angle of $45°$ with the downward vertical through O, the ring remains at rest relative to the wire only as long as the speed of rotation of the wire is between ω and 2ω. Calculate the value of ω and also the value of μ, the coefficient of friction between the ring and the wire, given that $\mu < 1$. (A.E.B.)

6 A particle of mass m is subject to a resistive force mkv^2, where v is the velocity of the particle and k is a constant. The particle is projected vertically upwards with velocity $(3g/k)^{\frac{1}{2}}$ from a point on the ground. Show that it reaches a maximum height

$$\frac{l}{k}\log_e 2$$

above the ground, and find its velocity when it returns to the ground.

Show that the total work done against the resistive force before the particle returns to the ground is $9mg/(8k)$. (C)

7 Two equal spheres A and B lie on a smooth horizontal plane and A is projected directly towards B along the line of centres. Show that when the spheres collide the total kinetic energy is reduced in the ratio $2:(1+e^2)$, where e is the coefficient of restitution between A and B.

After the collision B strikes a perfectly elastic wall at right angles to its direction of motion. Show that when the spheres collide again B is brought to rest, and that the kinetic energy lost in this final collision is equal to that lost in the first collision. (C)

8 A force of magnitude XY acting along XY from X towards Y is denoted by **XY**.
   (a) ABCD is a quadrilateral and M, N are the midpoints of AC, BD respectively. Show that the resultant of the forces **AB, AD, CB, CD** is 4**MN**.
   (b) PQR is a triangle, and the resultant of the forces **PQ, 2PR, 3RQ** cuts PR at S and QR at T. Show that RS $= \frac{1}{4}$RP, and find the position of T. Show also that the resultant is 12**ST**. (C)

9 A particle of mass m is attracted towards a fixed point O by a force of magnitude $2mk^2x(a^2-x^2)$, where $x(<a)$ is the distance of the particle from O, and k and a are positive constants. If the particle is projected from O with velocity u show that its velocity at distance $x(<a)$ from O is

$$[u^2-k^2x^2(2a^2-x^2)]^{\frac{1}{2}}.$$

If $u < ka^2$, show that the particle comes instantaneously to rest, and find its distance from O when this occurs.

If, on the other hand, $u = ka^2$, find the distance travelled by the particle in time t. (C)

10 A rod AB of length $2a$ is made to rotate in a horizontal plane with constant angular velocity ω about a vertical axis through A. A rod BC of length a is pivoted to AB at B and is made to rotate in a horizontal plane with constant angular velocity 2ω, both angular velocities being in the same sense. Initially A, B and C are in a straight line with B between A and C. Show that at time t later the velocity of C has magnitude $4a\omega |\cos\frac{1}{2}\omega t|$ and makes an angle $\frac{1}{2}(\pi+3\omega t)$ with the original direction of BC.

If M is the mid-point of AB, show that the velocity of C relative to M is at right angles to the acceleration of C. (C)

11 A force of magnitude XY acting along XY from X towards Y is denoted by **XY**.
ABCD is a quadrilateral and the resultant of **AB**, p**AD**, q**CB**, pq**CD** cuts AC at M and BD at N. Show that

$$AM/MC = q, \quad BN/ND = p,$$

and that the resultant is $(p+1)(q+1)$**MN**.
   Find the resultant if
   (a) M and N are coincident,
   (b) $p = -1$, $q \neq -1$,
   (c) $p = q = -1$. (C)

12 A rectangle ABCD has AB $= a$ and AD $= 2a$, and M is the mid-point of AD. Forces W, $2W$, $4W$, $6W$, $3W\sqrt{2}$, $W\sqrt{5}$ act along CB, DA, BA, CD, MB, DB respectively, the direction of the forces being indicated by the order of the letters.

Reduce the system to a single force acting through A and a couple; state the magnitude and direction of the force, and show that the couple has moment $6aW$. Where does the resultant of the system cut AD?

Find two parallel forces through B and D which are together equivalent to the system.   (C)

13 The diagram shows the cross-section of a wedge fixed to the horizontal ground. Its smooth faces PA and PB are inclined at $60°$ and $30°$ to the ground. A string

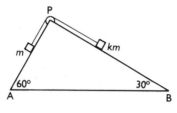

Fig. 175

passes over the small smooth pulley P, with particles of mass m and km attached at its ends. Show that the particle of mass m will accelerate towards P provided that $k > \sqrt{3}$.

If $k = 2$, find the tension in the string.

If $k = 2$, and the planes PA and PB are rough, μ being the coefficient of friction between each particle and plane, show that the particle of mass m will move towards P if

$$\mu < \frac{2-\sqrt{3}}{1+2\sqrt{3}} \tag{C}$$

14 A car starts from rest and moves with constant acceleration f. The wheels of the car are of radius a, and P is a point on one of the wheels halfway between the centre of the wheel and the point initially in contact with the ground. There is no slipping between the wheel and the ground. Prove that when the wheel has turned through an angle θ the velocity of P has magnitude $[\frac{1}{2}fa\theta(5-4\cos\theta)]^{\frac{1}{2}}$, and show that the angle which this velocity makes with the horizontal never exceeds $30°$.

Find the magnitude of the acceleration of P when the wheel has turned through $180°$.   (C)

15 A uniform rough sphere of radius a and weight W is placed on an inclined plane of slope $\tan^{-1}\frac{1}{2}$. A second uniform rough sphere of radius $4a$ and weight $4W$ is placed on the plane above the first sphere and in contact with it. The spheres rest in equilibrium, their points of contact with the plane lying along a line of greatest slope. Show that the frictional forces at each of the three points of contact are equal in magnitude.

Show also that the coefficient of friction between the spheres cannot be less than 2/3, and find the smallest possible value of the coefficient of friction at each of the other two points of contact.   (C)

16 A uniform rod AB of length $2a$ and mass $3m$ has a particle of mass m attached to it at B. The rod is free to rotate in a vertical plane about a horizontal axis perpendicular to the rod through a point X of the rod at a distance $x(<a)$ from A. Find the length of the simple equivalent pendulum when the rod is lightly displaced from its equilibrium position with B below A.

Show that the length is least when $x = \frac{1}{4}a(5-\sqrt{7})$.   (L)

17 Distances being measured in nautical miles and speeds in knots, a motor boat

sets out at 11 a.m. from a position $-6\mathbf{i}-2\mathbf{j}$ relative to a marker buoy and travels at a steady speed of magnitude $\sqrt{53}$ on a direct course to intercept a ship. The ship maintains a steady velocity vector $3\mathbf{i}+4\mathbf{j}$ and at 12 noon is at a position $3\mathbf{i}-\mathbf{j}$ from the buoy. Find the velocity vector of the motor boat, the time of interception, and the position vector of the point of interception from the buoy.

(L)

18 A point A of a lamina moves with constant acceleration f along a line Ox fixed in the plane of the lamina, and the lamina also rotates about an axis through A, perpendicular to its plane, with a constant anti-clockwise angular acceleration c. At time $t = 0$ the lamina is at rest. Prove that at any later instant of time one point P of the lamina has zero acceleration, and that if AP $= r$ and the angle xAP $= \theta$, $cr = f \sin \theta$.

If $f = \sqrt{3}$, and $r = 2$ when $t = 1$, find the value of c. (L)

19 Two particles are projected simultaneously in the same vertical plane, $\mathbf{i}$ and $\mathbf{j}$ being unit horizontal and vertical vectors in that plane. The first particle is projected from the origin with velocity vector $nV \cos \alpha \mathbf{i} + nV \sin \alpha \mathbf{j}$, and the second particle is projected from a position $h\mathbf{i} + k\mathbf{j}$ (where $h > 0$, $k > 0$) with velocity vector $-V \cos \beta \mathbf{i} + V \sin \beta \mathbf{j}$. Write down the position vectors of each of the particles after time t has elapsed.

Show that the particles cannot collide unless $\sin \beta < n \sin \alpha$, and if they do collide, prove that $\sin (\beta + \gamma) = n \sin (\alpha - \gamma)$, where $\tan \gamma = k/h$.

Find the condition imposed on V if the point of collision is above the level of the origin. (L)

20 A uniform rod AB, of length $2a$ and mass M, is fixed to a smooth pivot at A. A light elastic string of natural length $2a$ and modulus kMg is fastened to the end B and to a fixed point P vertically above A, where AP $= 2a$. The rod is released from rest when the angle PAB is $\pi/3$. If the rod next comes to rest when the angle PAB is $\pi/2$, prove that $2k = 3 + 2\sqrt{2}$ and find the angular acceleration of the rod at this instant. (L)

21 A thin circular wire of radius a and mass m has fastened to it three particles each of mass m at the corners of an equilateral triangle ABC. Find the moment of inertia of the system about the tangent to the circle at A.

If P is a point on the circle such that the arc AP subtends an angle θ at the centre of the circle, show that the moment of inertia of the system about the tangent at P is independent of θ. (L)

22 A small ring of mass m can slide freely on a smooth circular wire of radius a fixed in a vertical plane. A light elastic string of natural length a and modulus mg has one end fastened to the ring and the other end to the lowest point of the wire. If the ring is displaced slightly from rest at the highest point, show that until the string goes slack the velocity v of the ring is given by

$$v^2 = 4ag \, (\cos \tfrac{1}{2}\theta - \cos \theta),$$

where θ is the angle between the radius to the ring and the upward vertical.

Obtain an expression for the reaction between the ring and the wire, and find the values of θ for which the magnitude of the reaction is $2mg$. (L)

23 Given two vectors $\overrightarrow{OP}$ and $\overrightarrow{OQ}$ show how to construct geometrically the sum $(\overrightarrow{OP} + \overrightarrow{OQ})$ and the difference $(\overrightarrow{OP} - \overrightarrow{OQ})$.

If X, Y, Z are the mid-points of the lines BC, CA, AB respectively and O is any point in the plane of the triangle ABC, show that

$$\overrightarrow{OA} + \overrightarrow{OB} + \overrightarrow{OC} = \overrightarrow{OX} + \overrightarrow{OY} + \overrightarrow{OZ},$$

and find the position of the point D such that

$$\overrightarrow{OA} + \overrightarrow{OB} - \overrightarrow{OC} = \overrightarrow{OD}. \qquad \text{(L)}$$

24 Show that the centroid of a uniform solid hemisphere of radius a is at a distance $3a/8$ from O, the centre of the plane face.

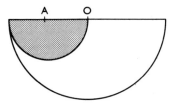

Fig. 176

The figure shows the central cross-section of a casting made in the form of a uniform solid hemisphere of radius a and centre O, with a hemispherical cavity of radius $\frac{1}{2}a$ and centre A. If this solid rests in equilibrium with its curved surface in contact with a horizontal plane, find the angle made by OA with the horizontal.
(L)

25 Two particles A and B of mass m and $3m$ respectively are connected by an elastic string of natural length l and modulus mg. Initially the particles are at rest on a smooth horizontal plane so that $AB = l$. The particle A is then given a velocity v in the direction BA. If, after time t, $AB = l+x$ and the distance of B from its initial position is y, prove that

$$nx = v \sin nt, \quad 4ny = v(nt - \sin nt)$$

where $n^2 = 4g/3l$. Hence prove that when AB is next equal to l,

$$y = \tfrac{1}{8}\pi v(3l/g)^{\frac{1}{2}}.$$ (L)

26 A tennis ball is dropped from a height h on to a horizontal pavement. At each bounce the ball loses half of the kinetic energy it possessed just before touching the pavement. Show that the height to which the ball bounces after the nth impact with the pavement is $h/2^n$ and hence show that the ball finally comes to rest after a time

$$\frac{\sqrt{2}+1}{\sqrt{2}-1}\left(\frac{2h}{g}\right)^{\frac{1}{2}}.$$ (NI)

27 (a) If ABC is a triangle and D, E, F are the mid-points of the sides BC, CA, AB respectively, prove that

$$\overrightarrow{AD} + \overrightarrow{BE} + \overrightarrow{CF} = 0.$$

(b) A particle of unit mass moves from a point A to a point B with position vectors

$$\mathbf{r}_A = \mathbf{i}+3\mathbf{j}, \quad \mathbf{r}_B = 7\mathbf{i}+5\mathbf{j}$$

under the action of constant force

$$\mathbf{F} = 3\mathbf{i}+4\mathbf{j}$$

where $\mathbf{i}$ and $\mathbf{j}$ are two perpendicular unit vectors.
If the particle starts from rest at the point A find:
(i) the work done by the force in moving the particle from A to B,
(ii) the velocity of the particle at the point B,
(iii) the rate of working of the force at the point B. (NI)

28 A parachutist of mass m is initially descending vertically with speed u. If the air resistance acting on the parachute is $m\alpha v$ where v is its downward speed and α is a positive constant such that $\alpha u < g$, find

    (i) the vertical speed of the parachutist at time t showing that this speed cannot exceed g/α,

    (ii) the vertical distance travelled by the parachutist after a time t has elapsed.
    (NI)

29 A pair of steps is constructed from two uniform sides AB and AC of equal lengths which are freely hinged at the top A, the weights of AB and AC being $3W$ and W respectively.

    The steps are placed in a vertical plane with the ends B and C resting on a rough horizontal floor, and are then gradually opened outwards until friction is limiting at one of the ends in contact with the floor. Find at which end this occurs and determine the coefficient of friction if the angle between the sides of the pair of steps is then 60°.
    (NI)

30 When a cyclist is riding towards the south-east the wind appears to him to be blowing from the east. When the cyclist changes direction and travels towards the south-west at the same speed, the wind appears to him to blow from the west with twice its previous speed. Determine the actual direction of the wind assuming that its velocity remains unaltered throughout the journey.
    (NI)

31 Find the length of a seconds pendulum, that is, a simple pendulum which takes 1 s to complete a swing from one extremity to the other, at a place where the acceleration of gravity is $9 \cdot 8$ m/s².

    A pendulum that takes 1 s to complete each swing at sea level is brought up to the summit of Slieve Donard mountain, which is at a height of 850 metres above sea level. Calculate the reduction in the number of swings made by the pendulum in a day, assuming that the radius of the Earth is 6400 kilometres and that the force of gravity varies inversely as the square of the distance from the centre of the Earth.
    (NI)

32 A cyclist and his bicycle have total mass M, the mass, radius, and radius of gyration of each wheel being m, r and k, respectively. The cyclist free-wheels down a hill making an angle α with the horizontal. If the total resistive force acting on the cyclist is a constant R and acts up the hill along the line of greatest slope, find the acceleration of the cyclist down the hill.
    (NI)

33 Show that the equation of the line of action of a force with components X, Y parallel to the Ox, Oy axes of a rectangular frame of reference $O(x,y)$ and moment G about the origin is

$$Yx - Xy = G.$$

    Three coplanar forces have x, y components $(F \sin \omega t, 0)$, $(F \sin \omega t, F \cos \omega t)$ and $(F \cos \omega t, -F \sin \omega t)$, which depend upon the time t, and lines of action which pass through the points (O,O), (a,b) and $(a,-b)$, respectively. Find the equation of the line of action of the resultant of the three forces showing that it passes through a fixed point on the OX axis at all times.
    (NI)

34 If a uniform spherical raindrop, falling under gravity through an atmosphere of water vapour, increases in mass by condensation of moisture at a rate which is proportional to its instantaneous surface area, show that the rate of increase of the radius of the raindrop is constant. Hence, find the acceleration of the raindrop if, initially, it is a spherical particle of negligible radius and mass.
    (NI)

35 A clock has a simple pendulum of length l with a bob of mass m. The effect of air resistance is to produce a force on the bob of magnitude $2km$ times its speed, where $k < \sqrt{(g/l)}$. Show that, when the pendulum is swinging freely with small amplitude, its angular displacement θ from the downward vertical at time t (measured from an instant when $\theta = 0$) is given approximately by

$$\theta = Ae^{-kt} \sin nt,$$

where

$$n = \sqrt{\left|\left(\frac{g}{l} - k^2\right)\right|}$$

and A is a constant.

Every time θ passes through the value zero the clock's mechanism applies an impulse which causes the pendulum's angular speed to increase by ω. Use the above formula for the motion in the interval between the impulse at $t = 0$ and the next impulse to determine the value of A, in terms of k, n and ω, for which the angular speed immediately after every impulse is the same. Hence show that, in a steady motion of this type, the maximum value of θ is

$$\frac{\omega e^{-k\tau}\sin n\tau}{n(1 - e^{-\pi k/n})},$$

where $\tan n\tau = n/k$.   (JMB)

36 A particle of mass m is attached to one end, B, of a light spring, AB, of natural length l and modulus mln^2. At time $t = 0$ the spring and particle are lying at rest on a smooth horizontal table, with the spring straight but unstretched. The end A is then moved in a straight line in the direction BA with constant acceleration f, so that, after t seconds, its displacement in this direction from its initial position is $\frac{1}{2}ft^2$. Show that the displacement, x, of the particle at time t in the direction BA from its initial position satisfies the equation

$$\frac{d^2x}{dt^2} + n^2x = \frac{1}{2}n^2ft^2.$$

By using the substitution $y = \frac{1}{2}ft^2 - x$, or otherwise, find the value of x at time t and show that the tension in the spring never exceeds $2ml$. (General solutions of differential equations may be quoted.)   (JMB)

37 A golf ball of mass m, initially at rest, is to be struck by a club-head so as to attain a speed v. The club-head is to be regarded as a freely moving sphere whose mass M can be chosen, and the impact is direct, with prescribed coefficient of restitution e. Show that (i) the required initial speed of the club-head decreases as M increases, but must be greater than $\frac{1}{2}v$, (ii) the required initial kinetic energy of the club-head is a minimum when $M = m$.   (JMB)

38 A light elastic spring, of natural length a, and modulus $8mg$ stands vertically with its *lower* end fixed and carries a particle of mass m fastened to its upper end. This particle is resting in equilibrium when a second particle, also of mass m, is dropped on to it from rest at a height $3a/8$ above it. The particles coalesce on impact. Show that the composite particle oscillates about a point which is at a height $3a/4$ above the lower end of the spring and that the equation of motion is

$$\frac{d^2x}{dt^2} = -\frac{4gx}{a}$$

where x is the displacement, at time t, of the composite particle from its centre of oscillation. State the period and find the amplitude of the resulting motion.

(Standard formulae for simple harmonic motion may be quoted without proof.)
                                                                              (JMB)

39 A small spherical air bubble rising in a liquid experiences an upward buoyancy force proportional to its volume and a resistance to the product of its radius and its speed. Its volume is inversely proportional to $(x + c)$, where x is its depth below the surface of the liquid and c is a positive constant. The mass of the bubble is negligibly small, so that in the motion the buoyancy force can be taken to be balanced exactly by the resistance. Show that

$$\frac{dx}{dt} = -k(x + c)^{-2/3}$$

where t is the time and k is a positive constant.

Such a bubble is observed to rise from a depth $7c$ to the surface in a time T. Find the value of k for this bubble and hence express, in terms of c and T, its speed when it reaches the surface. (JMB)

40 A particle of mass m is projected vertically upwards under gravity, the air resistance to the motion being mgv^2/a^2 when the speed is v, where a is a constant. Show that during the upward motion of the particle

$$v\frac{dv}{dx} = -\frac{g}{a^2}(a^2 + v^2),$$

where x is the upward vertical displacement, and find the greatest height reached if the speed of projection is u.

Obtain the corresponding differential equation for the downward motion, and show that the speed on returning to the point of projection is $ua/(u^2 + a^2)^{\frac{1}{2}}$. (JMB)

41 Two particles A_1, A_2 of masses m_1, m_2 respectively can move on a smooth horizontal table, and they attract each other with a mutual attraction acting along the line joining the particles. If $\mathbf{R}$ is the force exerted by A_1 on A_2, and $\mathbf{r}$ is the position vector of A_2 relative to A_1, show that

$$\mu\ddot{\mathbf{r}} = \mathbf{R} \quad \text{where} \quad \mu = m_1 m_2/(m_1 + m_2).$$

The magnitude of the attractive force is $\gamma m_1 m_2/x^2$ when the particles are at a distance x apart, where γ is a constant. Initially the particles are at a distance a apart and particle A_2 is moving away from A_1 with relative velocity v along the line A_1A_2. If

$$v^2 < 2\gamma(m_1 + m_2)/a$$

find the distance between the particles when both of them are moving with the same velocity. If A_1 is initially at rest find this common velocity. (JMB)

42 Find constants p and q such that $pt^2 + q$ is a particular integral of the differential equation $\ddot{z} + bz = ct^2$, where b and c are constants.

A particle of mass m hangs at rest suspended from a fixed point in a lift, which is also at rest, by an elastic string of natural length a and modulus of elasticity λ. The lift then begins to ascend with constant acceleration f. If, after time t, the particle has ascended a distance z (relative to ground level, *not* relative to the lift), find the resultant force then acting on the particle, in terms of t, z and the given constants, and show that

$$\ddot{z} + \frac{\lambda}{am}z = \frac{ft^2}{2am}.$$

Find an expression for z in terms of t and the given constants. (O)

43 The water in a tank is being heated by an electric heater which supplies a units of heat per second. Heat is lost to the surroundings at the rate kT units per second, where T is the number of degrees by which the temperature of the water exceeds the temperature of the surroundings. The amount of heat needed to raise the temperature of the water in the tank by one degree, if no heat be lost, is b units. When the heater is switched on, T is zero. Prove that, t s later,

$$\frac{dT}{dt} = (a - kT)/b$$

and, assuming a, b, k and the temperature of the surroundings to be constant, find an expression for T in terms of a, b, k and t. Prove that T is always less than a/k. (O)

44 A particle of mass m is attached to the end B of a light rod AB of length $2a$. The end A of the rod is in contact with a smooth vertical wall and the rod rests on a smooth horizontal rail which is parallel to the wall and at a distance $b(b < 2a)$

from it. The vertical plane through the rod is at right angles to the rail and the end B of the rod is uppermost. Find an expression for the potential energy of the system when it is inclined at an angle θ to the horizontal. Deduce the value of θ in the equilibrium position and show that the equilibrium is unstable.   (O)

45 A uniform rod, of length $2a$ and mass m, rests in equilibrium in a horizontal position on a fixed horizontal cylinder, of radius b, whose axis is horizontal. The rod is at right angles to the axis of the cylinder and its mid-point is at the point of contact with the cylinder. Find the period of small oscillations of the rod in a vertical plane about this equilibrium position, assuming that the cylinder is sufficiently rough to prevent any slipping.   (O)

46 A particle of mass m is moving with velocity u on a horizontal table when it strikes a uniform rod, of mass m and length $2a$, lying at rest on the table at right angles to the velocity of the particle. The distance of the point of impact from one end of the rod is $\frac{1}{2}a$, and the coefficient of restitution between the rod and the particle is e. Find the velocity of the mid-point of the rod, and its angular velocity, immediately after the impact.   (O)

47 One end of a light inelastic string of length πa is attached to a fixed cylinder, of radius a, at a point on its surface vertically above its axis, which is horizontal. A particle is attached to the other end of the string and is held with the string taut, horizontal, and at right angles to the axis of the cylinder. The particle is then released. Show that its velocity, when the straight part of the string makes an angle θ with the horizontal, is at right angles to this part of the string and equal to $a(\pi-\theta)\dot{\theta}$. Use the principle of conservation of energy to find this velocity in terms of g, a and θ; show that, when the straight part of the string is vertical, the particle is moving with speed $\sqrt{\{ag(\pi+2)\}}$.   (O)

48 A uniform circular hoop is projected with its plane vertical along a rough horizontal floor. The initial velocity, u, of its centre is horizontal and in the plane of the hoop, and its initial angular velocity is zero, so that it skids along the floor. Find the angular velocity of the hoop and the velocity of its centre at time t, when the hoop is still skidding. Show that skidding stops at time $u/2\mu g$, where μ is the coefficient of friction between the hoop and the floor. With what velocity does the hoop then roll along the floor?   (O)

49 A particle A, of mass m, rests on a rough horizontal table, the coefficient of friction between the particle and the table being μ. A light elastic string, of modulus of elasticity mg and natural length a, is connected at one end to the particle A, passes over a small smooth pulley fixed at the edge of the table and is attached at the other end to another particle, B, also of mass m. The particle B is held vertically below the pulley, with the string just taut, and is then released. Prove that, if $\mu < 2$, the particle A begins to move when B has descended a distance μa, and that the time taken for this descent is $\sqrt{(a/g)} \cos^{-1}(1-\mu)$.   (O)

50 A uniform rod AB, of mass M and length $2a$, is freely pivoted at its mid-point. When the rod is at rest in a horizontal position, it is struck at B by a particle of mass m falling vertically with speed u. The coefficient of restitution between the particle and the rod is e and the particle is reduced instantaneously to rest by the impact. Prove that $m/M = e/3$ and find, in terms of a, e and u, the time taken for the rod to perform a complete revolution after the impact.   (O)

51 A uniform rod AB, of length $2a$ and mass m, is rotating freely with angular velocity ω on a smooth horizontal table, its end A being smoothly hinged to a fixed point of the table. A small smooth ring of mass m, threaded on the rod, is held at A and is connected to B by a light elastic string of natural length a and modulus of elasticity λ. The ring is then released. Use the principles of conservation of angular momentum and of conservation of energy to find the angular velocity of the rod when the length of the string is a, and the velocity of the ring relative to the rod at this instant.   (O)

52 A river is of width $2a$. Its speed of flow varies uniformly as the distance from the nearer bank, being zero at the bank and the constant V in midstream. Starting from a point O on one bank a man rows a boat across the river. The velocity of the boat relative to the water has the constant magnitude U and direction at right angles to the stream. Show that at time t, where $0 \leqslant t \leqslant a/U$, the boat is at a point $\frac{1}{2}UVt^2/a$ downstream from O. Find the corresponding result for the case $a/U \leqslant t \leqslant 2a/U$ and prove that the boat reaches the opposite bank at a point aV/U downstream from O.   (O&C)

53 A particle is sliding down the smooth face, inclined at angle α, of a wedge. At the moment when it is passing a point A with speed V the wedge is given a constant horizontal acceleration f towards the particle. This acceleration is continued for a time T and for a further time T the wedge is kept moving with the constant velocity it has then attained. Prove that, if $f = 2g \tan \alpha$, the velocity of the particle relative to the wedge at the end of the total time $2T$ is the same as at the start. Prove also that, if in addition $T = 2V/(g \sin \alpha)$ the particle is then again passing A.   (O&C)

54 Prove that, for the ellipse $\dfrac{x^2}{a^2}+\dfrac{y^2}{b^2} = 1$,

$$\frac{x}{a^2}+\frac{y}{b^2}\frac{dy}{dx} = 0, \quad \frac{1}{a^2}+\frac{1}{b^2}\left(\frac{dy}{dx}\right)^2 +\frac{y}{b^2}\frac{d^2y}{dx^2} = 0.$$

An endless smooth wire is in the form of this ellipse and is fixed in a vertical plane with its minor axis $(2b)$ vertical. A bead of mass m which is threaded on the wire is projected from the highest point with speed V. Find the speed of the bead and the reaction of the wire on it (i) at the lowest point; (ii) at one end of the major axis.   (O&C)

55 One end A of a uniform heavy chain AB of length a is held on a smooth horizontal table at a point which is at a distance $\frac{2}{5}a$ from the edge of the table. The end B is hanging freely in equilibrium. The end A is suddenly released. Prove that when the end A is still on the table and x is the depth of B below the table

$$a\left(\frac{dx}{dt}\right)^2 = g\{x^2-(\tfrac{3}{5}a)^2\}.$$

Prove that the chain becomes free of the table after a time $(a/g)^{\frac{1}{2}}\log_e 3$.   (O&C)

56 Two particles, of weight $3W$ and W, are joined by a light inelastic string, which passes over a small smooth fixed pulley. They are also joined by a light elastic string of modulus $4W$ and natural length l. If the particles are released from rest at the same level, find the depth to which the heavier particle falls, and show that the period of the simple harmonic motion which the particles describe when the elastic string is taut is $\pi\sqrt{(l/g)}$.   (O&C)

57 A long light inelastic string carries three equal particles one at each end and one at its mid-point O. The string passes over two small smooth pulleys, fixed at points A and B on the same horizontal level and at a distance $2a$ apart. The middle particle is held at the mid-point of AB and released. Obtain the energy equation, taking the angle OAB as the variable θ, and hence or otherwise show that it will first come to rest when $\theta = \tan^{-1}\frac{4}{3}$.

Show also that in this position the angular acceleration of AO is of magnitude $9g/95a$.   (O&C)

58 A particle of mass m is attached to a fixed point A by a light elastic string of modulus mg and natural length l. At a depth $a(l < a < 2l)$ below the point A is a smooth horizontal table and the particle rests on the table directly below A. The particle is now projected along the table with speed V. Prove that so long as the particle remains on the table its speed v is given by

$$v^2+\frac{g}{l}z^2 = V^2 +\frac{g}{l}(a-l)^2$$

where $l+z$ is the length of the string.

Prove that the particle will lose contact with the table if

$$V^2 > g\frac{l^4-(a-l)^4}{l(a-l)^2}.$$ (O&C)

59 If two points A and B have position vectors **a** and **b** with respect to an origin O, prove that the point which divides AB in the ratio $\lambda:1$ has position vector $(\mathbf{a}+\lambda\mathbf{b})/(1+\lambda)$.

The position vectors of the vertices of the triangle ABC, with respect to an origin O, not necessarily in the plane of the triangle, are **a, b** and **c**. Prove from first principles that the lines joining the vertices to the mid-points of the opposite sides meet in a point (the centroid of the triangle) whose position vector is $\frac{1}{3}(\mathbf{a}+\mathbf{b}+\mathbf{c})$.

Each vertex of a tetrahedron is joined to the centroid of the opposite face. Prove that these lines meet in a point, and that this point divides each line in the ratio 3:1.   (O&C)

60 Two lines OA and OB are such that the angle AOB is α. If a vector OC, of magnitude c, makes an angle θ with OA (in the same sense as α), find the magnitudes of vectors OX and OY along OA and OB whose vector sum is OC.

If c and α are constant, and θ is proportional to the time, show that the acceleration of X is directed towards O and has magnitude proportional to OX, and similarly for the acceleration of Y, with the same constant of proportionality.   (O&C)

61 A bead is threaded on a smooth wire in the shape of a cycloid $x = a(\theta-\sin\theta)$, $y = a(1+\cos\theta)$, which is fixed in a vertical plane with the positive y-axis as the upward vertical. The bead is released from the position given by $\theta = 0$. Prove that, in the subsequent motion

(i) $\dfrac{d\theta}{dt}$ is constant,

(ii) the acceleration vector has constant magnitude.   (O&C)

62 A light framework ABCFDE consists of equilateral triangles smoothly jointed at the vertices and in one plane.

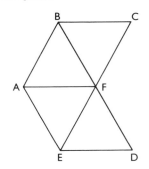

Fig. 177

(i) A force of 10 kg wt is applied at A in the direction FA and the framework is balanced by parallel forces at C and D. Determine the resulting forces in the framework distinguishing between tensions and compressions.

(ii) The external forces of (i) are removed and CD is now joined by a strut in which there is a compression of $5\sqrt{3}$ kg wt. Determine the resulting forces in the framework.

If both sets of forces are superposed, state the resultant force in BC.   (S)

63 ABCD is a square of side a. The anti-clockwise moment of a set of forces in the plane of the square is $10aP$ about A, $-20aP$ about B and $10aP$ about C. Taking the x-axis along AB and the y-axis along AD, determine the resultant of the set of forces and the equation of its line of action.

Determine the couple and the single force at the centre of the square which would be equivalent to this resultant. (S)

64 Inelastic particles of mass m and $2m$ are connected by a light inelastic string of length $3l$ which runs over a small smooth light pulley at a height $2l$ above a horizontal table. The particle of mass m is on the table when the system is released.

(i) Show that it reaches a height of $\frac{4}{3}l$ above the table.

(ii) Show that it does not reach the table again, and determine its least height above the table.

(iii) Find the total time from the moment of release to the moment when the mass $2m$ hits the table the second time. (S)

65 A particle A of mass $2m$ is held on a smooth horizontal table and is attached to one end of an inelastic string which runs over a smooth light pulley at the edge of the table. At the other end of the string there hands a particle B of mass m. The distance from A to the pulley is $l(> 2u^2/g)$. The particle A is then projected towards the pulley with velocity u.

(i) Find an expression for the time taken before the string becomes taut.

(ii) Show that after the string becomes taut, the initial common velocity of A and B is $4u/3$.

(iii) Find an expression for the common velocity when A reaches the pulley (assuming that B has not yet reached the ground).

(iv) Show that the total time taken is

$$\{\sqrt{(4u^2 + 6gl)} - 2u\}/g. \tag{S}$$

66 A battleship maintains a speed of 25 knots on bearing 045°, and a destroyer maintains a speed of 30 knots on bearing 090°. When the first is 9 sea miles North of the second, a launch is lowered from the side of the destroyer remote from the battleship, and maintains a speed of 40 knots on a bearing such that its velocity relative to the destroyer is in the same direction as that of the destroyer relative to the battleship.

By a drawing using the scale 1 cm $\equiv$ 5 knots, or otherwise, find the bearing on which the launch goes.

If the launch is first noticed by the battleship 20 minutes after it set off from the destroyer, find its distance and bearing from the battleship at that moment. (S)

67 Four thin pegs project horizontally from a vertical wall at the corners of a square ABCD, AB being horizontal and below DC. A mass m is suspended from the peg at A by a light inextensible string of length $4a$, and is given a horizontal velocity u in a plane parallel to the wall. If the string remains taut and comes successively into contact with the pegs at B, C and D, and the mass strikes the peg at A, show that $u^2 \geqslant 17ag$.

If $u^2 = 17ag$, show that the string must be able to withstand a tension of at least $10mg$. (S)

68 A uniform straight rod AB, of length a and mass m, can rotate freely in a vertical plane about its end A, which is fixed. The end B is attached to a fixed point O, vertically above A and at a distance a from it, by a light elastic string of natural length $b(< 2a)$ and modulus of elasticity λ. Show that if $\lambda \geqslant mgb/(2a-b)$, there are positions of equilibrium in which the angle 2θ between AO and AB is determined by the equation

$$\sin \theta = \lambda b/(2a\lambda - mgb).$$

If $\lambda > mgb/(2a-b)$, investigate the stability of the position of equilibrium in which B is vertically below A. (W)

69 O is a fixed point in an evacuated chamber at a height a above its horizontal floor. Cartesian axes are chosen with origin O and Oy vertically downwards. At time $t = 0$, a particle P of mass m is projected with speed U from O in the direction Ox. It falls under gravity and also experiences an electromagnetically applied force in the direction of the positive x-axis of magnitude mk times the vertical distance of P below O, where k is a constant. Write down cartesian equations of motion for P and show *by integration* that at time t, $y = \frac{1}{2}gt^2$, provided P has not reached the floor. Find an expression for x in terms of t and show that P strikes the floor at a distance $\{ka^2 + 6U(2ag)^{\frac{1}{2}}\}/6g$ from the point on the floor vertically below O. (W)

70 A smooth sphere A of mass m is lying at rest on a horizontal plane when it is struck by a second smooth sphere B of the same radius and mass m' moving on the plane. Immediately after the impact the direction of motion of A makes an angle $\frac{1}{4}\pi$ with the original direction of motion of B and an angle $\tan^{-1}\frac{12}{5}$ with the new direction of motion of B. Show that the coefficient of restitution between A and B is
$$(7m' - 5m)/12m.$$
What does this result imply about the range of possible values of the ratio $m:m'$? (W)

71 Define the resolute of a vector in a given direction. Show that if the resolutes of a vector **a** are given in two different directions in the same plane as **a**, then **a** is uniquely determined.

The unit vectors $\mathbf{t_1}$, $\mathbf{t_2}$, in the first quadrant of the x,y plane, have directions making angles $\frac{1}{4}\pi$, $\tan^{-1}\frac{3}{4}$ respectively with the x-axis. If the resolutes of **a** in the directions of $\mathbf{t_1}$ and the positive x-axis are $\sqrt{2}$, -1 respectively, and the resolutes of **b** in the directions of $\mathbf{t_1}$ and $\mathbf{t_2}$ are $\sqrt{2}$, -1 respectively, find the cartesian components of both **a** and **b**. Find the components in the directions of $\mathbf{t_1}$ and $\mathbf{t_2}$ of the vector **c** with resolutes 4, $3\sqrt{2}$ in the directions of $\mathbf{t_1}$ and $\mathbf{t_2}$ respectively. (If **c** has components α, β in the directions of $\mathbf{t_1}$ and $\mathbf{t_2}$, then $\mathbf{c} = \alpha\mathbf{t_1} + \beta\mathbf{t_2}$.) (W)

72 Two straight uniform rods AB, BC are freely jointed together at B, and A and C are freely hinged at two points of a vertical wall with A vertically above C and below the level of B. AB is of length $\frac{2}{3}\sqrt{3}a$ and mass m_1, and BC is of length $2a$ and mass m_2, and B is at a distance a from the wall. A load P of mass M is suspended from B. Show that the horizontal reaction on the wall at A is of magnitude $\frac{1}{4}\sqrt{3}g(2M + m_1 + m_2)$ and find the magnitude of the vertical reaction.

Find the magnitudes of the reactions at A if P were suspended from one end of a light string passing over a small smooth pulley at B and attached to a point of the wall vertically above A and on the same level as B. (W)

73 A uniform circular disc of radius a and mass M stands on a plane inclined at an angle α to the horizontal, with its plane in the vertical plane containing a line l of greatest slope. A straight rod AB is freely hinged at a point A of l above the point P of contact between disc and plane, and at a distance $a \cot \beta$ from it. The rod rests on the rim of the disc at a point C between A and B. If the coefficients of friction at both P and C are μ, and the disc is just on the point of slipping, show that friction is limiting only at C.

If $\mu = \sqrt{3}$, $\beta = \frac{1}{6}\pi$, show that the magnitude of the normal reaction at C is $\frac{1}{3}\sqrt{3}Mg \sin \alpha$, and find the magnitudes of the normal and frictional reactions at P. (W)

74 A uniform circular disc of radius a and mass m is free to rotate in its own plane, which is vertical, about its centre O. A particle P of mass m' is fixed to the rim of the disc, which is controlled by a hair spring that exerts a restoring couple of magnitude $k|\theta|$ on the disc when OP is displaced through an angle θ from the downward vertical, k being a constant. Show that if V is the speed of P when $\theta = 0$ then
$$(m + 2m')(V^2 - a^2\dot{\theta}^2) = 2k\theta^2 + 4m'ga(1 - \cos \theta).$$
Find the period of small oscillations of OP about the downward vertical. (W)

Appendix A

The international system of units (SI)

The following extracts are from PD 5686:1969, 'The Use of SI Units', and are reproduced by permission of the British Standards Institution, 2 Park Street, London W1A 2BS, from whom copies of the complete publication may be obtained.

Historical note

The idea of a decimal system of units was conceived by Simon Stevin (1548–1620) who also developed the even more important concept of decimal fractions. Decimal units were also considered in the early days of the French Académie des Sciences founded in 1666, but the adoption of the metric system as a practical measure was part of the general increase in administrative activity in Europe which followed the French Revolution. Advised by the scientists of his day, the statesman Talleyrand aimed at the establishment of an international decimal system of weights and measures 'à tous les temps, à tous les peuples'. It was based on the metre as the unit of length (it was intended to be one ten-millionth part of the distance from the North Pole to the equator at sea level through Paris, but the circumstances did not permit this aim to be achieved with any great accuracy) and the gramme as the unit of quantity of matter. The gramme was to be the mass of one cubic centimetre of water at $0°$ C.

Although the metric system was primarily devised as a benefit to industry and commerce, physicists soon realized its advantages and it was adopted also in scientific and technical circles. In 1873 the British Association for the Advancement of Science selected the centimetre and the gramme as basic units of length and mass for physical purposes.

Measurement of other quantities called for a base-unit of time and the adoption of the second for this purpose gave the centimetre-gramme-second system (c.g.s.). In about 1900 practical measurements in metric units began to be based on the metre, the kilogramme and the second (the MKS system). In 1935, the International Electrotechnical Commission (IEC) accepted the recommendation of Professor Giorgi that this system of units of mechanics should be linked with the electro-magnetic units by the adoption of any one of the latter as a fourth base-unit. The ampere, the unit of electrical current, was adopted by the IEC in 1950 as the fourth base-unit, giving the MKSA (or Giorgi) system.

Since 1875 all international matters concerning the metric system have been the responsibility of the Conférence Générale des Poids et Mesures (CGPM) which was constituted following the Convention held in Paris in that year. The CGPM meets in Paris, and controls the Comité International des Poids et Mesures (CIPM) and various Sub-committees as well as the Bureau International des Poids et Mesures (BIPM).

The laboratories of BIPM at Sèvres are the repository of the standard kilogramme and the former standard metre. The kilogramme is still defined in terms of the international prototype at Sèvres but the metre is now defined in terms of a number of wavelengths of a particular radiation of light. The United Kingdom participates in CGPM work, the Government department responsible being the Ministry of Technology.

At its tenth meeting, in 1954, the CGPM adopted a rationalized and coherent system of units based on the four MKSA units, the kelvin as the unit of temperature and the candela as the unit of luminous intensity. The eleventh CGPM in 1960 formally gave it the full title 'Système International d'Unités' for which the abbreviation is 'SI' in all languages.

A.2.5   *Decimal multiples and sub-multiples of the SI units are formed by means of the prefixes given below:*

Factor by which the unit is multiplied	Prefix	Symbol
10^{12}	tera	T
10^{9}	giga	G
10^{6}	mega	M
10^{3}	kilo	k
10^{2}	hecto	h
10	deca	da
10^{-1}	deci	d
10^{-2}	centi	c
10^{-3}	milli	m
10^{-6}	micro	μ
10^{-9}	nano	n
10^{-12}	pico	p
10^{-15}	femto	f
10^{-18}	atto	a

The symbol of a prefix is considered to be combined with the unit symbol to which it is directly attached, forming with it a new unit symbol which can be raised to a positive or negative power and which can be combined with other unit symbols to form symbols for compound units.

Examples

$$1 \text{ cm}^3 = (10^{-2} \text{ m})^3 = 10^{-6} \text{ m}^3$$
$$1 \text{ } \mu\text{s}^{-1} = (10^{-6} \text{ s})^{-1} = 10^6 \text{ s}^{-1}$$
$$1 \text{ mm}^2/\text{s} = (10^{-3} \text{ m})^2/\text{s} = 10^{-6} \text{ m}^2/\text{s}$$

Compound prefixes should not be used, for example write nm (nano-metre) instead of mμm.

List of SI units and a selection of recommended decimal multiples and sub-multiples of the SI units together with other units or other names of units which may be used

An asterisk against a unit means that the unit may be used in the UK but is not yet included in the ISO draft recommendation.

Quantity	SI unit	Selection of recommended decimal multiples and sub-multiples of SI unit	Other decimal multiples and sub-multiples of SI unit	Other units or other names of units which may be used
Part I: Space and Time				
plane angle	rad (radian)			degree (...°), $1° = \dfrac{\pi}{180}$ rad
		mrad		minute (...′), $1' = \dfrac{1°}{60}$
		μrad		second (...″), $1'' = \dfrac{1'}{60}$
length	m (metre)	km		*International nautical mile (1 n mile = 1852 m)
			dm	
			cm	
		mm		
		μm		
		nm		
area	m²	km²		hectare (ha), 1 ha = 10^3 m²
			dm²	are (a), 1 a = 10^2 m²
			cm²	
		mm²		

Quantity	SI unit	Selection of recommended decimal multiples and sub-multiples of SI unit	Other decimal multiples and sub-multiples of SI unit	Other units or other names of units which may be used
volume	m^3			hectolitre (hl),
			dm^3	$1\ hl = 10^{-1}\ m^3$
				litre (l),
			cm^3	$1\ l = 10^{-3}\ m^3 = 1\ dm^3$
		mm^3		centilitre (cl),
				$1\ cl = 10^{-5}\ m^3$
				millilitre (ml),
				$1\ ml = 10^{-6}$
				$m^3 = 1\ cm^3$
time				day (d),
		ks		$1\ d = 24\ h$
	s			hour (h),
	(second)			$1\ h = 60\ min$
		ms		minute (min),
		μs		$1\ min = 60\ s$
		ns		
angular velocity	rad/s			
velocity				kilometre per hour (km/h)
	m/s			$1\ km/h = \dfrac{1}{3\cdot6}\ m/s$
				*knot (kn)
				$1\ kn = 1\ n\ mile/h$
				$= 0\cdot514\,444\ m/s$

Part II: Periodic and related phenomena

frequency		THz		
		GHz		
		MHz		
		kHz		
	Hz			
	(hertz)			
rotational frequency	$1/s$			revolution per minute (rev/min)
				revolution per second (rev/s)

Quantity	SI unit	Selection of recommended decimal multiples and sub-multiples of SI unit	Other decimal multiples and sub-multiples of Si unit	Other units or other names of units which may be used
Part III: Mechanics				
mass	kg (kilo-gramme)	Mg g mg μg		tonne (t), 1 t $=$ 10^3 kg
density (mass density)	kg/m^3	Mg/m^3	1 kg/dm^3 $=$ 1 g/cm^3	1 t/m^3 $=$ 1 kg/l $=$ 1 g/ml g/l
momentum	kg m/s			
moment of momentum, angular momentum	kg m^2/s			
moment of inertia	kg m^2			
force	N (newton)	MN kN mN μN	daN	
moment of force	N m	MN m kN m μN m	daN m	

Quantity	SI unit	Selection of recommended decimal multiples and sub-multiples of SI unit	Other decimal multiples and sub-multiples of Si unit	Other units or other names of units which may be used
pressure and stress	N/m²	GN/m² MN/m² kN/m² mN/m² μN/m²	daN/mm² N/mm² N/cm²	1 hbar = 10^7 N/m² 1 bar = 10^5 N/m² 1 mbar = 10^2 N/m² 1 μbar = 10^{-1} N/m²
energy, work	J (joule)	GJ MJ kJ mJ		kilowatt hour (kW h) 1 kW h = $3\cdot6 \times 10^6$ J = 3·6 MJ electronvolt (eV) 1 eV = $(1\cdot602\,10 \pm 0.000\,07)$ $\times 10^{-19}$ J
power	W (watt)	GW MW kW mW μW		

Values of some imperial units in terms of SI units

Length

1 yd	**0·9144** m
1 ft	**304·8** mm
1 in	**25·4** mm
1 mile	**1·609 344** km

Area

1 in²	**645·16** mm²
1 ft²	0·092 903 0 m²
1 yd²	0·836 127 m²
1 mile²	2·589 99 km²

Volume

1 in³	16 387·1 mm³
1 ft³	0·028 316 8 m³
1 UKgal	4·546 09 dm³*

Velocity

1 ft/s	**0·3048** m/s
1 mile/h	**0·447 04** m/s

Mass

1 lb	**0·453 592 37** kg

Density

1 lb/in³	2·767 99 × 10⁴ kg/m³
1 lb/ft³	16·0185 kg/m³
1 lb/UKgal	0·099 776 3 Mg/m³
	(i.e. 0·099 776 3 kg/dm³*)

Force

1 pdl	0·138 255 N
1 lbf	4·448 22 N

Pressure

1 lbf/in²	6·894 76 kN/m²

Energy (work, heat)

1 ft pdl	0·042 140 1 J
1 ft lbf	1·355 82 J

Power

1 hp	745·700 W

Numbers printed in bold type are exact

---

* By a resolution of the twelfth CGPM in 1964 the word 'litre' (symbol l) is now recognized as a special name for the cubic decimetre, but is not used to express high precision measurements.

In 1901 the litre was defined as the volume of 1 kilogramme of pure water at normal atmospheric pressure and maximum density, equal therefore to 1·000 028 dm³. This 1901 definition still applies for the purposes of the 1963 Weights and Measures Act. On the basis of the 1901 definition, 1 UK gal = 4·545 96 litres, but this small difference may be disregarded for most purposes.

Appendix B

The British Imperial (BI) System of Units

In books and articles published before 1970 the student is likely to find reference to BI units. A few notes on this system (far from exhaustive) are listed here for easy reference.

The BI system is based on the foot (ft), pound (lb) and the second.

Force is measured in one of two ways:

(1) in lb wt, i.e. in terms of the gravitational pull on a given mass, sometimes written as lbf to distinguish it from mass,

(2) in poundals (pdl) which is the force required to give a mass of 1 lb an acceleration of 1 ft/s^2.

The acceleration due to gravity on the Earth, g, is approximately 32 ft/s^2, and so 1 lb wt is equivalent to approximately 32 pdl. However, since g varies on the Earth, one man's measure of a force in lb wt may not equal another's, and so measurement in lb wt is not universally applicable—it is not absolute. By contrast, the poundal is the same everywhere, and is referred to as the absolute unit of force.

Two units of work correspond to the two units of force. If the force is measured in lb wt, then work is measured in foot-pound weight (ft-lb wt or ft-lbf). If the force is in poundals, work is measured in foot-poundals (ft-pdl).

Power may be expressed in ft-lb wt/s (ft-lbf/s), or ft-pdl/s. It is alternatively measured in Horse Power (hp) where 1 hp is equivalent to 550 ft-lb wt/s.

BI-SI equivalents are listed in Appendix A.

Answers to Exercises

EXERCISE 1

1 $1/25$ m/s^2 **2** 18 kg **3** $1/(1\cdot44 \times 10^4)$ mN **4** 9·42 m/s^2
5 $33\frac{1}{3}$ m/s; $8\cdot52 \times 10^{-3}$ m/s^2

EXERCISE 2

1 $5\frac{5}{9}$ s **2** 16 s; 600 m; 16 s
3 $4\frac{1}{2}$ s; 100/81 m/s^2 **4** 96 km/h; $3\frac{5}{9}$ m/s^2
5 $4\frac{1}{2}$ s; $9\frac{1}{2}$ s **6** 10 m; 29 m; 57 m
7 $8/75$ m/s^2; $22\frac{2}{3}$ m/s **8** 8/9 km; 2 min 46 s

EXERCISE 3

1 25·9 m **3** 187·5 m **4** $2\sqrt{2}$ m/s; 10·79 m/s
5 1 min 50 s **6** 1/3 **7** $\frac{1}{2}$ in; 3/4 km
8 26·7 m/s; 76·2 m **9** $10\frac{1}{3}$ km; $166\frac{2}{3}$ m; $5\frac{1}{2}$ min.
10 $h < 60V^2/g$ **11** 0·49 mN; 5790 m/s; 64·9 ms
12 $18\frac{17}{21}$; 291 m **13** About 1·46 m/s^2

EXERCISE 4

1 2·8 m/s^2; 4·41 N **2** 5/3; 3/5 **4** $(2\cdot40+d):(2\cdot40-d)$
5 $\dfrac{2m_1 d}{m_1+m_2}$ **7** 52/81 m **8** 2·63 m/s; 3·19 m/s
9 $9mg/7$; $g/7$ **10** $g/5$; $6mg/5$ **11** $3m_2 m_3/(m_3+4m_2)$.
12 $g/17$ downwards

EXERCISE 5

1 21·6 N at 56° 21′ to OX **2** $2\sqrt{2}$ N; 45° to OC and OD
3 (a) 1·61 N at 308° 15′; (b) 20·2 N at 242° 58′; (c) 14·0 N at 97° 47′
4 3·11 N at 75° to OA towards B
6 $1\cdot2P$; 150° clockwise to first-named force
7 61 m/s^2 at $\tan^{-1}(45+26\sqrt{3})$ to OA
8 4 along OC; $R = 3, Q = \sqrt{3}$ **9** 16·3 N; 109° 10′

EXERCISE 6

1 $49\sqrt{3}$ N; 98 N along XY **2** $49\sqrt{3}$ mN at 30° to the wall
3 $a(\frac{4}{\sqrt{15}}-1)$; $\sqrt{15}mg$ **4** 22° 40′ to the vertical; 9·2 N
6 $\sqrt{2}mg$ **7** 4·42 N **8** $W/3$

EXERCISE 7

1 3:1 **2** $6\frac{7}{8}$ kg **3** 38 cm **4** $28\frac{8}{11}g$ N; $13\frac{3}{11}g$ N **5** 2·21 m

6 50·0 N and 38·2 N;   40·6 cm from the centre

7 0·11 kg. 0–100 g at 1 cm/5 g;   0–10 g at 2 cm/g. Most suitably: 4 cm and 11 cm from zero.

8 $\frac{\sqrt{3}}{2}g$ N; $\frac{g}{2}(10+4\sqrt{3})^{\frac{1}{2}}$ N at $\tan^{-1}\frac{\sqrt{3}}{2+\sqrt{3}}$ to AB

EXERCISE 8

1 $\sqrt{13}F$, through B at $\tan^{-1}(3/2)$ to AB   **3** $3P/2, -5P/2;$ $-12P$

4 $\sqrt{10}P$ at $\tan^{-1}3$ to BA, 2 units from A on BA produced. $15P$

5 $2\sqrt{5}P;$ $R = -\frac{55}{12}P, Q = -\frac{25}{12}P. 10aP$

6 $\sqrt{34};$ $3y = 5x-12;$ $3y-5x+12$

7 AD:DC $= 2:1;$ BE:EC $= 3:1;$ $n = 12$

9 AD:DC $= 3:2;$ BE:EC $= 5:2;$ $\frac{35}{2}\overrightarrow{DE}$

11 26·2 cm   **12** $151W/91$ **13** $3mg/4\sqrt{2}$

EXERCISE 9

3 $1/3\sqrt{3}$ **4** 0·46   **5** $\frac{15}{16}\tan\alpha;$ $\frac{15}{26}\tan\alpha$ **7** $g/13$

9 $M(2-\frac{3\sqrt{3}}{22})$ **10** $\mu mg/(\cos\alpha+\mu\sin\alpha)$ **11** $\sin^{-1}(5/3g)$

EXERCISE 10

1 $\sqrt{13}W/4$ at $\tan^{-1}2\sqrt{3}$ to the vertical

2 $\sqrt{5}W/2$ at $\tan^{-1}2$ to the vertical

4 $\sqrt{\frac{7}{12}}W$ at $\tan^{-1}(2/\sqrt{3})$ to the vertical

5 $\tan^{-1}2;$ $5W/4$ at $\tan^{-1}\frac{3}{4}$ to the vertical

6 $2W/3;$ $\tan^{-1}\frac{3}{4}$ to the horizontal

EXERCISE 11

1 $20\sqrt{2}g$ N along AC;   compression: AB, CD, DA all $20g$ N, tension: BC, $20g$ N, DB, $20\sqrt{2}g$ N

2 $22\frac{2}{3}$ N, compression

3 Compression: AB, CD, both $195g$ N, BC, $385g$ N;   tension: DE, EA, both $120g$ N, EB, EC, both $330g$ N

4 Compression: BC, AF, AO, BO, all $100g/\sqrt{3}$ N, CD, FE, both $100\sqrt{3}g$ N, CO, FO, both $200g/\sqrt{3}$ N, DE, $400g/\sqrt{3}$ N; tension: DO, EO, both $500g/\sqrt{3}$ N;   no stress, AB. Over rigid with AB.

5 CF

6 Compression: BC, DE, both 25·5 N, CD, 16 N, EA 41·5 N;   tension: AB, 10 N, AC, AD, both 25·5 N;   reaction at A, 51 N, force at E 41·5 N.

7 Maximum shearing force, W; maximum bending moment, aW

8 Values of bending moments at B, C and D are $170g$, $260g$, and $190g$. Values of shearing force are $-85g/2, -45g/2, 35g/2, 95g/2.$

9 $\frac{mg}{4\sqrt{3}l}(l+6x);$ $\frac{mg}{4l}(2x-l);$ $\frac{xmg}{4l}(l-x)$

10 Maximum M $= 5Wa/2$

Support Exercise A

1 3:4;   0·4 s   **2** $8\frac{8}{11}$ m/s^2 **3** 470 N

4 $\frac{at(3t+2T)}{(3t+T)^2}$ m/s^2; $\frac{at(3t+2T)}{3t+T}$ m/s; $\frac{1}{3}(7t+3T)$ s

5 16 m/s^2 at 32 m/s;   252 km/h   **6** $a > 2;$ $2\frac{1}{3}$ units/s or 2 units/s

7 0·19%   **8** $\frac{200}{7a}(183a-8-16a^2)$ m   **9** 3:8   **10** No

11 $\dfrac{4u}{3t}$; $-\dfrac{3u}{t}$ and $-\dfrac{u}{2t}$; 4 min 30 s   **12** 36° 32'; 5·6 m/s

13 $\dfrac{2Mg(4+7x)}{11+7x}$; $x \leqslant 17/7$ **14** 42g N/tonne

15 $\frac{34}{35}$ m. 0·524 m/s   **16** 1·8 m/s²; 6·3 m

17 $g/3$ m/s²; $20g/3$ N

18 $g/9$ downwards, $7g/27$ downwards, $13g/27$ upwards.

19 1/275; 655 N   **20** 1·36 at 17° to 3 between 3 and 4; 0·7

21 2·2 m/s² up; 1·8 m/s² down

22 91 N at 14°; weak stay at 257°, strong stay at 167°, or weak stay at 130° and strong stay at 220°.

23 $\sqrt{\dfrac{6u}{b}}$ **25** Safe   **26** $\cos^{-1} \frac{1}{2}\sqrt{\frac{3}{2}}$ to the vertical

28 $\cos^{-1} \frac{1}{2\sqrt{2}}$ to the vertical. $\sqrt{2}W/3$, $2\sqrt{2}W/3$

29 $4\sqrt{3}$ N bisecting angle AOB; 7 N   **30** $\pi/6$; $\sqrt{3}:1$

31 $W/2$; $\dfrac{W\sqrt{11}}{2\sqrt{2}}$ at $\sin^{-1} \dfrac{3\sqrt{7}}{4\sqrt{22}}$ to the vertical.   **32** 10:13; 5:8

33 D is $\frac{1}{6}$ m from A, E is $\frac{5}{6}$ m from B; D is $\frac{1}{3}$ m from A, E is $\frac{2}{3}$ m from B; $24\sqrt{5}g$ N.

34 $\sqrt{3}:1$; $xmg/2$ **35** $15\sqrt{3}g/4$ N; $15g/2$N   **36** $x = 2\frac{1}{2}$ or 3

37 $x = -3, y = -2\sqrt{2}$ **38** $10g/\sqrt{6}$ N

39 $x = -1, y = 5$; $13\sqrt{3}aP/2$; $\sqrt{21}P$ at $\tan^{-1} 2/\sqrt{3}$ to AB

40 $\cos^{-1} 3\sqrt{(5/61)}$; $\dfrac{45Mg}{2\sqrt{61}}$ and $\dfrac{9Mg}{2\sqrt{61}}$ **42** $\dfrac{ma}{12(M+m)}$ **44** 3/4; $56W/15$

45 $2\sqrt{7}mg$ **46** $2P$ parallel to AC, $\sqrt{15}$ from AC towards B; $7\sqrt{15}P/2$

47 $\dfrac{\sin 2\phi}{2-\cos 2\phi}$ **48** W; $\sqrt{3}W$ **49** $2\frac{1}{4}$; 18 m   **51** $\sqrt{3}mg/2$

52 0·29 m/s   **53** $y(g-2y) = 2x^2 + \mu xg$ **54** $\tan^{-1} \dfrac{a}{h-a\mu}$

56 $\sqrt{39}W/2$ at $\tan^{-1} 2\sqrt{3}$ to horizontal. $(24/\sqrt{7}+\sqrt{3})W$

57 1·11 m/s²; 2·37 m/s²; 1080 N; 77 km/h; 97 km/h

60 $\frac{1}{2}$; $8\sqrt{2}a$

61 $4\frac{1}{4}W$; $\frac{\sqrt{21}}{2}W$ at $\tan^{-1} \frac{\sqrt{3}}{5}$ to horizontal

62 $4\sqrt{2}F$, $-\sqrt{2}F$; $8\sqrt{2}F$ at 45° to AD cutting AD $a/4$ from A.

63 $6mg/11\sqrt{3}$

64 Compression: CD, EA, both $8g/\sqrt{15}$ kN, DE $6g/\sqrt{15}$ kN; tension: AB, BC, both $2g/\sqrt{15}$ kN; no stress in EB, BD.

65 30°

66 Compression: AB, BC, DE, EF, all 0·5g kN, EF 1·6g kN; tension: CF 0·7g kN; no stress: AF, BF, DF; reaction 2·1g kN at $13\frac{1}{2}°$ to the vertical.

EXERCISE 12

1 $5i+5j$; $-8i+2j$; $9i-5j$; C   **2** C

3 $a-b+c$; $\frac{1}{2}(a+c)$ or $\frac{1}{2}(b+d)$. 5 and $\sqrt{5}$

4 $3i+j$; $r = (9\pm3\sqrt{3})/2i+(5\mp3\sqrt{3})/2j$

5 $8i-9j$; $9i-2j$; $i-8j$ **6** $4i-2j+3k$; $5i-9j+20k$

7 $4i+j-k$; $2i-j+k$; $3\frac{1}{4}i+\frac{1}{4}j-\frac{1}{4}k$ **8** $y = x+1$; $r = ti+(t+1)j$

EXERCISE 13

1 $\frac{1}{4}i+\frac{7}{8}j$ **2** $2\frac{3}{8}i-\frac{1}{4}j-k$ **3** $-1/4$ **4** 5/12 cm   **5** $\tan^{-1} \frac{2}{3\sqrt{3}}$

7 $\dfrac{hl}{3(r+l)}$ where l is $(r^2+h^2)^{\frac{1}{2}}$ **8** $(56-12\pi)/(8-\pi)$ **9** $\sqrt{3}a/2\pi$

EXERCISE 14

1 $12\sqrt{13}$ km/h at $\tan^{-1}\frac{3\sqrt3}{5}$ to the road of the faster car.
2 $036°$ $(12')$ **3** $27\cdot9$ km/h; $103\cdot8°$ $(283\cdot8°)$
4 21 min   **5** $294°$;   0248 hrs   **6** $23\cdot5$ km/h
7 $\tan^{-1}0\cdot3$ to horizontal, $\sqrt{109}$ m/s; $\tan^{-1}\frac{9}{10\sqrt{17}}$ to horizontal, $14\cdot1$ m/s

EXERCISE 15

1 (a) (i) $\mathbf r=t\mathbf i+(3t-1)\mathbf j$, etc.   (b) (ii) $x+y=2$, etc.
2 $\mathbf r=(7+t)\mathbf i+(2-t)\mathbf j$; $\mathbf r=t\mathbf i+10\mathbf j$; $\mathbf r=(13+a+7t)\mathbf i+(14-a+t)\mathbf j$
3 $-\frac43\mathbf i-\frac13\mathbf j$; $7\frac23\mathbf i-1\frac13\mathbf j$ **4** $5\mathbf i+\mathbf j$; $(2+4t)\mathbf i+(4+3t)\mathbf j$, etc.
5 $\mathbf r=(2+\sqrt3)\mathbf i\pm3\mathbf j$; $\mathbf r(2-\sqrt3 s)\mathbf i+3s\mathbf j$, etc.
6 $2\mathbf i+2\mathbf j$, $7\mathbf i+14\mathbf j$, $19\mathbf i+9\mathbf j$; $\mathbf r=(14+5t)\mathbf i+(12t-3)\mathbf j$;
  $\mathbf r=(7+12t)\mathbf i+(14-5t)\mathbf j$; $\mathbf r=(7+7t)\mathbf i+(14-17t)\mathbf j$
7 $8\mathbf i+4\mathbf j$ **8** $t=3/5$; $\sqrt{\frac52}$
9 $12\mathbf i-11\mathbf j$ through $-6/11\mathbf i$, $\mathbf r=(12t-\frac{6}{11})\mathbf i-11t\mathbf j$
10 $16\frac23$ min. $-2\frac23\mathbf i+10\frac12\mathbf j$; $-9\cdot6\mathbf i+37\cdot8\mathbf j$
11 2 km; $1129\frac12$ hrs   **12** $13\cdot4$ m

EXERCISE 16

1 $35\cdot4$ m; $5\cdot1$ m   **2** 255 m; $35\cdot4\mathbf i+15\cdot8\mathbf j$, $35\cdot4\mathbf i-3\cdot8\mathbf j$
3 $-46\frac23\mathbf i-40\mathbf j+40\mathbf k$; $-10\mathbf i-20\mathbf j+20\mathbf k$; $10\mathbf i-10\mathbf j$ and $26\mathbf i+38\mathbf j$
4 $10\cdot6\mathbf i+16\cdot6\mathbf j$ **5** 153 m   **6** $23°$ $34'$ or $72°$ $50'$
7 The boy cannot dislodge the bird as $9gT^2-300T+9g+240=0$ has no real solution.
8 $-6°$ to the horizontal; $4\cdot8$ m

EXERCISE 17
1 14 m   **2** 40 m down the plane; $30°$ **4** $14\cdot5$ m
5 $\sin\alpha\sqrt{2ag\tan\alpha}$ **6** $21°$ **8** $\frac{2h}{R}\cos\alpha\mathbf i+\left(\frac{2h}{R}\sin\alpha-gh^2/(2V^2R^2)\right)\mathbf j$

Support Exercise B

1 $\mathbf b+\frac12\mathbf d$; $\frac23\mathbf b+\frac13\mathbf d$ **2** $\dfrac{\sin\alpha\cos(\alpha+30°)}{\sqrt3-\cos\alpha\cos(\alpha+30°)}$
4 W horizontally; $90°$; $7/9$
5 $-a\cos(\theta+\alpha)\mathbf i-a\sin(\theta+\alpha)\mathbf j$; $-\alpha$, maximum, and $\pi-\alpha$
6 6; $2\sqrt5$; $10\sqrt6$ **7** $\frac29(10\mathbf i-\mathbf j)$ **8** $\frac a2$ m/s^2; a m/s^2
9 $\mathbf i+2\mathbf j-2\mathbf k$; $\mathbf j-\mathbf k$ **11** $3:1$ **12** $255/28\mathbf i+180/7\pi\mathbf j$
13 $3\mathbf i-\frac56\mathbf j-\frac56\mathbf k$; $\tan^{-1}\dfrac{\sqrt{2t}}{3(2-t)}$ **14** $6/13$ **15** $(l+m-n):(m+n-l)$
16 20 min; 17 min   **17** $\tan^{-1}(7-4\sqrt2)/7$ **18** $\dfrac{875v}{72}$ m; 47 s
19 $-\frac{43}{23}\mathbf i+\frac{11}{23}\mathbf j$ **20** $7\sqrt{\frac{2}{17}}$ N at $\tan^{-1}\frac53$ to YX; $-3\frac{84}{85}$ N m
21 $154°$; 1410 hours; $3\cdot1$ km   **22** $136/35$
23 $5\mathbf i+6\mathbf j-11\mathbf k$; $\mathbf r=(5+4z)\mathbf i+(6+4z)\mathbf j-(11+9z)\mathbf k$; $-\frac13\mathbf i+\frac23\mathbf j+\mathbf k$
24 $15\sqrt5$ N (tension); 45 N (compression); 30 N (compression), shearing force, -35 N $(x<a)$, -25 N $(x>a)$, bending moment, $35x(x<a)$, $25x+10a(x>a)$
26 $350°$; 1 min 3 s   **27** $757/770$
30 $8\sqrt{3g}$ kN, $8(1+\sqrt3)$ kN, $16g$ kN, $8(1+\sqrt3)g$ kN, $16g$ kN all tensions.
31 $12\cdot6$ m/s, at $7°$ $48'$ to horizontal   **32** $\tan^{-1}\frac{4\sqrt3}{5}$ to the horizontal

33 $\sqrt{3}W/2$ horizontally; $\sqrt{7}W/2$ at $\tan^{-1} 2/\sqrt{3}$ to horizontal; $\sqrt{19}W/2$ at $\tan^{-1}\sqrt{3}/4$ to the vertical; $\tan^{-1}\sqrt{3}/4$.

34 $\mathbf{q} = (t^2-1)\mathbf{i}+2t\mathbf{j}$; $\sqrt{\frac{11}{22}}$; $\sqrt{22}\mathbf{i}+\mathbf{j}$ **35** $\mathbf{r} = (1-6s)\mathbf{i}+(2-2s)\mathbf{j}+(s-3)\mathbf{k}$

37 $2(1-v)\mathbf{i}+(4+6v)\mathbf{j}$; $-2(2+v)\mathbf{i}+2(1+3v)\mathbf{j}$; $-4\mathbf{i}+2\mathbf{j}$

38 $17\frac{1}{2}°$ to the horizontal   **39** $\tan^{-1} 5/12$; $0.2g$ and $0.03g$ N

40 $\tan^{-1}\dfrac{2\sqrt{2}}{\sqrt{3}t}$; $\sqrt{35}\cos^{-1}\sqrt{\dfrac{3}{5}}(= 4.05$ units/s$)$

41 $(2\frac{2}{3}, 0)$ **42** 15; BE:EC $= 1:2$; AF:FB $= 3:2$

EXERCISE 18

1 Consistent: $[ML^2T^{-2}]$; inconsistent: $[LT^{-1}]$, $[M^2L^{-4}T^2]$; consistent: $[T]$
2 $p = 1, q = 2$ **3** $54°\,44'$; $50°\,35'$; $33°\,28'$ **4** 1.04 N; 4.93 J
5 $30g$ N; $15g$ W   **7** 86 N/t   **8** 161.7 W; 12900 J
9 0.389 MW; 123 km/h   **10** $34\frac{1}{2}$ km/h; 0.145 m/s^2

EXERCISE 19

1 0.236 J   **2** 13.9 h   **4** 1970 W   **5** $2a$ below O
6 $\sqrt{3}m_1g/16\sqrt{7}$ J; $[m_2-(\frac{2}{5}+\frac{\sqrt{21}}{16})m_1]g/7$ **7** 8.13 m/s
8 $2\sqrt{\dfrac{ag}{3}}$ and $\sqrt{\dfrac{ag}{3}}$; $2a$ from the initial position of the lighter mass.
9 $2\sqrt{16-ga}$; $16m-mga/2$; $\sqrt{(16-5ga/2)}$ **10** $19mga/4$

EXERCISE 20

1 $\sqrt{21}W/(4\sqrt{7}-\sqrt{21}-2\sqrt{3})(= 1.81W)$ **2** $4W/\sqrt{3}$
6 2230 W; 69.4 N   **7** $2\frac{7}{9}$ μJ   **8** 0.24 m; 9.14; 151 J

EXERCISE 21

2 $1/3$ **3** $43\frac{1}{2}°$ **4** $2/5$ **5** $\dfrac{1+e}{1-e}\sqrt{\dfrac{2}{g}}$ **6** $6\sqrt{\dfrac{ga}{7}}$

EXERCISE 22

1 $-3v/25$ and $7v/25$ **2** $2/3$ **3** $51v/25$ and $81v/25$
8 $783mv^2/50$ **9** $3(e^2-e-2)/(e^2+7e+6)$

EXERCISE 23

1 $22\frac{2}{5}$ kg m/s   **2** $40\,500$ N   **3** 18.5 N
4 10 m/s   **5** 44.7 m/s; 716 W
6 $3v/13$ along BA; $\sqrt{34}v/13$ at $\cot^{-1}\frac{3}{5}$ to BA produced.
7 $\sqrt{2}J/7$ **8** $\tan^{-1}\dfrac{\sqrt{3}M}{M+m}$ **9** $15mv\,\sec\theta$
10 AB:$2\sqrt{3}mV/11$; BC:$3\sqrt{3}mV/11$ **11** $\dfrac{m}{2}(3\sqrt{3}ga)^{\frac{1}{4}}$
12 $\sqrt{5}V/3$ at $\tan^{-1}\frac{1}{2}$ to the impulse, and $2\sqrt{2}V/3$ at $45°$ to the impulse.
13 $J/\sqrt{2}(M+m)\cdot\dfrac{J}{2(M+m)}\left[\dfrac{2M+m}{M}\right]^{\frac{1}{2}}$ at $\tan^{-1}\sqrt{\dfrac{M+m}{M}}$ to the impulse.
14 $2J/(m_1+m_2)$ in the line of the impulse.

EXERCISE 24

2 $6\frac{2}{4}\mathbf{i}-10\mathbf{j}$ and $9\frac{1}{4}\mathbf{i}-2\mathbf{j}$; 1197 $m/32$ **3** $\frac{1}{2}mv(1+e)\cos\theta$
4 $(19m^2-7mM+M^2)^{\frac{1}{2}}v/(M+m)$ at $\tan^{-1}\dfrac{(M+m)}{\sqrt{3}(5m-M)}$ to the line of impact;

$(13M^2 - 10Mm + 4m^2)^{\frac{1}{2}}v/(M+m)$ at $\tan^{-1}\dfrac{(M+m)}{\sqrt{3}(2M-m)}$ to the line of impact.

5 $(\sqrt{3}-1)/(2\sqrt{3}+1);\quad v(\sqrt{3}-1)$
6 $\mathbf{r} = (2+3t)\mathbf{i}+(3+2t)\mathbf{j};\quad \mathbf{r} = 2(1+3t)\mathbf{i}+3(1-2t)\mathbf{j};\quad 20m$
9 $(3-2T)\mathbf{i}+(3+8T)\mathbf{j};\quad 5\mathbf{i}+(1+4T)\mathbf{j}$ **10** $mv(2\sqrt{2}+1)/6$

Support Exercise C

1 $1:1\cdot60$ **2** $\sin\beta:\sin\alpha$ **3** $(625g+94)M/25$ N
4 $\mathbf{r} = (7 \text{ or } 9+t)\mathbf{i}+t\mathbf{j};\quad -8$
5 $4W/3;\quad \dfrac{W}{2}\sqrt{\dfrac{13}{3}}$ at $\tan^{-1} 2\sqrt{3}$ to the horizontal; $\sqrt{91}\,W/6$ at $\tan^{-1}\frac{8}{3\sqrt{3}}$ to the
horizontal.

6 $-3\mathbf{i}+15\mathbf{j};\quad -2\mathbf{i}+10\mathbf{j};\quad 0940$ hours   **8** 600 W. 60 N   **9** $3\overrightarrow{AB}$
10 $\mathbf{v}_a = -\frac{20}{3}\mathbf{i}+4(\frac{5}{3\sqrt{3}}+6)\mathbf{j};\quad \mathbf{v}_b = \frac{16}{3}\mathbf{i}+\frac{88}{3}\mathbf{j}.\ 5/\sqrt{3}$ km north of S. 4 km north of S.
12 $56\sqrt{2}:11\sqrt{3}$ **13** $\dfrac{x(x+1)g}{3200}$ J; $1\cdot52$ m/s
                     15 $W/\sqrt{3};\quad 1/\sqrt{3};\quad 49°\ 6'$ to the horizontal
17 $93g$ N; $174g$ N at $27°\ 40'$ to the vertical;   compression: AB, BC both $186g$ N;
tension: CD $161g$ N., DA $308g$ N, BD $263g$ N
18 $12\cdot5$ kW. $3\frac{1}{4}$ min.
19 $2\sqrt{10}F$ at $\tan^{-1}\frac{4}{3}$ to AB cutting AB produced $11a/2$ units from B; $-8aF$.
21 $(\frac{39}{2}-6t+18t^2)m;\quad 12m(t^2+1)$ **22** $3:2$ or $3:11$
24 $\dfrac{2aW-3Fh}{6a};\quad \dfrac{2aW+3Fh}{6a};\quad \dfrac{W}{3};\quad \dfrac{2aW}{3h}$ **25** $26\mathbf{i}+46\mathbf{j}$
27 $64\cdot3$ kW; $6\cdot17$ km/h/s   **28** $\frac{5}{3}\mathbf{i}+\mathbf{j}.\ -7\mathbf{i}-4\mathbf{j}$
29 $\cot\theta = \frac{1}{2}(\tan\alpha-\tan\beta);$ unstable
30 $\sqrt{127W/2}$ at $\tan^{-1}\frac{19}{7\sqrt{3}}$ to the horizontal
31 $e < \frac{1}{4}$ **32** $gT(\cos\alpha+\cos2\alpha)/2\sin\alpha$
33 $\frac{1}{4}(\mathbf{a}+\mathbf{b}+\mathbf{c})$ **34** $\frac{7}{3\sqrt{3}}m;$ $36°\ 20'$ to AC
36 $\frac{4}{9}$ of the length from the foot   **38** $m/\sqrt{7}$
39 $\sqrt{97V}/4$ **42** $\frac{1}{4}\sqrt{(13+6\sqrt{3})}$ kg m/s
43 $\frac{3\sqrt{3}}{5}mv;$ $\sqrt{1\cdot3}v$ at $\tan^{-1}\sqrt{0\cdot3}$ to the string
45 $r/\pi;\quad h/4;\quad \sqrt{\pi}:2$ **46** $\sqrt{2},\ \sqrt{6}$ at $\tan^{-1}\sqrt{2}$ to the groove
47 $(3+2\sqrt{3})a;\quad 6a$

48 48 cm; $3\sqrt{5}$ cm/s at $\tan^{-1}2$ to DA, 1 cm/s parallel to AD;   F on AB where
AF $= 60$ cm; $2\cdot1\ \mu$J
49 $4/3\mathbf{k},\ 5/3\mathbf{k};\quad \mathbf{r} = 3(s-3)\mathbf{i}-4s\mathbf{j}$

EXERCISE 25

1 $cm\omega^2 d^2$ **2** $3\cdot89$ N; $6\cdot8$ rad/s   **3** $2\sqrt{\dfrac{3g}{7a}}$ rad/s

4 $2\cdot24$ N   **5** 2ω rad/s; $2m\omega^2a$ **6** $13mg/5,\ 16mg/5$

7 $\sqrt{\dfrac{7g}{3a}}$ rad/s   **8** $5a-\dfrac{4g}{\omega^2}\cos^{-1}\frac{1}{4}$

EXERCISE 26

1 $25\cdot8$ km/h   **2** $21\cdot6$ km/h   **3** Slide; 68 km/h

4 $27\cdot5$ m; 50 km/h   **5** $2/3;\quad 46\cdot0$ km/h   **6** $\dfrac{10R}{r}$ rad/s; $20R$ units/s

7 $-2\mathbf{i}+5\mathbf{j};\quad -12;\quad -3\mathbf{i}-15\mathbf{j}$ **8** $2t\mathbf{i}+2\mathbf{j}$ **9** 282 mm; $11\cdot34$ kN

EXERCISE 27

1 $\cos^{-1}\frac{1}{3}$

2 $2a/9$

3 374 mN; $\cos^{-1}\frac{8}{3g}$ to the vertical

4 $\cos^{-1}\frac{1}{\sqrt{6}}$

5 $a/4$; $21mg/4$

6 $\frac{m}{r}(3gr\cos\phi - 2gr - u^2)$

7 $\frac{1}{2}mg(20+3\sqrt{3})$

8 $\frac{m}{2a}(v^2 - ga)$

9 $60°$

11 $\sqrt{7ga}$

13 $\sqrt{\dfrac{7ga}{2}}$

EXERCISE 28

2 $\frac{1}{3}(2t+4)^{\frac{3}{2}} - \frac{8}{3}$

3 327 mm/s

4 60 mm from A

5 75 mm; π s

·6 $\sqrt{5}:2\sqrt{2}$; $\frac{T}{2\pi}(\sin^{-1}\frac{2}{3} - \sin^{-1}\frac{1}{3})$

7 3·6 m/s²; 0·3 m/s

8 $8\pi^2$ m/s²; π m/s; 0·8π m/s; 4·8π^2 m/s²

9 22·6 mm; 15·8 mm or 399·8 mm

10 $2\pi\sqrt{\dfrac{2a}{g}}$; $g/8$; $\frac{1}{8}\sqrt{2ga}$

11 $3\sqrt{5ga}$; $\sqrt{\dfrac{a}{5g}}\left(\dfrac{\pi}{2}+\dfrac{1}{3}\right)$

12 $\pi\sqrt{\dfrac{2ma}{\lambda}}$

13 $5mg/2$; $\sqrt{10g/2\pi}$ Hz

14 60 mm; 1·72 Hz

15 $5g/8$ N and $3g/8$ N

EXERCISE 29

1 1·55 s

2 89 mm

3 147 mm

4 0·7 Hz

5 45 mm

6 22 s

7 1·05; 225 mm

8 9·85 Hz; 9·70 Hz

11 5·26 N

Support Exercise D

1 $x = \frac{1}{3}t^3 - \frac{49}{9}t + \frac{956}{81}, 0 \leqslant t \leqslant \frac{7}{3}$; $x = 6t^2 - 28t + 36, t \geqslant \frac{7}{3}$

2 $\frac{25r}{7}(1 - 2/\sqrt{13})$; $25mg/24$

3 $v/2, \sqrt{3}v/2$ at $\tan^{-1}\frac{1}{\sqrt{2}}$ to AB; C stationary, A and B both v

4 $7m\dfrac{6-\sqrt{2}}{7\sqrt{2}+12\sqrt{.7}}$

5 $5\sqrt{6}$; $10\sqrt{2}$; $(35t-4)/2(325t^2 - 70t + 4)^{\frac{1}{2}}$

6 4:1

7 $\left[\dfrac{2g}{3a}(15+8\sqrt{3})\right]^{\frac{1}{2}}$ rad/s. $\left[\dfrac{2g}{3a}(15-8\sqrt{3})\right]^{\frac{1}{2}}$ rad/s.

8 $\left(1+\dfrac{3W_1}{2W_2}\right)\sin\theta/(1+\cos\theta)$

9 $7\sqrt{2u^2/g}$; $7\sqrt{2u/g}$

10 $6\cdot0\times10^{24}$ kg; 2·34 h; 1600 m/s

11 $u\sqrt{e}$

12 $\dfrac{I}{m}\left[\sin^2\alpha + \dfrac{(e-1)^2}{4}\cos^2\alpha\right]^{\frac{1}{2}}$ at $\tan^{-1}[2\tan\alpha/(e-1)]$ to the line of impact;

$\dfrac{I}{2m}(1+e)\cos\alpha$ along the line of impact. $\dfrac{I^2}{4m}\cos^2\alpha(1-e^2)$

14 $\sqrt{15}/48, 5\sqrt{15}/48$

15 $\tan^{-1}\frac{7\sqrt{3}}{29}$; $\frac{355}{247}W, \frac{139}{247}W$

17 $3\mathbf{i}+4\mathbf{j}+\mathbf{k}$; $\mathbf{r} = (1+3t)\mathbf{i}+(1+4t)\mathbf{j}+(1+t)\mathbf{k}$; $-3\mathbf{i}-4\mathbf{j}-\mathbf{k}$; 9; $2\mathbf{i}-\mathbf{j}-2\mathbf{k}$

18 $30\mathbf{i}+50\mathbf{j}$; parallel to $\mathbf{i}$; 13/15; 1/3

19 $3\frac{1}{8}m$; 0·125 N

20 $\sqrt{\frac{3}{2}}W$; $W/\sqrt{6}$

23 $m\sqrt{\dfrac{ga}{2}}$

24 $1\cdot79\times10^6$ N

25 $3W/2$

26 BC internally in the ratio $3:2$; $\sqrt{31}F$ at $\tan^{-1}\frac{5\sqrt{3}}{7}$ to CB; $-5\sqrt{3}aF$

27 $\cos^{-1}(2/\sqrt{3}-1)$ **29** $\frac{m}{5}(4g-3a)$ **30** $\frac{3a}{8}\mathbf{i}$; $\frac{3}{8}a(\mathbf{i}+\mathbf{j}+\mathbf{k})$

31 $6mg$ **32** $\dfrac{2e(5e+1)}{(3e+1)^2 g}$

33 $228\cdot5\times10^6$ km; $24\cdot2$ km/s   **34** $1\cdot78$ ms on, $0\cdot72$ ms off

35 $a(1+\pi)^2/16$ **36** $-2\mathbf{a}$ and $6\mathbf{a}$

39 Compression: AB $1\cdot125$ kN, CD $4\cdot25$ kN, AD $3\cdot2$ kN;   tension: BC $4\cdot05$ kN, DE $1\cdot00$ kN, DB $3\cdot2$ kN;   no stress: EA;   reaction at A, $4\cdot25$ kN at $18°$ to the horizontal.

40 $0\cdot08g$ N   **41** $m\dot\theta^2(b^2+a^2)/4$ **42** 308 W; $15\cdot5$ N

EXERCISE 30

1 $4Ma^2/3$ **2** $4266\frac{2}{3}m$ kg mm^2; $2400m$ kg mm^2

6 $7ml^2/18$; $5ml^2/18$; $\sqrt{\frac{7}{6}}l$

EXERCISE 31

1 $\frac{1}{2}I_x$; $\frac{1}{2}I_x$; $\frac{1}{2}I_x-4M$; $\frac{1}{2}I_x-4M$; I_x-4M; I_x-4M; I_x-8M

2 $8Ma^2$; $4Ma^2$; $5Ma^2$; $9Ma^2$ **3** $\frac{31}{12}mr^2$

4 $4\cdot09\times10^{-3}$ kg m^2 **5** $\dfrac{M}{12(r+l)}(l^3+3rl^2+6r^2l+3r^3)$

6 $4M(a^2+b^2)/3$; $M(b^2+c^2)/3$; $4M(a^2+b^2)/3$

7 $255Ma^2/4$; $251Ma^2/4$

8 $M(2h^2+3r^2)/20$; $3M(h^2+4r^2)/80$; $M(2h^2+3r^2)/20$

9 $\dfrac{4m}{75}(16x^2+36x+27)$ **10** $20\frac{2}{9}m$; $\left[\dfrac{5g}{96a}(\cos\theta-\cos\phi)\right]^{\frac{1}{2}}$

EXERCISE 32

1 $4\mathbf{j}-12\mathbf{k}$; $25\mathbf{j}$; 19 **2** $24\mathbf{j}+18\mathbf{k}$; $2\mathbf{i}-4\mathbf{j}-2\mathbf{k}$; $3\mathbf{i}-9\mathbf{k}$

3 $-7\mathbf{i}+8\mathbf{j}$; $-4\mathbf{i}+2\mathbf{j}$ **4** $6mV\mathbf{i}-3mV\mathbf{j}+mV\mathbf{k}$ **6** $177\frac{7}{9}$ rad/s^2

7 $15\,500$ J; $98\cdot5$ s   **8** 60 rad/s; 90 W   **9** $\frac{5}{4}Ma^2\log_e\left(1+\dfrac{2\omega_1}{Mga}\right)$

10 $\omega=\omega_0+kt$; $\theta=\omega_0 t+\frac{2}{3}kt^2$; $\omega^2=\omega_0^2+2\theta k$

12 $13\cdot9$ N   **13** 109 rad/s^2 **15** $2\pi\sqrt{\dfrac{7r^2+20ar+24a^2}{(13a+5r)g}}$

16 $2a/3$ **17** $2\pi\sqrt{\dfrac{2r}{g}}$ **18** $5a/2\sqrt{3}$

EXERCISE 33

1 $5d/3$ **2** $a/2$; $3mv^2/2$

3 $mv/4$; $3v/8a$; $\cos^{-1}\left(1-\dfrac{3v^2}{32ga}\right)$ **4** $5ma\omega/6$

5 $3/4$; $3v/4$

6 $1/12$ from the bottom; $13/24$ from the bottom

7 $15m\omega r/32$; $-13\omega/32$ rad/s

EXERCISE 34

1 $\mathbf{r}=5(1+\cos\theta)\mathbf{i}+5\sin\theta\mathbf{j}+\frac{1}{2}(\theta-\cos^{-1}\frac{4}{5})\mathbf{k}$

3 2; $\frac{1}{2}a(1+68\pi^2+4\pi^4)^{\frac{1}{2}}$

4 $\frac{1}{2}a(5+\cos\theta)\mathbf{i}+\frac{1}{2}a\sin\theta\mathbf{j}+a\mathbf{k}$; $\frac{1}{2}a(1-\cos\theta)\mathbf{i}-\frac{1}{2}a\sin\theta\mathbf{j}$

5 $[e^{2t}(1+\omega^2)+\omega^2]^{\frac{1}{2}}$ **6** $8/\sqrt{6}$

7 $\mathbf{r} = (2-x)\mathbf{i}+(3x-1)\mathbf{j}+(4x-1)\mathbf{k}$ **8** $\mathbf{b}$ is nearest L_2; $\sqrt{\frac{69}{14}}$
9 $44m/3$ **10** $\frac{1}{6}(3\mathbf{j}+5\mathbf{k})$
12 $\mathbf{p}.(33\mathbf{i}+14\mathbf{j}+\mathbf{k}) = 48$ **13** $\mathbf{b}$, $2\sqrt{3}-3$
14 $\cos^{-1}(25/\sqrt{663})$; $\frac{1}{2}$ unit^3 **15** $\mathbf{r} = 3t\mathbf{i}+4(1-t)\mathbf{j}+(1-t)\mathbf{k}$

EXERCISE 35

1 $2(1-2t^2)\mathbf{e}+8t\mathbf{e}_\theta$
2 $\dot{\mathbf{p}} = 2ct\cos ct^2\mathbf{e}_r+2ct(1+\sin ct^2)\mathbf{e}_\theta$;
  $\ddot{\mathbf{p}} = 2c[\cos ct^2-4ct^2\sin ct^2-2ct^2]\mathbf{e}_r+2c(4ct^2\cos ct^2+\sin ct^2+1)\mathbf{e}_\theta$
3 $2\sqrt{2}ma\omega^2(1+\sin\omega t)^{\frac{1}{2}}$ **4** π/ω

EXERCISE 36

1 $x = k(y^2+1)^{\frac{1}{2}}$; $x+2(1-y)^{\frac{1}{2}} = c$; $\ln kx = x-\frac{1}{y}$; $\frac{1}{2}x^2+e^{-y}+c = 0$

4 $m\sqrt{\dfrac{52k}{3}}$ **6** $x = [\frac{3}{2}(\sqrt{2}kt+d)]^{\frac{2}{3}}$

10 $v = \sqrt{\dfrac{a}{b}}(1-e^{-2bx})^{\frac{1}{2}}$ **11** 39·4 m/s; 5·44 s   **12** 7.0×10^{-5}

EXERCISE 37

1 (a) $x = Ae^{-2t}+Be^{-3t}$; (b) $x = pe^{-t/2}\cos\left(\dfrac{\sqrt{7}}{2}t+\varepsilon\right)$;
  (c) $x = pe^{-kt/2}\cos(t+\varepsilon)+2t-2k$
2 (a) $x = 4e^{-3t}-2e^{-4t}$; (b) $x = \frac{\sqrt{17}}{8}e^{-\frac{1}{2}t}\cos\{2t+\tan^{-1}(-\frac{1}{4})\}+\frac{1}{2}\sin 2t$
5 $x = \dfrac{ae^{-kt}}{2b}[(a+b)e^{bt}-(a-b)e^{-bt}]$ **6** $x = \frac{1}{4}e^{-2t}(e^{\sqrt{2}t}+e^{-\sqrt{2}t})+t-\frac{1}{2}$

Support Exercise E

1 $50\,000ma^2\pi^2/3$; 125π rad   **2** 3/7; $\dfrac{55v}{392}$; $\dfrac{73v}{392}$
3 $(23\mathbf{i}+66\mathbf{j}+102\mathbf{k})/56$
6 BA produced $7a/2$ from A; $-2Q$; $-\sqrt{3}aQ$; $-4Q$ and Q
7 $\sqrt{\frac{41}{2\sqrt{5}}}W$; $9W/2\sqrt{5}$ **8** $2\mathbf{i}-5\mathbf{j}$; $6\mathbf{i}-6\mathbf{j}$; 36   **9** $431ma^2/57$
11 $\dfrac{a(2g-\omega^2a)}{8(g-\omega^2a)}$; $\sqrt{\dfrac{2g}{3a}}$, $2\sqrt{\dfrac{g}{7a}}$, $2\sqrt{\dfrac{g}{5a}}$
12 $20g$ kN, tension; $10\sqrt{5}$ kN, compression; $10g$ kN, compression; $32\frac{1}{8}g$ kN;
  $5\sqrt{269g}/2$ kN at $\tan^{-1}\frac{10}{13}$ to the horizontal
13 560 kg m^2; $\frac{3500}{3}\pi$ **14** $\sqrt{3}mv/4$; $\sqrt{5}v/4$ at $\tan^{-1}\frac{1}{2}$ to CD
15 0·0934; 5050 kg m/s   **16** $\frac{251}{108}ma^2$
17 $4\pi n/T$; $\dfrac{mghrT^2}{4\pi n(2\pi nr+h)}$ **18** $\dfrac{W}{2+\sqrt{3}}$; $\dfrac{1}{2+\sqrt{3}}$; $\dfrac{24W}{147+2\sqrt{3}}$
19 $\dfrac{31mr^2}{70}$ **21** $(7e+3):4$; $\cos^{-1}\dfrac{16-21e}{5(16+49e^2)^{\frac{1}{2}}}$
23 2160 N; 79·7 m   **24** $\cos^{-1}\dfrac{g}{a\omega^2}$. $5\sqrt{\dfrac{g}{6a}}$; $mg/5$; $4mg$
26 $(2-e)\mathbf{i}+3\mathbf{j}$, $(3e+2)\mathbf{i}+2\mathbf{j}$; 27:13   **27** 55° 18′
28 $(4+3\sqrt{3})/11$; $(3\sqrt{3}-4)/11$; $(4+3\sqrt{3})/11$
33 $m\sqrt{\dfrac{5ga}{2}}$ **34** $g/4n^2$
35. $\cos^{-1}\frac{1}{4}$; $\frac{1}{2}\mathbf{e}_1$, $-\frac{7}{4}\mathbf{e}_2$; $\frac{15}{2}\mathbf{e}_1$, $\frac{15}{4}\mathbf{e}_2$; **36** J

36 $\dfrac{5V}{162a}$;   7·6 m/s   **37** 81 km/h   **39** $3Ma^2/10$; $\pi a\sqrt{\dfrac{6M}{5\lambda}}$

41 $4\pi/\omega$; $\omega(b^2+1)^{\frac{1}{2}}$; $\cos^{-1}(\omega/\sqrt{2\pi g})$; $2(2\pi g-\omega^2)^{\frac{1}{2}}\mathbf{i}+b\omega\mathbf{j}-\omega\mathbf{k}$

42 $3W/4$; $\sin^{-1}(3/2R)$ **44** 29·3 kW;   800 N

46 $\mathbf{i}-4\mathbf{j}+5\mathbf{k}$; $10/\sqrt{38}$ **47** $\dfrac{mv^2l}{l^2-h^2}$;   15·9 N;   2·28 m/s;   32·7 N

48 $\dfrac{v}{u}\tan\alpha\left(\dfrac{M+m}{m}\right)+\dfrac{Mv}{mu}\cot\alpha-1$

49 32·9 knots at 008° 45′;   1026 hours;   1·2 nm

50 $\cot^{-1}\left[\left(\dfrac{\mu g}{kd}\right)^2-1\right]^{\frac{1}{2}}$

51 $\mathbf{p}.(2\mathbf{i}-2\mathbf{j}+\mathbf{k})=6$; $(17\mathbf{i}-20\mathbf{j}+28\mathbf{k})/17$

52 $3\cdot84\times10^5$ km   **53** $(1-\sqrt{\tfrac{10}{7}})V$ **54** $2mv/3$; $2mv^2/9a$

55 $\left(\dfrac{3kt}{\sqrt{2}}+a^3\right)^{1/3}$ **56** $4\pi/\sqrt{\pi^2-4}$ cm; $8\pi/\sqrt{\pi^2-4}$ s

57 $\cos^{-1}(-2/\sqrt{29})$ **58** $\dfrac{mgdh}{d+h}+\tfrac{1}{2}mv^2$ **59** $\dfrac{7Mmg}{3M+8m}$; $\dfrac{(5m+M)Mg}{3M+8m}$

60 420 N m   **61** $\dfrac{8\pi}{3}\sqrt{\dfrac{a}{g}}$; $129mg/8$

65 $(\tfrac{13}{9}\mp1/\sqrt{2})\mathbf{i}+(13/9\pm1/\sqrt{2})\mathbf{j}-2/9\mathbf{k}$. $\mathbf{p}.(\mathbf{i}+\mathbf{j}+4\mathbf{k})=2$

66 $t=5\ln\dfrac{5g}{5g-v}$; $x=25g\ln\dfrac{5g}{5g-v}-5v$

4·1 m/s;   5·6 m/s

Support Exercise F

2 $1/3k$; $5W/12, 11W/12, 2W/3$; $35lW/48k$

3 $\dfrac{a(\lambda^2-12\lambda+48)}{3(8-\lambda)}$, $\dfrac{2a(6-\lambda)}{8-\lambda}$;   4   **4** $8\sqrt{3}$ knots, 120°; $\sqrt{7}$ nm, 130° 54′

5 $\left(\dfrac{g}{\sqrt{2a}}\right)^{\frac{1}{2}}$; $\tfrac{1}{3}$ **6** $\left(\dfrac{3g}{4k}\right)^{\frac{1}{2}}$ **8** $RT=\tfrac{1}{3}RQ$

9 $x=(a^2-\sqrt{a^4-u^2/k^2})^{\frac{1}{2}}$; $a\tanh akt$ or $\left(\dfrac{e^{2akt}-1}{e^{2akt}+1}a\right)$

11 0; $(1+q)\mathbf{DB}$ through M;   couple of moment $2\times$ area ABCD.

12 $10W$ at $\tan^{-1}\tfrac{3}{4}$ to AD;   M; $3W$ at $\tan^{-1}\tfrac{3}{4}$ to AB; $7W$ at $\tan^{-1}\tfrac{3}{4}$ to CD

13 $(1+\sqrt{3})mg/3$ **14** $f(9/4+\pi^2)^{\frac{1}{2}}$ **15** $\tfrac{2}{3}, \tfrac{2}{3}, \tfrac{2}{5}$

16 $\dfrac{2(4a^2-5ax+2x^2)}{5a-4x}$ **17** $7\mathbf{i}+2\mathbf{j}$;   12·30 p.m.; $4\tfrac{1}{2}\mathbf{i}+\mathbf{j}$

18 $1/\sqrt{2}$ **19** $V^2>\dfrac{gh}{2n\sin\alpha(n\cos\alpha+\cos\beta)}$

20 $3g(2\sqrt{2}+1)/4\sqrt{2}a$ **21** $13ma^2/2$

22 $mg\left(1-\cos\dfrac{\theta}{2}+2\cos\theta\right)$;   0 and $\cos^{-1}(-\tfrac{3}{4})$

23 On CZ produced such that CZ = DZ   **24** $\tan^{-1}\tfrac{8}{45}$

27 6·5 units; $(3\mathbf{i}+\mathbf{j})\sqrt{\tfrac{13}{10}}$; $13\sqrt{\tfrac{13}{10}}$ units/s

28 $v=\dfrac{g}{\alpha}-\left(\dfrac{g}{\alpha}-u\right)e^{-\alpha t}$; $x=\dfrac{g}{\alpha}t+\dfrac{1}{\alpha}\left(\dfrac{g}{\alpha}-u\right)e^{-\alpha t}$

29 C; $\dfrac{2}{3\sqrt{3}}$ **30** From N 71° 30′ W

31 993 mm;   11·38 swings less   **32** $\dfrac{(Mg\sin\alpha-R)r^2}{Mr^2+2mk^2}$

33 $(x-a-b)(c\cos\omega t-\sin\omega t)=y(\sin\omega t+\cos\omega t)$

34 $g - K\frac{v}{r}$ where K is a constant and v the speed

42 $p = \dfrac{c}{b}, \quad q = -\dfrac{2c}{b^2}; \quad z = \dfrac{maf}{\lambda}\left(\cos\sqrt{\dfrac{\lambda}{ma}}\,t - 1\right) + \tfrac{1}{2}ft^2$

43 $T = \dfrac{a}{k}(1 - e^{-kt/b})$ **44** $\cos^{-1}\left(\dfrac{b}{2a}\right)^{1/3}$ **45** $\dfrac{2\pi a}{\sqrt{3bg}}$

46 $\dfrac{4u}{11}(1+e); \ \dfrac{6u}{11a}(1+e)$ **48** $-\mu g t/r; \quad u - \mu g t; \quad \tfrac{1}{2}u$ **50** $\dfrac{2\pi a}{eu}$

51 $\dfrac{4\omega}{7}; \quad \left(\dfrac{\lambda a}{2m} + \dfrac{4a^2}{7}\omega^2\right)^{\frac{1}{2}}$

54 $(V^2 + 4gb)^{\frac{1}{2}}, \dfrac{mb}{a^2}(V^2 + 4bg) + mg; \quad (V^2 + 2gb)^{\frac{1}{2}}, \dfrac{ma}{b^2}(V^2 + 2gb)$ **56** l

62 Compression: BF, EF, both 5g N;   tension: AB, AE, AF, BC, ED, all 5g N; FC, FD, no stress. Compression: AE, AB, ED, BC, all 5g N;   tension: AF, EF, BF, all 5g N, FC, FD, both 10g N. Zero.

63 $30\sqrt{2}P$ along $y = x - \dfrac{a}{3}; \quad 30\sqrt{2}P$, and couple of moment $10aP$

64 $\tfrac{8}{9}l; \quad 7\sqrt{\dfrac{2l}{3g}}$ **65** $\dfrac{2u}{g}; \quad \dfrac{2}{3}\left(u^2 + \dfrac{3gl}{g}\right)^{\frac{1}{2}}$ **66** $106°; \quad 14\tfrac{1}{2}$ nm at $152°$

68 Unstable   **71** $\tfrac{34}{47}; \quad \tfrac{22\sqrt{2}}{46}$

72 $\dfrac{g}{4}(2M - m_1 + m_2); \quad \dfrac{\sqrt{3g}}{4}(2M + m_1 + m_2) - \tfrac{1}{2}Mg; \quad \dfrac{g}{4}(2M - m_1 + m_2) - \dfrac{Mg}{\sqrt{3}}$

73 $(\cos\alpha + \tfrac{2}{\sqrt{3}}\sin\alpha)Mg, \ Mg\sin\alpha$ **74** $\pi a\sqrt{\dfrac{2(m + 2m')}{m'ga + k}}$

Index